Volume 1

Mathematics I

Custom Edition for Utah School Districts

Randall I. Charles
Basia Hall
Dan Kennedy
Laurie E. Bass
Allan E. Bellman
Sadie Chavis Bragg
William G. Handlin
Art Johnson
Stuart J. Murphy
Grant Wiggins

PEARSON

Acknowledgments appear on page Z42, which constitutes an extension of this copyright page.

Taken from:

High School Math 2014 Common Core Integrated Math 1 Write-In Student Edition Volume 1
Copyright © 2014 by Pearson Education, Inc.
Published by Pearson Education, Inc.
One Lake Street, Upper Saddle River, New Jersey 07458

High School Math 2014 Common Core Integrated Math 1 Write-In Student Edition Volume 2
Copyright © 2014 by Pearson Education, Inc.
Published by Pearson Education, Inc.
One Lake Street, Upper Saddle River, New Jersey 07458

Algebra 2 Common Core Edition
Copyright © 2012 by Pearson Education, Inc.
Published by Pearson Education, Inc.
One Lake Street, Upper Saddle River, New Jersey 07458

Pearson Learning Solutions, 501 Boylston Street, Suite 900, Boston, MA 02116
A Pearson Education Company
www.pearsoned.com

Printed in the United States of America

4 5 6 7 8 9 10 V011 18 17 16 15 14

000200010271798628

AH

PEARSON

ISBN 10: 1-269-54664-3
ISBN 13: 978-1-269-54664-5

From the **Authors**

Welcome

Math is a powerful tool with far-reaching applications throughout your life. We have designed a unique and engaging program that will enable you to tap into the power of mathematics and mathematical reasoning. This award-winning program has been developed to align fully to the Common Core State Standards.

Developing mathematical understanding and problem-solving abilities is an ongoing process—a journey both inside and outside the classroom. This course is designed to help make sense of the mathematics you encounter in and out of class each day and to help you develop mathematical proficiency.

You will learn important mathematical principles. You will also learn how the principles are connected to one another and to what you already know. You will learn to solve problems and learn the reasoning that lies behind your solutions. You will also develop the key mathematical practices of the Common Core State Standards.

Each chapter begins with the "big ideas" of the chapter and some essential questions that you will learn to answer. Through this question-and-answer process you will develop your ability to analyze problems independently and solve them in different applications.

Your skills and confidence will increase through practice and review. Work through the problems so you understand the concepts and methods presented and the thinking behind them. Then do the exercises. Ask yourself how new concepts relate to old ones. Make the connections!

Everyone needs help sometimes. You will find that this program has built-in opportunities, both in this text and online, to get help whenever you need it.

The problem-solving and reasoning habits and problem-solving skills you develop in this program will serve you in all your studies and in your daily life. They will prepare you for future success not only as a student, but also as a member of a changing technological society.

Best wishes,

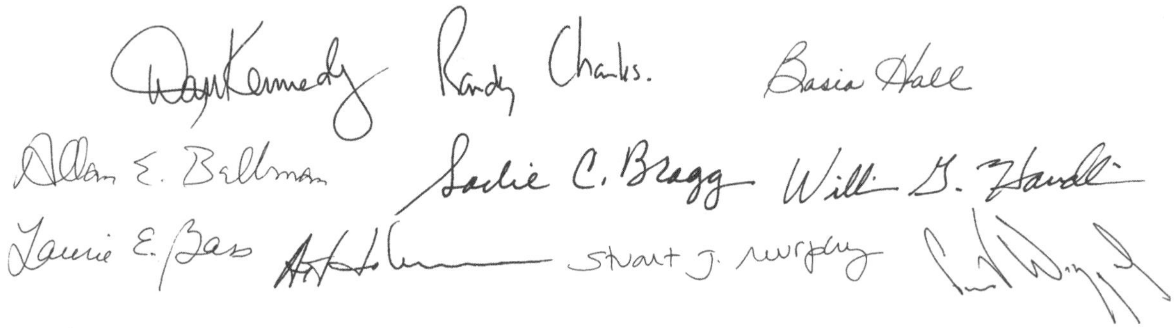

Series *Authors*

Randall I. Charles, Ph.D., is Professor Emeritus in the Department of Mathematics at San Jose State University, San Jose, California. He began his career as a high school mathematics teacher, and he was a mathematics supervisor for five years. Dr. Charles has been a member of several NCTM committees including the writing team for the Curriculum Focal Points. He is the former Vice President of the National Council of Supervisors of Mathematics. Much of his writing and research has been in the area of problem solving. He has authored more than 90 mathematics textbooks for kindergarten through college.

Dan Kennedy, Ph.D., is a classroom teacher and the Lupton Distinguished Professor of Mathematics at the Baylor School in Chattanooga, Tennessee. A frequent speaker at professional meetings on the subject of mathematics education reform, Dr. Kennedy has conducted more than 50 workshops and institutes for high school teachers. He is coauthor of textbooks in calculus and precalculus, and from 1990 to 1994 he chaired the College Board's AP Calculus Development Committee. He is a 1992 Tandy Technology Scholar and a 1995 Presidential Award winner.

Basia Hall currently serves as Manager of Instructional Programs for the Houston Independent School District. With 33 years of teaching experience, Ms. Hall has served as a department chair, instructional supervisor, school improvement facilitator, and professional development trainer. She has developed curricula for Algebra 1, Geometry, and Algebra 2 and co-developed the Texas state mathematics standards. A 1992 Presidential Awardee, Ms. Hall is past president of the Texas Association of Supervisors of Mathematics and is a state representative for the National Council of Supervisors of Mathematics (NCSM).

Consulting *Authors*

Stuart J. Murphy is a visual learning author and consultant. He is a champion of helping students develop visual learning skills so they become more successful students. He is the author of MathStart, a series of children's books that presents mathematical concepts in the context of stories, and *I See I Learn,* a Pre-Kindergarten and Kindergarten learning initiative that focuses on social and emotional skills. A graduate of the Rhode Island School of Design, he has worked extensively in educational publishing and has been on the authorship teams of a number of elementary and high school mathematics programs. He is a frequent presenter at meetings of the National Council of Teachers of Mathematics, the International Reading Association, and other professional organizations.

Grant Wiggins, Ed.D., is the President of Authentic Education in Hopewell, New Jersey. He earned his B.A. from St. John's College in Annapolis and his Ed.D. from Harvard University Dr. Wiggins consults with schools, districts, and state education departments on a variety of reform matters; organizes conferences and workshops; and develops print materials and web resources on curricular change. He is perhaps best known for being the coauthor, with Jay McTighe, of *Understanding by Design®* and *The Understanding by Design® Handbook*[1], the award-winning and highly successful materials on curriculum published by ASCD®. His work has been supported by the Pew Charitable Trusts, the Geraldine R. Dodge Foundation, and the National Science Foundation.

[1] ASCD®, publisher of the "Understanding by Design® Handbook" co-authored by Grant Wiggins and registered owner of the trademark "Understanding by Design®", has not authorized or sponsored this work and is in no way affiliated with Pearson or its products.

Program *Authors*

Algebra Topics

Allan E. Bellman, Ph.D., is an Associate Professor of Mathematics Education at the University of Mississippi. He previously taught at the University of California, Davis for 12 years and in public school in Montgomery County, Maryland for 31. He has been an instructor for both the Woodrow Wilson National Fellowship Foundation and the Texas Instruments' T^3 program. Dr. Bellman has expertise in the use of technology in education and assessment-driven instruction and speaks frequently on these topics. He is a recipient of the Tandy Award for Teaching Excellence and has twice been listed in Who's Who Among America's Teachers.

Sadie Chavis Bragg, Ed.D., is Senior Vice President of Academic Affairs and professor of mathematics at the Borough of Manhattan Community College of the City University of New York. She is a past president of the American Mathematical Association of Two-Year Colleges (AMATYC). In recognition for her service to the field of mathematics locally, statewide, nationally, and internationally, she was awarded AMATYC's most prestigious award, The Mathematics Excellence Award for 2010. Dr. Bragg has coauthored more than 60 mathematics textbooks for kindergarten through college.

William G. Handlin, Sr., is a classroom teacher and Department Chair of Mathematics and former Department Chair of Technology Applications at Spring Woods High School in Houston, Texas. Awarded Life Membership in the Texas Congress of Parents and Teachers for his contributions to the well-being of children, Mr. Handlin is also a frequent workshop and seminar leader in professional meetings.

Geometry Topics

Laurie E. Bass is a classroom teacher at the 9–12 division of the Ethical Culture Fieldston School in Riverdale, New York. A classroom teacher for more than 30 years, Ms. Bass has a wide base of teaching experiences, ranging from Grade 6 through Advanced Placement Calculus. She was the recipient of a 2000 Honorable Mention for the Radio Shack National Teacher Awards. She has been a contributing writer for a number of publications, including software-based activities for the Algebra 1 classroom. Among her areas of special interest are cooperative learning for high school students and geometry exploration on the computer. Ms. Bass is a frequent presenter at local, regional, and national conferences.

Art Johnson, Ed.D., is a professor of mathematics education at Boston University. He is a mathematics educator with 32 years of public school teaching experience, a frequent speaker and workshop leader, and the recipient of a number of awards: the Tandy Prize for Teaching Excellence, the Presidential Award for Excellence in Mathematics Teaching, and New Hampshire Teacher of the Year. He was also profiled by the Disney Corporation in the American Teacher of the Year Program. Dr. Johnson has contributed 18 articles to NCTM journals and has authored over 50 books on various aspects of mathematics.

Using **Your Book** with Success

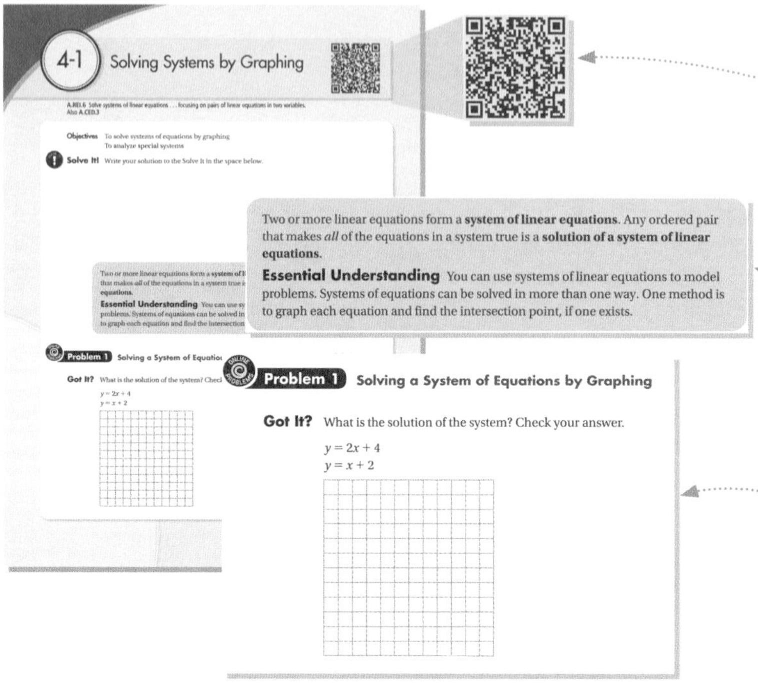

4-1 Solving Systems by Graphing

Two or more linear equations form a **system of linear equations**. Any ordered pair that makes *all* of the equations in a system true is a **solution of a system of linear equations**.

Essential Understanding You can use systems of linear equations to model problems. Systems of equations can be solved in more than one way. One method is to graph each equation and find the intersection point, if one exists.

Problem 1 Solving a System of Equations by Graphing

Got It? What is the solution of the system? Check your answer.

$y = 2x + 4$

$y = x + 2$

- You will find a QR code on each lesson opener. Each code links to a unique instructional video developed by **Virtual Nerd**™.
- The **Essential Understanding** presents the key concept of the lesson and connects to the Big Ideas that are introduced in the Chapter Opener.
- After working through the Problem in the Interactive Digital Path, you complete a **Got It?** exercise in your book. For exercises that require graphing, a blank grid is provided.

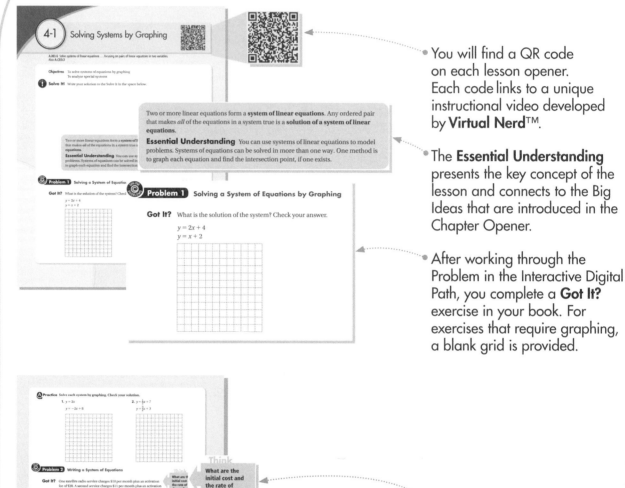

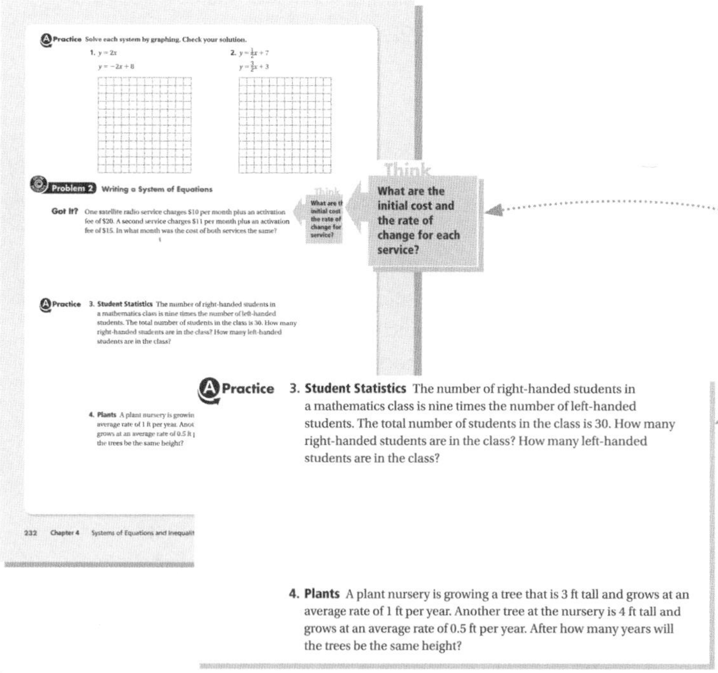

Think What are the initial cost and the rate of change for each service?

Practice 3. **Student Statistics** The number of right-handed students in a mathematics class is nine times the number of left-handed students. The total number of students in the class is 30. How many right-handed students are in the class? How many left-handed students are in the class?

4. **Plants** A plant nursery is growing a tree that is 3 ft tall and grows at an average rate of 1 ft per year. Another tree at the nursery is 4 ft tall and grows at an average rate of 0.5 ft per year. After how many years will the trees be the same height?

- The **Think** and **Plan** boxes suggest questions to help you make sense of the problem and develop a solution plan.
- Each **Got It?** exercise is followed by additional exercises that focus on the same math concept and skill. You complete these exercises in your book.

You can use the instructional summaries in the **Take Note** boxes to review concepts when completing homework or studying for an assessment.

At the end of each lesson is a **Lesson Check** that you complete in your book. The Do you know HOW? section focuses on skills and the Do you UNDERSTAND? section targets your understanding of the math concepts related to the skills.

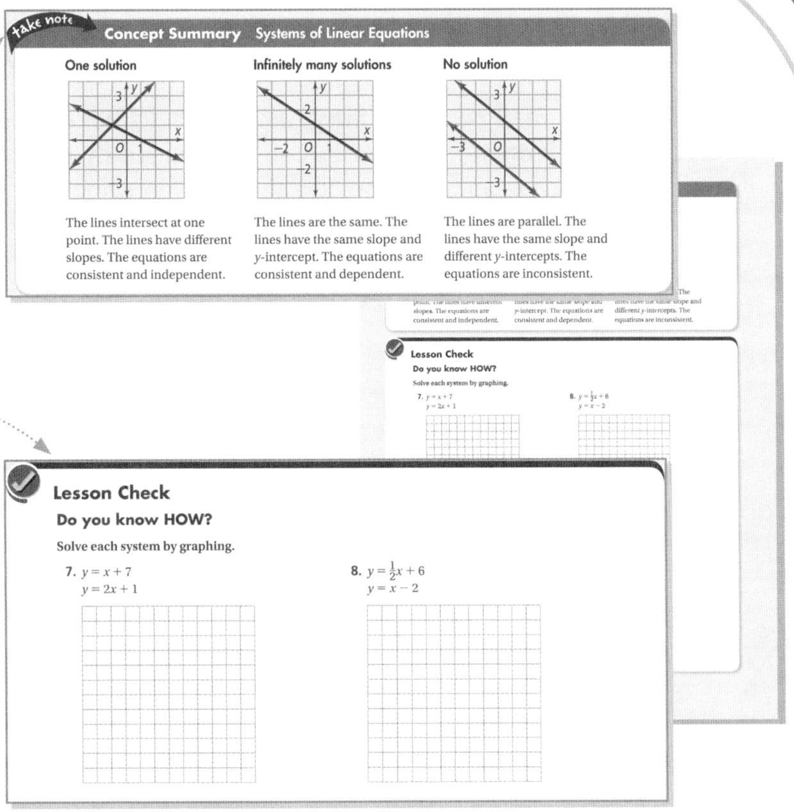

Each lesson ends with **More Practice and Problem Solving** Exercises. You will complete these exercises in your homework notebook or on a separate sheet of paper.

The exercises with the **Common Core logo** help you become more proficient with the Standards for Mathematical Practice. Those with the **STEM** logo provide practice with science, technology, or engineering topics.

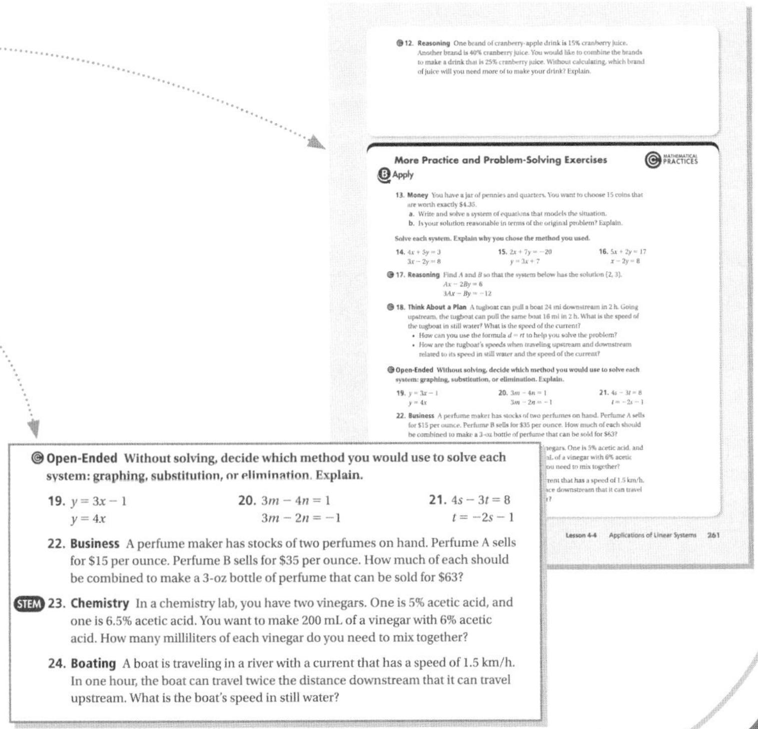

What is a **QR code** *and how do I use it?*

A unique feature of Pearson's ***Integrated High School Mathematics*** is the QR code on every lesson opener. QR codes can be scanned by any electronic device with a camera, such as a smart phone, tablet, and even some laptop computers. The QR codes on the lesson openers link to Virtual Nerd™ tutorial videos that directly relate to the content in the lesson. To learn more about Virtual Nerd tutorial videos and its exclusive dynamic whiteboard, go to virtualnerd.com.

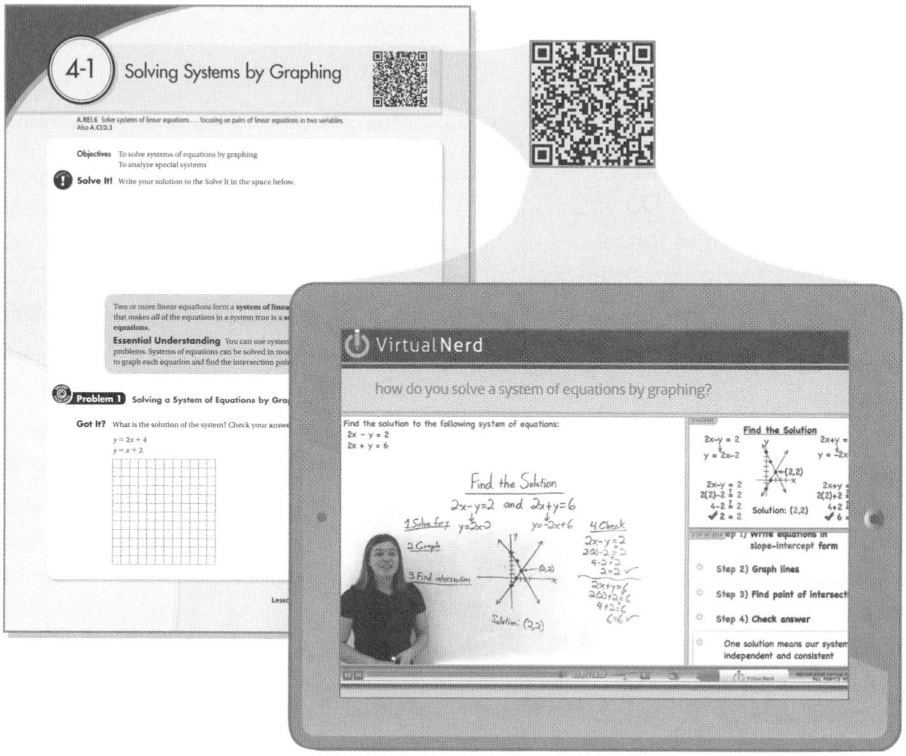

You must have a QR code reader on your mobile device or computer. You can download a QR reader app at the app store for your mobile device.

Step 1: Go to the app store for your camera-enabled smart phone or tablet.

Step 2: Search for "QR" or "QR readers". Download the QR reader app.

Step 3: Open that app and follow the instructions to scan. Whenever you want to scan a QR code, you will need to open the QR reader app first, otherwise you will just end up taking a picture of a QR code.

Step 4: After scanning the QR code, the appropriate Virtual Nerd tutorial video will play.

What **Resources** can I use when studying?

Pearson's ***Integrated High School Mathematics*** offers a range of resources that you can use out of class.

Student Worktext Your book is more than a textbook. Not only does it have important summaries of key math concepts and skills, it will also have your worked-out solutions to the *Got It?* and *Practice* exercises and your own notes for each lesson or problem. Use your book to:

- Refer back to your worked-out solutions and notes.
- Review the key concepts of each lesson by rereading the *Essential Understanding* and *Take Note* boxes.
- Access video tutorials of the concepts addressed in the lesson by scanning the QR codes.

Pearson SuccessNet You have full access to all of the resources on Pearson SuccessNet, including the **Interactive Digital Path** where you will find all of the *Solve Its!* and Problems presented in class. Revisit the animated, stepped-out problems presented in-class to clarify and solidify your math knowledge. Additional resources available to you include:

- Interactive Student Worktext
- Homework Video Tutors in English and Spanish
- Online Glossary with audio in English and Spanish
- MathXL for School Interactive Math Practice
- Math Tools and Online Manipulatives
- Multilingual Handbook
- Assessments with immediate feedback

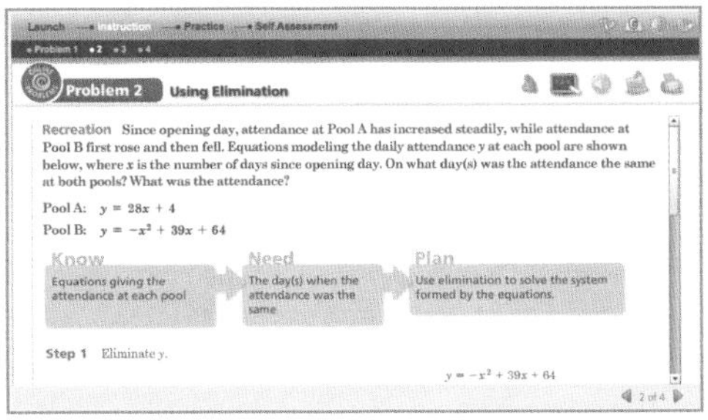

Mobile eText You may wish to access your student book on the go, either online or offline via download. Pearson's ***Integrated High School Mathematics*** also offers you a complete mobile etext of the Student Worktext.

- Use the notes, highlight, and bookmark features to personalize your eText.
- Watch animated problem videos with step-by-step instruction for every lesson.

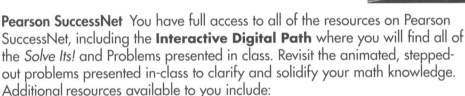

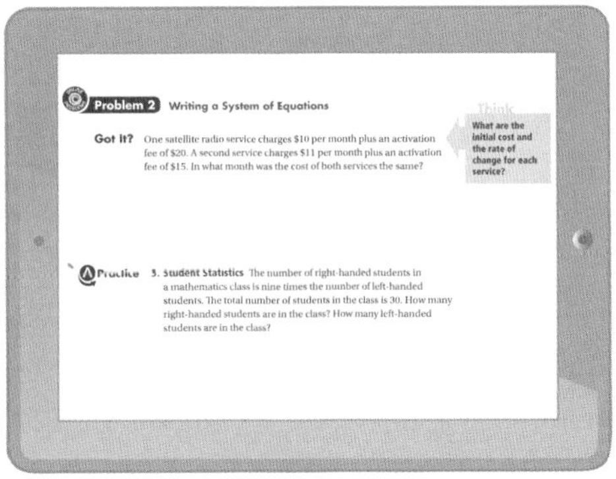

Pearson SuccessNet

Pearson SuccessNet is the gateway to all of the digital components of the program. You can use the online content to review the day's lesson, complete lessons independently, get help with your homework assignments, and prepare for and/or take an assessment. You will be given a username and password to log into www.pearsonsuccessnet.com.

The Homepage

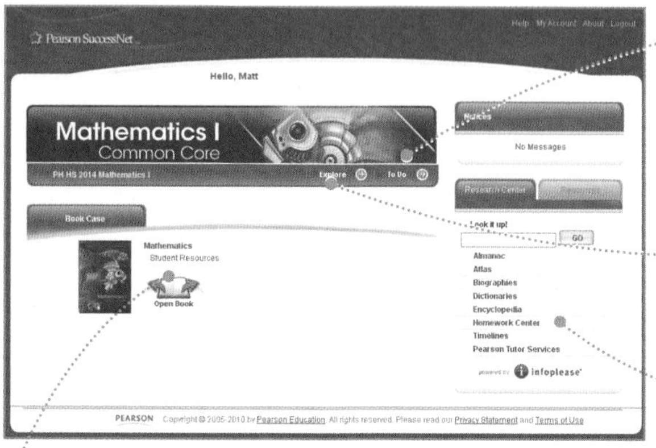

The **To Do** tab contains a list of assignments that you need to complete. You can also access your gradebook and review past assignments.

The **Explore** tab provides you access to the Table of Contents and all of the digital content for the program.

You can also access the following student resources: Practice Worksheets, Homework Video Tutors, and a Multilingual Handbook

Your eText includes links to animated lesson videos, highlighting and note taking tools, and a visual glossary with audio.

Table of Contents

To access the Table of Contents, click on *Explore* from your Homepage.

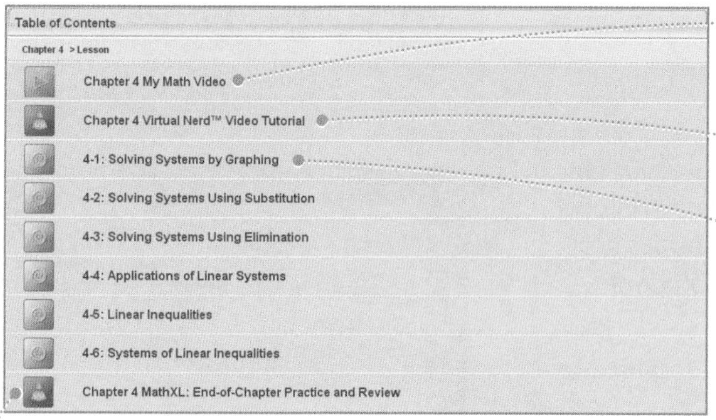

Student-developed videos bring real-life context to mathematics.

Step-by-step video tutorials offer additional support for every lesson.

Digital lessons include access to animated problems, math tools, homework exercises, and self-assessments.

MathXL for School exercises provide additional practice. Examples and tutorials support every problem, and instant feedback is provided as you complete each exercise.

Interactive Digital Path

To access the **Interactive Digital Path**, click on the appropriate lesson from the Table of Contents.

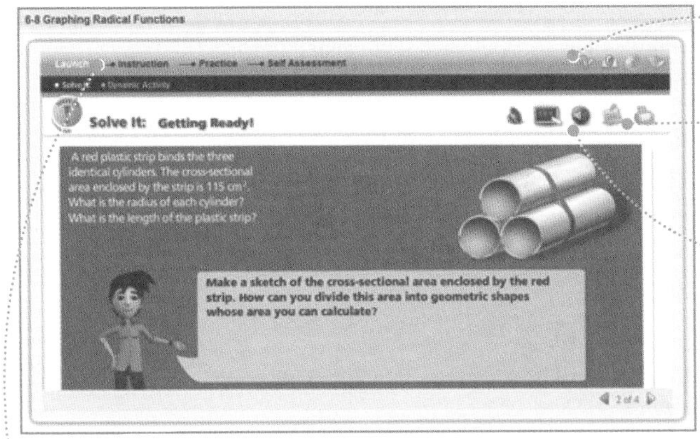

Math Tools help you explore and visualize concepts.

You'll find opportunities to review formulas, properties, and other key concepts.

Interactive Glossary is available in English and Spanish with audio.

Every lesson includes the following:

Launch: Interactive lesson opener connects the math to real-world applications.

Instruction: All lesson problems are stepped out with detailed instruction. You can complete the subsequent *Got It?* exercises in your Student Worktext.

Practice: Exercises from your Student Worktext are available for view.

Self-Assessment: You can take the self-check lesson quiz, and then check your answers on the second screen.

MathXL for School

To access *MathXL for School,* click on the Chapter Review and Practice link from the Table of Contents.

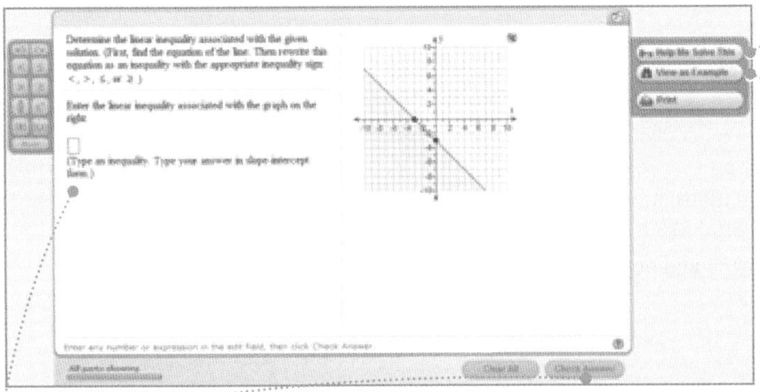

Select **Help Me Solve This** for an interactive step-by-step tutorial.

Select **View an Example** to see a similar worked out problem.

Input your answer and select **Check Answer** to get immediate feedback. After completing the exercise, a new exercise automatically regenerates, so you have unlimited practice opportunities.

Common Core *State Standards*

Mathematics I

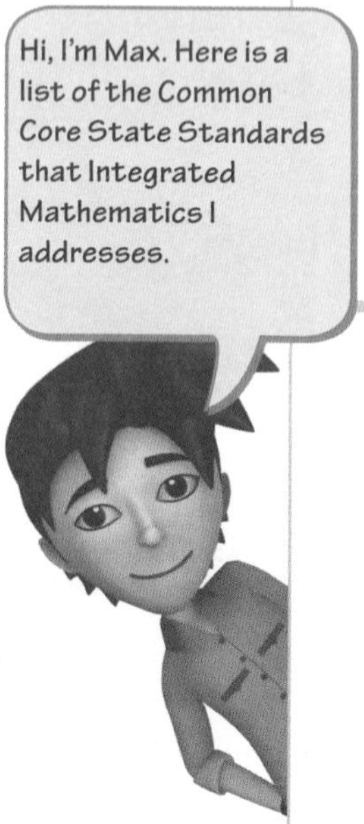

Number and Quantity

Quantities

Reason quantitatively and use units to solve problems

N.Q.1 Use units as a way to understand problems and to guide the solution of multi-step problems; choose and interpret units consistently in formulas; choose and interpret the scale and the origin in graphs and data displays.

N.Q.2 Define appropriate quantities for the purpose of descriptive modeling.

N.Q.3 Choose a level of accuracy appropriate to limitations on measurement when reporting quantities.

Algebra

Seeing Structure in Expressions

Interpret the structure of expressions

A.SSE.1.a Interpret expressions that represent a quantity in terms of its context.★ Interpret parts of an expression, such as terms, factors, and coefficients.

A.SSE.1.b Interpret expressions that represent a quantity in terms of its context.★ Interpret complicated expressions by viewing one or more of their parts as a single entity.

Write expressions in equivalent forms to solve problems

A.SSE.3.c Choose and produce an equivalent form of an expression to reveal and explain properties of the quantity represented by the expression.★ Use the properties of exponents to transform expressions for exponential functions.

Creating Equations★

Create equations that describe numbers or relationships

A.CED.1 Create equations and inequalities in one variable and use them to solve problems. Include equations arising from linear and exponential functions.

A.CED.2 Create equations in two or more variables to represent relationships between quantities; graph equations on coordinate axes with labels and scales.

A.CED.3 Represent constraints by equations or inequalities, and by systems of equations and/or inequalities, and interpret solutions as viable or nonviable options in a modeling context.

A.CED.4 Rearrange formulas to highlight a quantity of interest, using the same reasoning as in solving equations.

Reasoning with Equations and Inequalities

Solve equations and inequalities in one variable

A.REI.3 Solve linear equations and inequalities in one variable, including equations with coefficients represented by letters.

Solve systems of equations

A.REI.5 Prove that, given a system of two equations in two variables, replacing one equation by the sum of that equation and a multiple of the other produces a system with the same solutions.

A.REI.6 Solve systems of linear equations exactly and approximately (e.g., with graphs), focusing on pairs of linear equations in two variables.

★ Indicates a modeling standard

Represent and solve equations and inequalities graphically

A.REI.10 Understand that the graph of an equation in two variables is the set of all its solutions plotted in the coordinate plane, often forming a curve (which could be a line).

A.REI.11 Explain why the x-coordinates of the points where the graphs of the equations $y = f(x)$ and $y = g(x)$ intersect are the solutions of the equation $f(x) = g(x)$; find the solutions approximately, e.g., using technology to graph the functions, make tables of values, or find successive approximations. Include cases where $f(x)$ and/or $g(x)$ are linear and exponential functions.★

A.REI.12 Graph the solutions to a linear inequality in two variables as a half-plane (excluding the boundary in the case of a strict inequality), and graph the solution set to a system of linear inequalities in two variables as the intersection of the corresponding half-planes.

Functions

Interpreting Functions

Understand the concept of a function and use function notation

F.IF.1 Understand that a function from one set (called the domain) to another set (called the range) assigns to each element of the domain exactly one element of the range. If f is a function and x is an element of its domain, then $f(x)$ denotes the output of f corresponding to the input x. The graph of f is the graph of the equation $y = f(x)$.

F.IF.2 Use function notation, evaluate functions for inputs in their domains, and interpret statements that use function notation in terms of a context.

F.IF.3 Recognize that sequences are functions, sometimes defined recursively, whose domain is a subset of the integers.

Interpret functions that arise in applications in terms of the context

F.IF.4 For a function that models a relationship between two quantities, interpret key features of graphs and tables in terms of the quantities, and sketch graphs showing key features given a verbal description of the relationship. *Key features include: intercepts; intervals where the function is increasing, decreasing, positive, or negative; relative maximums and minimums; symmetries; end behavior; and periodicity.*★

F.IF.5 Relate the domain of a function to its graph and, where applicable, to the quantitative relationship it describes.★

F.IF.6 Calculate and interpret the average rate of change of a function (presented symbolically or as a table) over a specified interval. Estimate the rate of change from a graph.★

Analyze functions using different representations

F.IF.7.a Graph functions expressed symbolically and show key features of the graph, by hand in simple cases and using technology for more complicated cases.★ Graph linear functions and show intercepts, maxima, and minima.

F.IF.9 Compare properties of two functions each represented in a different way (algebraically, graphically, numerically in tables, or by verbal descriptions).

Building Functions

Build a function that models a relationship between two quantities

F.BF.1.a Write a function that describes a relationship between two quantities.★ Determine an explicit expression, a recursive process, or steps for calculation from a context.

F.BF.2 Write arithmetic and geometric sequences both recursively and with an explicit formula, use them to model situations, and translate between the two forms.★

Linear, Quadratic, and Exponential Models

Construct and compare linear and exponential models and solve problems.

F.LE.1.a Distinguish between situations that can be modeled with linear functions and with exponential functions. Prove that linear functions grow by equal differences over equal intervals, and that exponential functions grow by equal factors over equal intervals.

F.LE.1.b Distinguish between situations that can be modeled with linear functions and with exponential functions. Recognize situations in which one quantity changes at a constant rate per unit interval relative to another.

F.LE.1.c Distinguish between situations that can be modeled with linear functions and with exponential functions. Recognize situations in which a quantity grows or decays by a constant percent rate per unit interval relative to another.

F.LE.2 Construct linear and exponential functions, including arithmetic and geometric sequences, given a graph, a description of a relationship, or two input-output pairs (include reading these from a table).

F.LE.3 Observe using graphs and tables that a quantity increasing exponentially eventually exceeds a quantity increasing linearly.

Interpret expressions for functions in terms of the situation they model

F.LE.5 Interpret the parameters in a linear or exponential function in terms of a context.

Geometry

Congruence

Experiment with Transformations in the Plane

G.CO.2 Represent transformations in the plane using, e.g., transparencies and geometry software; describe transformations as functions that take points in the plane as inputs and give other points as outputs. Compare transformations that preserve distance and angle to those that do not (e.g., translation versus horizontal stretch).

G.CO.3 Given a rectangle, parallelogram, trapezoid, or regular polygon, describe the rotations and reflections that carry it onto itself.

G.CO.4 Develop definitions of rotations, reflections, and translations in terms of angles, circles, perpendicular lines, parallel lines, and line segments.

G.CO.5 Given a geometric figure and a rotation, reflection, or translation, draw the transformed figure using, e.g., graph paper, tracing paper, or geometry software. Specify a sequence of transformations that will carry a given figure onto another.

Understand congruence in terms of rigid motions

G.CO.6 Use geometric descriptions of rigid motions to transform figures and to predict the effect of a given rigid motion on a given figure; given two figures, use the definition of congruence in terms of rigid motions to decide if they are congruent.

G.CO.7 Use the definition of congruence in terms of rigid motions to show that two triangles are congruent if and only if corresponding pairs of sides and corresponding pairs of angles are congruent.

G.CO.8 Explain how the criteria for triangle congruence (ASA, SAS, and SSS) follow from the definition of congruence in terms of rigid motions.

Prove geometric theorems

G.CO.10 Prove theorems about triangles. *Theorems include: measures of interior angles of a triangle sum to 180°; base angles of isosceles triangles are congruent; the segment joining midpoints of two sides of a triangle is parallel to the third side and half the length; the medians of a triangle meet at a point.*

Statistics and Probability★

Interpreting Categorical and Quantitative Data

Summarize, represent, and interpret data on a single count or measurement variable

S.ID.1 Represent data with plots on the real number line (dot plots, histograms, and box plots).

S.ID.2 Use statistics appropriate to the shape of the data distribution to compare center (median, mean) and spread (interquartile range, standard deviation) of two or more different data sets.

S.ID.3 Interpret differences in shape, center, and spread in the context of the data sets, accounting for possible effects of extreme data points (outliers).

Summarize, represent, and interpret data on two categorical and quantitative variables

S.ID.5 Summarize categorical data for two categories in two-way frequency tables. Interpret relative frequencies in the context of the data (including joint, marginal, and conditional relative frequencies). Recognize possible associations and trends in the data.

S.ID.6.a Represent data on two quantitative variables on a scatter plot, and describe how the variables are related. Fit a function to the data; use functions fitted to data to solve problems in the context of the data. Use given functions or choose a function suggested by the context. Emphasize linear and exponential models.

S.ID.6.c Represent data on two quantitative variables on a scatter plot, and describe how the variables are related. Fit a linear function for a scatter plot that suggests a linear association.

Interpret linear models

S.ID.7 Interpret the slope (rate of change) and the intercept (constant term) of a linear model in the context of the data.

S.ID.8 Compute (using technology) and interpret the correlation coefficient of a linear fit.

S.ID.9 Distinguish between correlation and causation.

BIGideas

These Big Ideas are the organizing ideas for the study of important areas of mathematics: algebra, geometry, and statistics.

Stay connected! These Big Ideas will help you understand how the math you study in high school fits together.

Algebra

Properties

- In the transition from arithmetic to algebra, attention shifts from arithmetic operations (addition, subtraction, multiplication, and division) to the use of the *properties* of these operations.
- All of the facts of arithmetic and algebra follow from certain properties.

Variable

- Quantities are used to form expressions, equations, and inequalities.
- An expression refers to a quantity but does not make a statement about it. An equation (or an inequality) is a statement about the quantities it mentions.
- Using variables in place of numbers in equations (or inequalities) allows the statement of relationships among numbers that are unknown or unspecified.

Equivalence

- A single quantity may be represented by many different expressions.
- The facts about a quantity may be expressed by many different equations (or inequalities).

Solving Equations & Inequalities

- Solving an equation is the process of rewriting the equation to make what it says about its variable(s) as simple as possible.
- Properties of numbers and equality can be used to transform an equation (or inequality) into equivalent, simpler equations (or inequalities) in order to find solutions.
- Useful information about equations and inequalities (including solutions) can be found by analyzing graphs or tables.
- The numbers and types of solutions vary predictably, based on the type of equation.

Proportionality

- Two quantities are *proportional* if they have the same ratio in each instance where they are measured together.
- Two quantities are *inversely proportional* if they have the same product in each instance where they are measured together.

Function

- A function is a relationship between variables in which each value of the input variable is associated with a unique value of the output variable.
- Functions can be represented in a variety of ways, such as graphs, tables, equations, or words. Each representation is particularly useful in certain situations.
- Some important families of functions are developed through transformations of the simplest form of the function.
- New functions can be made from other functions by applying arithmetic operations or by applying one function to the output of another.

Modeling

- Many real-world mathematical problems can be represented algebraically. These representations can lead to algebraic solutions.
- A function that models a real-world situation can be used to make estimates or predictions about future occurrences.

Statistics and Probability

Data Collection and Analysis

- Sampling techniques are used to gather data from real-world situations. If the data are representative of the larger population, inferences can be made about that population.
- Biased sampling techniques yield data unlikely to be representative of the larger population.
- Sets of numerical data are described using measures of central tendency and dispersion.

Data Representation

- The most appropriate data representations depend on the type of data—quantitative or qualitative, and univariate or bivariate.
- Line plots, box plots, and histograms are different ways to show distribution of data over a possible range of values.

Probability

- Probability expresses the likelihood that a particular event will occur.
- Data can be used to calculate an experimental probability, and mathematical properties can be used to determine a theoretical probability.
- Either experimental or theoretical probability can be used to make predictions or decisions about future events.
- Various counting methods can be used to develop theoretical probabilities.

Geometry

Visualization

- Visualization can help you see the relationships between two figures and help you connect properties of real objects with two-dimensional drawings of these objects.

Transformations

- Transformations are mathematical functions that model relationships with figures.
- Transformations may be described geometrically or by coordinates.
- Symmetries of figures may be defined and classified by transformations.

Measurement

- Some attributes of geometric figures, such as length, area, volume, and angle measure, are measurable. Units are used to describe these attributes.

Reasoning & Proof

- Definitions establish meanings and remove possible misunderstanding.
- Other truths are more complex and difficult to see. It is often possible to verify complex truths by reasoning from simpler ones using deductive reasoning.

Similarity

- Two geometric figures are similar when corresponding lengths are proportional and corresponding angles are congruent.
- Areas of similar figures are proportional to the squares of their corresponding lengths.
- Volumes of similar figures are proportional to the cubes of their corresponding lengths.

Coordinate Geometry

- A coordinate system on a line is a number line on which points are labeled, corresponding to the real numbers.
- A coordinate system in a plane is formed by two perpendicular number lines, called the *x*- and *y*-axes, and the quadrants they form. The coordinate plane can be used to graph many functions.
- It is possible to verify some complex truths using deductive reasoning in combination with the distance, midpoint, and slope formulas.

1

Solving Equations and Inequalities

Chapter 1

Number and Quantity

Quantities
Reason quantitatively and use units to solve problems

Algebra

Seeing Structure in Expressions
Interpret the structure of expressions

Creating Equations
Create equations that describe numbers or relationships

Reasoning with Equations and Inequalities
Understand solving equations as a process of reasoning and explain the reasoning

Represent and solve equations and inequalities graphically

2

An Introduction to Functions

Chapter 2

Number and Quantity

Quantities
Reason quantitatively and use units to solve problems

Algebra

Seeing Structure in Expressions
Interpret the structure of expressions

Creating Equations
Create equations that describe numbers or relationships

Reasoning with Equations and Inequalities
Represent and solve equations and inequalities graphically

Functions

Interpreting Functions
Understand the concept of a function and use function notation
Interpret functions that arise in applications in terms of the context

Building Functions
Build a function that models a relationship between two quantities
Build new functions from existing functions.

3

Linear Functions

Chapter 3

Algebra

Seeing Structure in Expressions
Interpret the structure of expressions

Creating Equations
Create equations that describe numbers or relationships

Functions

Interpreting Functions
Interpret functions that arise in applications in terms of the context
Analyze functions using different representations

Building Functions
Build new functions from existing functions

Linear and Exponential Models
Construct and compare linear and exponential models and solve problems.
Interpret expressions for functions in terms of the situation they model

4

Systems of Equations and Inequalities

Chapter 4

Number and Quantity

Quantities
Reason quantitatively and use units to solve problems

Algebra

Creating Equations
Create equations that describe numbers or relationships

Reasoning with Equations and Inequalities
Represent and solve equations and inequalities graphically

H

Honors Appendix

A Matrices

B Reasoning and Proof

CHAPTER 1

Get Ready!

Factors — a # ÷'s into another # evenly.

Find the greatest common factor of each set of numbers.

1. 12, 18 **2.** 25, 35 **3.** 13, 20 **4.** 40, 80, 100

Least Common Multiple (LCM)

Find the least common multiple of each set of numbers.

5. 5, 15 **6.** 11, 44 **7.** 8, 9 **8.** 10, 15, 25

Using Estimation

Estimate each sum or difference.

9. $956 - 542$ **10.** $1.259 + 5.312 + 1.7$ **11.** $\$14.32 + \$1.65 + \$278.05$

Simplifying Fractions

Write in simplest form.

12. $\frac{12}{15}$ **13.** $\frac{20}{28}$ **14.** $\frac{8}{56}$ **15.** $\frac{48}{52}$

Fractions and Decimals

Write each fraction as a decimal.

16. $\frac{7}{10}$ **17.** $\frac{3}{5}$ **18.** $\frac{13}{20}$ **19.** $\frac{93}{100}$ **20.** $\frac{7}{15}$

Adding and Subtracting Fractions

Find the sum or difference.

21. $\frac{4}{7} + \frac{3}{14}$ **22.** $6\frac{2}{3} + 3\frac{4}{5}$ **23.** $\frac{9}{10} - \frac{4}{5}$ **24.** $8\frac{3}{4} - 4\frac{5}{6}$

VOCABULARY Looking Ahead Vocabulary

25. A mailman *distributes* mail to each resident of a neighborhood. What does it mean to *distribute* the 4 in the product $4(10 + 7)$?

26. An *interval* of time is a duration between two moments. What is an *interval* between two numbers a and b?

27. When two things are *identical,* they are the same. What does it mean for an equation to be an *identity*?

CHAPTER 1

Solving Equations and Inequalities

Big Ideas

1 Solving Equations and Inequalities

Essential Question How can you solve equations?

Essential Question How can you solve inequalities?

2 Equivalence

Essential Question Can equations that appear to be different be equivalent?

Domains

- Quantities
- Creating Equations
- Reasoning with Equations and Inequalities

Chapter Preview

Interactive Digital Path

Log in to **pearsonsuccessnet.com** and click on Interactive Digital Path to access the Solve Its and animated Problems.

Vocabulary

English/Spanish Vocabulary Audio Online:

English	Spanish
coefficient, *p. 6*	coeficiente
compound inequality *p. 70*	desigualidad compusta
conversion factor, *p. 38*	factor de conversión
formula, *p. 31*	ecuaciones equivalentes
identity, *p. 24*	identidad
like terms, *p. 7*	terminus semejantes
literal equation, *p. 29*	ecuación literal
proportion, *p. 52*	proporción
rate, *p. 37*	tasa
ratio, *p. 37*	razón
term, *p. 6*	término
unit rate, *p. 37*	razón de unidades

1-1 The Distributive Property

A.SSE.1.a Interpret parts of an expression . . . Also **A.SSE.1**

Objective To use the Distributive Property to simplify expressions

Solve It! Write your solution to the Solve It in the space below.

To solve problems in mathematics, it is often useful to rewrite expressions in simpler forms. The **Distributive Property**, illustrated by the area model below, is one property of real numbers that helps you to simplify expressions.

$x + 5$

x 5

> The model shows that
> $8(x + 5) = 8(x) + 8(5)$.

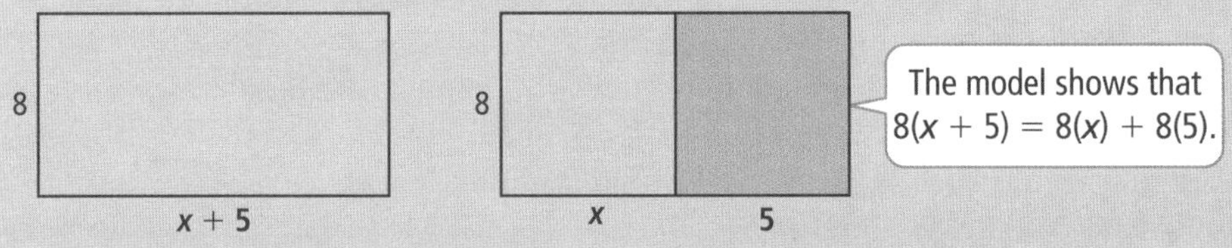

Essential Understanding You can use the Distributive Property to simplify the product of a number and a sum or difference.

take note

Property Distributive Property

Let a, b, and c be real numbers.

Algebra

$a(b + c) = ab + ac$

$(b + c)a = ba + ca$

$a(b - c) = ab - ac$

$(b - c)a = ba - ca$

Examples

$4(20 + 6) = 4(20) + 4(6)$

$(20 + 6)4 = 20(4) + 6(4)$

$7(30 - 2) = 7(30) - 7(2)$

$(30 - 2)7 = 30(7) - 2(7)$

Problem 1 Simplifying Expressions

Got It? What is the simplified form of each expression?

a. $5(x + 7)$

b. $12\left(3 - \frac{1}{6}t\right)$

c. $(0.4 + 1.1c)3$

d. $(2y - 1)(-y)$

Practice **Use the Distributive Property to simplify each expression.**

1. $\frac{1}{4}(4f - 8)$

2. $(-8z - 10)(-1.5)$

A fraction bar may act as a grouping symbol. A fraction bar indicates division. Any fraction $\frac{a}{b}$ can also be written as $a \cdot \frac{1}{b}$. You can use this fact and the Distributive Property to rewrite some fractions as sums or differences.

Problem 2 Rewriting Fraction Expressions

Got It? What sum or difference is equivalent to each expression?

a. $\frac{4x - 16}{3}$

b. $\frac{11 + 3x}{6}$

c. $\frac{15 + 6x}{12}$

d. $\frac{4 - 2x}{8}$

A Practice Write each fraction as a sum or difference.

3. $\frac{22 - 2n}{2}$

4. $\frac{42w + 14}{7}$

The Multiplication Property of -1 states that $-1 \cdot x = -x$. To simplify an expression such as $-(x + 6)$, you can rewrite the expression as $-1(x + 6)$.

Problem 3 Using the Multiplication Property of -1

Got It? What is the simplified form of each expression?

a. $-(a + 5)$

$-a - 5$

b. $-(-x + 31)$

$x - 31$

c. $-(4x - 12)$

$-4x + 12$

d. $-(6m - 9n)$

Think

What does the negative sign in front of the parentheses mean?

A Practice Simplify each expression.

5. $-(-m + n + 1)$

6. $-(x + 3y - 3)$

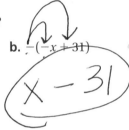

You can use the Distributive Property to make calculations easier to do with mental math. Some numbers can be thought of as simple sums or differences.

Problem 4 Using the Distributive Property for Mental Math

Got It? Julia commutes to work on the train 4 times each week. A round-trip ticket costs \$7.25. What is her weekly cost for tickets? Use mental math.

Practice 7. One hundred five students see a play. Each ticket costs \$45. What is the total amount the students spend for tickets? Use mental math.

8. Suppose the distance you travel to school is 5 mi. What is the total distance for 197 trips from home to school? Use mental math.

Essential Understanding You can simplify an algebraic expression by combining the parts of the expression that are alike.

In an algebraic expression, a **term** is a number, a variable, or the product of a number and one or more variables. A **constant** is a term that has no variable. A **coefficient** is a numerical factor of a term. Rewrite expressions as sums to identify these parts of an expression.

$6a^2$, $-5ab$, $3b$, and -12 are terms.

$$6a^2 - 5ab + 3b - 12 = 6a^2 + (-5ab) + 3b + (-12)$$

coefficients (6, −5, 3) — constant (−12)

In the algebraic expression $6a^2 - 5ab + 3b - 12$, the terms have coefficients of 6, −5, and 3. The term −12 is a constant.

Like terms have the same variable factors. To identify like terms, compare the variable factors of the terms, as shown below.

Terms	$4x^2$ and $12x^2$	$6ab$ and $-2a$	xy^2 and x^2y
Variable Factors	x^2 and x^2	ab and a	xy^2 and x^2y
Like Terms?	yes	no	no

An algebraic expression in simplest form has no like terms or parentheses.

Not Simplified	**Simplified**
$2(3x - 5 + 4x)$	$14x - 10$

You can use the Distributive Property to help combine like terms. Think of the Distributive Property as $ba + ca = (b + c)a$.

Problem 5 Combining Like Terms

Got It? What is the simplified form of each expression in parts (a)–(c)?

Plan
Which terms can you combine?

a. $3y - y$ = 2y

Only combine variables that are the exact same when + or −

b. $-7mn^4 - 5mn^4$

$-12mn^4$

c. $7y^3z - 6yz^3 + y^3z$

7 − 6 + 1 = $2y^3z$

d. Reasoning Can you simplify $8x^2 - 2x^4 - 2x + 2 + xy$ further? Explain.

leave it alone

Practice Simplify each expression by combining like terms.

9. $-7h + 3h^2 - 4h - 3$

$\widehat{-11h + 3h^2 - 3}$

$3h^2 - 11h - 3$

10. $10ab + 2ab^2 - 9ab$

$1ab$

$2ab^2 + 1ab$

Lesson Check

Do you know HOW?

11. What is the simplified form of each expression? Use the Distributive Property.

a. $(j + 2)7$

$7(j+2)$

b. $-8(x - 3)$

c. $-(4 - c)$

d. $-(11 + 2b)$

Rewrite each expression as a sum.

12. $-8x^2 + 3xy - 9x - 3$

13. $2ab - 5ab^2 - 9a^2b$

Tell whether the terms are like terms.

14. $3a$ and $-5a$

15. $2xy^2$ and $-x^2y$

Do you UNDERSTAND?

MATHEMATICAL PRACTICES

16. Vocabulary Does each equation demonstrate the Distributive Property? Explain.

a. $-2(x + 1) = -2x - 2$

b. $(s - 4)8 = 8(s - 4)$

c. $5n - 45 = 5(n - 9)$

d. $8 + (t + 6) = (8 + t) + 6$

17. Mental Math How can you express 499 to find the product 499×5 using mental math? Explain.

18. Reasoning Is each expression in simplified form? Justify your answer.

a. $4xy^3 + 5x^3y$

b. $-(y - 1)$

c. $5x^2 + 12xy - 3yx$

More Practice and Problem-Solving Exercises

MATHEMATICAL PRACTICES

B Apply

Write a word phrase for each expression. Then simplify each expression.

19. $3(t - 1)$ **20.** $4(d + 7)$ **21.** $\frac{1}{3}(6x - 1)$

STEM **22. Physiology** The recommended heart rate for exercise, in beats per minute, is given by the expression $0.8(200 - y)$ where y is a person's age in years. Rewrite this expression using the Distributive Property. What is the recommended heart rate for a 20-year-old person? For a 50-year-old person? Use mental math.

23. Error Analysis Identify and correct the error shown at the right.

~~$4(x + 5) = (4 \cdot x)(4 \cdot 5)$~~
~~$= 80x$~~

24. Error Analysis A friend uses the Distributive Property to simplify $4(2b - 5)$ and gets $8b - 5$ as the result. Describe and correct the error.

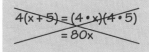

Geometry **Write an expression in simplified form for the area of each rectangle.**

25. Rectangle with sides 11 and $3x + 2$

26. Rectangle with sides $5 + 2y$ and 5

27. Rectangle with sides 7 and $5n - 9$

28. Think About a Plan You are replacing your regular shower head with a water-saving shower head. These shower heads use the amount of water per minute shown. If you take an 8-min shower, how many gallons of water will you save?

- Which would you use to represent water saved each minute, an expression involving addition or an expression involving subtraction?
- How can you use the Distributive Property to find the total amount of water saved?

Simplify each expression.

29. $6yz + 2yz - 8yz$

30. $-2ab + ab + 9ab - 3ab$

31. $-9m^3n + 4m^3n + 5mn$

32. $3(-4cd - 5)$

33. $12x^2y - 8x^2y^2 + 11x^2y - 4x^3y^2 - 9xy^2$

34. $a - \frac{a}{4} + \frac{3}{4}a$

35. Reasoning The Distributive Property also applies to division, as shown.

$$\frac{a+b}{c} = \frac{a}{c} + \frac{b}{c}$$

Use the Distributive Property of Division to rewrite $\frac{9 + 12n}{3}$. Then simplify.

36. Lawn Game You play a game where you throw a pair of connected balls at a structure, as shown at the right. When a pair wraps around a bar, you earn the points shown. You toss 3 pairs, and all of them wrap around a bar. Which expression could represent your total score if a pairs of balls wrap around the blue bar?

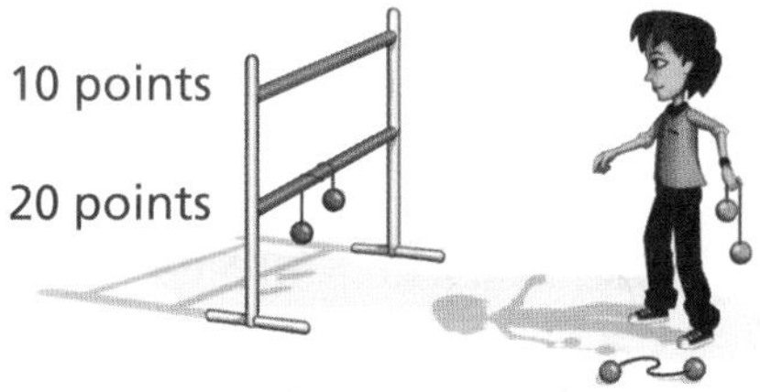

Ⓐ $30 + 10a$ Ⓑ $20a + 3 - 10a$ Ⓒ $10a + 20(3 - a)$ Ⓓ $30a + 10$

37. Open-Ended Suppose you used the Distributive Property to get the expression $3m - 6n - 15$. With what expression could you have started?

Challenge

38. Writing Your friend uses the order of operations to find the value of $11(39 - 3)$. Would you prefer to use the Distributive Property instead? Explain.

Simplify each expression.

39. $5(2d + 1) + 7(5d + 3)$

40. $6(4t - 3) + 6(4 - 3t)$

41. $9(5 + t) - 7(t + 3)$

42. $4(r + 8) - 5(2r - 1)$

43. $-(m + 9n - 12)$

44. $-6(3 - 3x - 7y) + 2y - x$

1-2 Solving Multi-Step Equations

A.CED.1 Create equations and inequalities in one variable and . . . solve problems . . . Also **A.REI.1, A.REI.3**

Objective To solve multi-step equations in one variable

Solve It! Write your solution to the Solve It in the space below.

In this lesson, you will learn to write and solve multi-step equations.

Essential Understanding To solve multi-step equations, you form a series of simpler equivalent equations. To do this, use the properties of equality, inverse operations, and properties of real numbers. You use the properties until you isolate the variable.

Problem 1 Combining Like Terms

Think How can you simplify the left side of each equation?

Got It? What is the solution of each equation? Check each answer.

a. $11m - 8 - 6m = 22$

$5m - 8 = 22$

$+8 \quad +8$

$\frac{5m}{5} = \frac{30}{5}$

$m = 6$

b. $-2y + 5 + 5y = 14$

$3y + 5 = 14$

$-5 \quad -5$

$\frac{3y}{3} = \frac{9}{3}$

$y = 3$

A **Practice** Solve each equation. Check your answer.

1. $17 = p - 3 - 3p$

$17 = 2p - 3$

$+3 \qquad +3$

$20 = -2p$

$\dfrac{}{-2} \quad \dfrac{}{-2}$

$\boxed{p = -10}$

2. $-23 = -2a - 10 + a$

$-23 = -1a - 10$

$+10 \qquad +10$

$-13 = -1a$

$\dfrac{}{-1} \quad \dfrac{}{-1}$

$\boxed{a = 13}$

Problem 2 Solving a Multi-Step Equation

Got It? Noah and Kate are shopping for new guitar strings in a music store. Noah buys 2 packs of strings. Kate buys 2 packs of strings and a music book. The book costs $16. Their total cost is $72. How much is one pack of strings?

> **Think**
> How can a model help you write an equation for this situation?

N $\bigcirc\!\!\!2$

K $\bigcirc\!\!\!2$ + MB

16

$\cancel{4}S + 16 = 72$

slope \quad I \qquad T

A **Practice** Write an equation to model each situation. Then solve the equation.

3. **Employment** You have a part-time job. You work for 3 h on Friday and 6 h on Saturday. You also receive an allowance of $20 per week. You earn $92 per week. How much do you earn per hour at your part-time job?

C \quad 3h

\quad 6h

$\dfrac{9h + 20 = 92}{\text{slope} \quad I \quad T}$

4. Travel A family buys airline tickets online. Each ticket costs $167. The family buys travel insurance with each ticket that costs $19 per ticket. The Web site charges a fee of $16 for the entire purchase. The family is charged a total of $1132. How many tickets did the family buy?

T $167. + 16

19t   19t + 183 = 1,132

Problem 3 Solving an Equation Using the Distributive Property

Got It? **a.** What is the solution of $18 = 3(2x - 6)$? Check your answer.

b. Reasoning Can you solve the equation in part (a) by using the Division Property of Equality instead of the Distributive Property? Explain.

Bobby was here!?

Practice **Solve each equation. Check your answer.**

5. $n + 5(n - 1) = 7$

6. $-4(r + 6) = -63$

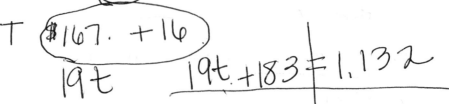

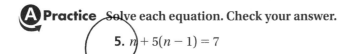

You can use different methods to solve equations that contain fractions.

Problem 4 Solving an Equation That Contains Fractions

Got It? What is the solution of each equation? Why did you choose the method you used to solve each equation?

a. $\frac{2b}{5} + \frac{3b}{4} = 3$

b. $\frac{1}{9} = \frac{5}{6} - \frac{m}{3}$

A Practice **Solve each equation. Choose the method you prefer to use. Check your answer.**

7. $\frac{11z}{16} + \frac{7z}{8} = \frac{5}{16}$

8. $\frac{x}{3} - \frac{7x}{12} = \frac{2}{3}$

You can clear decimals from an equation by multiplying by a power of 10. First, find the greatest number of digits to the right of any decimal point, and then multiply by 10 raised to that power.

Problem 5 Solving an Equation That Contains Decimals

Got It? What is the solution of $0.5x - 2.325 = 3.95$? Check your answer.

Practice **Solve each equation. Check your answer.**

9. $25.24 = 5g + 3.89$

10. $0.25n + 0.1n = 9.8$

Lesson Check

Do you know HOW?

Solve each equation. Check your answer.

11. $7p + 8p - 12 = 59$

12. $-2(3x + 9) = 24$

13. $\frac{2m}{7} + \frac{3m}{14} = 1$

14. $1.2 = 2.4 - 0.6x$

15. Gardening There is a 12-ft fence on one side of a rectangular garden. The gardener has 44 ft of fencing to enclose the other three sides. What is the length of the garden's longer dimension?

Do you UNDERSTAND?

MATHEMATICAL PRACTICES

Explain how you would solve each equation.

16. $1.3 + 0.5x = -3.41$

17. $7(3x - 4) = 49$

18. $-\frac{2}{9}x - 4 = \frac{7}{18}$

19. Reasoning Ben solves the equation $-24 = 5(g + 3)$ by first dividing each side by 5. Amelia solves the equation by using the Distributive Property. Whose method do you prefer? Explain.

More Practice and Problem-Solving Exercises

MATHEMATICAL PRACTICES

B Apply

Solve each equation.

20. $6 + \frac{v}{-8} = \frac{4}{7}$

21. $\frac{2}{3}(c - 18) = 7$

22. $3d + d - 7 = \frac{25}{4}$

23. $0.25(d - 12) = 4$

24. $8n - (2n - 3) = 12$

25. $\frac{2}{3} + n + 6 = \frac{3}{4}$

26. $0.5d - 3d + 5 = 0$

27. $-(w + 5) = -14$

28. $\frac{a}{20} + \frac{4}{15} = \frac{9}{15}$

29. Think About a Plan Jillian and Tyson are shopping for knitting supplies. Jillian wants 3 balls of yarn and 1 set of knitting needles. Tyson wants 1 ball of yarn and 2 sets of knitting needles. Each ball of yarn costs $6.25. If their total cost is $34.60, what is the cost of 1 set of knitting needles?

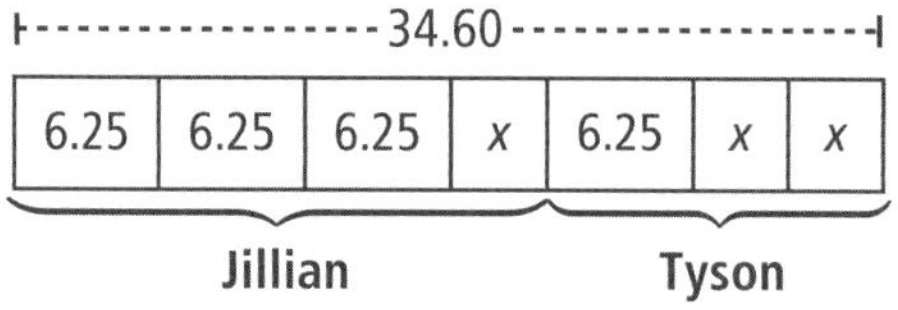

- How can the model at the right help you solve the problem?
- How does the model tell you which operations to use in the equation?

30. Online Video Games Angie and Kenny play online video games. Angie buys 1 software package and 3 months of game play. Kenny buys 1 software package and 2 months of game play. Each software package costs $20. If their total cost is $115, what is the cost of one month of game play?

31. Error Analysis Describe and correct the error in solving the equation at the right.

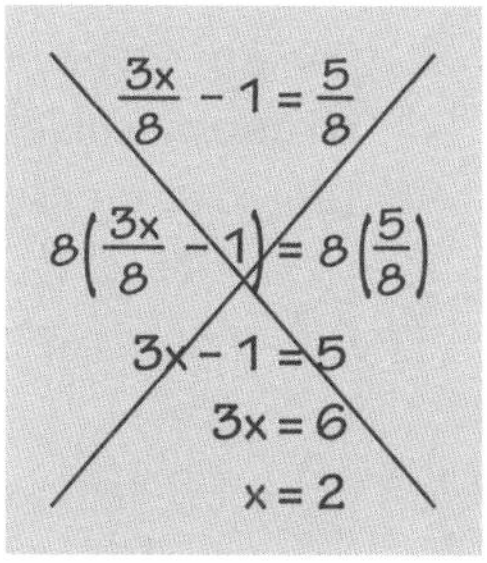

32. Reasoning Suppose you want to solve $-4m + 5 + 6m = -3$. What would you do as your first step? Explain.

33. Writing Describe two ways in which you can solve $-\frac{1}{2}(5x - 9) = 17$.

34. Bowling Three friends go bowling. The cost per person per game is $5.30. The cost to rent shoes is $2.50 per person. Their total cost is $55.20. How many games did they play?

35. Moving Expenses A college student is moving into a campus dormitory. The student rents a moving truck for $19.95 plus $.99 per mile. Before returning the truck, the student fills the tank with gasoline, which costs $65.32. The total cost is $144.67. How many miles did the student drive the truck?

Geometry **Find the value of x. (*Hint*: The sum of the angle measures of a quadrilateral is 360°.)**

36.

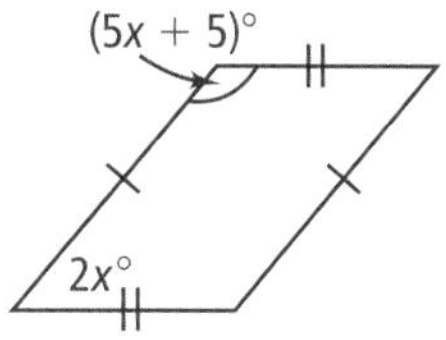

37.

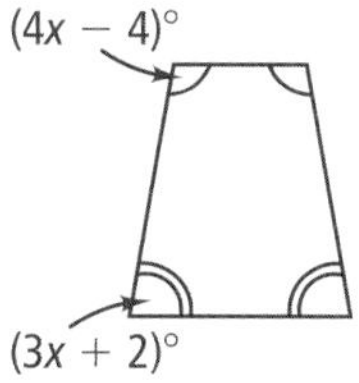

38.

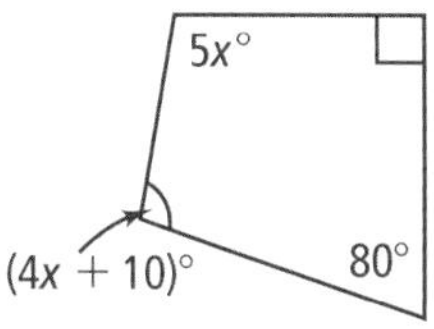

39. Dining Out You are ordering a meal and have \$15 to spend. The restaurant charges 6% sales tax. You plan to leave a 15% tip. The equation $c = x + 0.06x + 0.15x$ gives the total cost c of your meal, where x is the cost before tax and tip. What is the maximum amount you can spend before tax and tip?

40. Savings You have \$85 in your bank account. Each week you plan to deposit \$8 from your allowance and \$15 from your paycheck. The equation $b = 85 + (15 + 8)w$ gives the amount b in your bank account after w weeks. How many weeks from now will you have \$175 in your bank account?

Challenge

41. Find three consecutive integers with a sum of 45. Show your work.

42. Cooking A cook buys two identical bags of rice and uses some of the rice in each bag so that one bag is half full and the other is one-third full. The cook combines them into one bag, which then contains $3\frac{1}{3}$ cups of rice. How much rice was in a full bag?

43. Painting Tim can paint a house in 6 days. Tara can paint the same house in 3 days.

a. What fraction of the house can Tim paint in one day? What fraction of the house can Tara paint in one day?

b. What fraction of the house can Tim paint in d days? What fraction of the house can Tara paint in d days?

c. What fraction of the house can Tim and Tara together paint in one day? What fraction of the house can Tim and Tara together paint in d days?

d. Write and solve an equation to find the number of days it will take Tim and Tara to paint the whole house working together.

1-3 Solving Equations With Variables on Both Sides

A.CED.1 Create equations and inequalities in one variable and . . . solve problems . . . Also **A.REI.1, A.REI.3**

Objectives To solve equations with variables on both sides
To identify equations that are identities or have no solution

Solve It! Write your solution to the Solve It in the space below.

The problem in the Solve It can be modeled by an equation that has variables on both sides.

Essential Understanding To solve equations with variables on both sides, you can use the properties of equality and inverse operations to write a series of simpler equivalent equations.

Problem 1 Solving an Equation With Variables on Both Sides

Got It? **a.** What is the solution of $7k + 2 = 4k - 10$?

b. Reasoning Solve the equation in Problem 1 by subtracting $5x$ from each side instead of $2x$. Compare and contrast your solution with the solution in Problem 1.

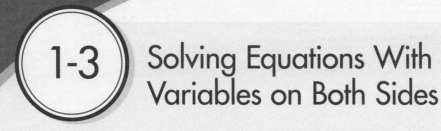

A Practice **Solve each equation. Check your answer.**

1. $-3c - 12 = -5 + c$

2. $-n - 23 = 5 + n$

Problem 2 Using an Equation With Variables on Both Sides

Got It? An office manager spent $650 on a new energy-saving copier that will reduce the monthly electric bill for the office from $112 to $88. In how many months will the copier pay for itself?

A Practice **Write and solve an equation for each situation. Check your solution.**

STEM **3. Architecture** An architect is designing a rectangular greenhouse. Along one wall is a 7-ft storage area and 5 sections for different kinds of plants. On the opposite wall is a 4-ft storage area and 6 sections for plants. All of the sections for plants are of equal length. What is the length of each wall?

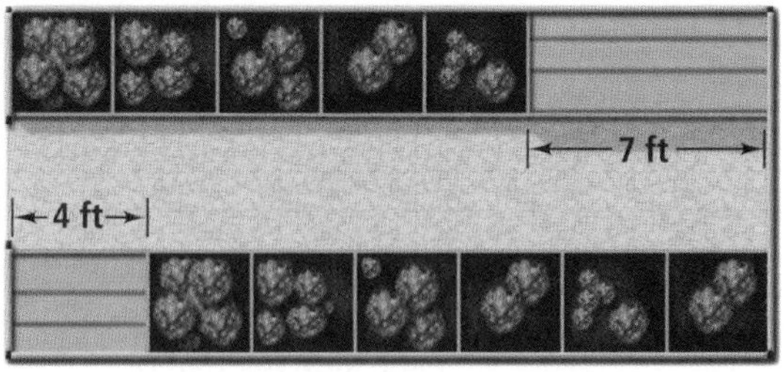

4. Business A hairdresser is deciding where to open her own studio. If the hairdresser chooses Location A, she will pay $1200 per month in rent and will charge $45 per haircut. If she chooses Location B, she will pay $1800 per month in rent and will charge $60 per haircut. How many haircuts would she have to give in one month to make the same profit at either location?

ONLINE PROBLEMS

Problem 3 Solving an Equation With Grouping Symbols

Plan

How do you get started?

Got It? What is the solution of each equation?

a. $4(2y + 1) = 2(y - 13)$

b. $7(4 - a) = 3(a - 4)$

A Practice Solve each equation. Check your answer.

5. $2r - (5 - r) = 13 + 2r$

6. $5g + 4(-5 + 3g) = 1 - g$

An equation that is true for every possible value of the variable is an **identity**. For example, $x + 1 = x + 1$ is an identity. An equation has no solution if there is no value of the variable that makes the equation true. The equation $x + 1 = x + 2$ has no solution.

ONLINE PROBLEMS

Problem 4 Identities and Equations With No Solution

Think

How can you tell how many solutions an equation has?

Got It? What is the solution of each equation?

a. $3(4b - 2) = -6 + 12b$

b. $2x + 7 = -1(3 - 2x)$

Practice **Determine whether each equation is an *identity* or whether it has *no solution*.**

7. $-6a + 3 = -3(2a - 3)$

8. $4 - d = -(d - 4)$

When you solve an equation, you use reasoning to select properties of equality that produce simpler equivalent equations until you find a solution. The steps below provide a general guideline for solving equations.

take note

Concept Summary Solving Equations

Step 1 Use the Distributive Property to remove any grouping symbols. Use properties of equality to clear decimals and fractions.

Step 2 Combine like terms on each side of the equation.

Step 3 Use the properties of equality to get the variable terms on one side of the equation and the constants on the other.

Step 4 Use the properties of equality to solve for the variable.

Step 5 Check your solution in the original equation.

Lesson Check

Do you know HOW?

Solve each equation. Check your answer.

9. $3x + 4 = 5x - 10$

10. $5(y - 4) = 7(2y + 1)$

11. $2a + 3 = \frac{1}{2}(6 + 4a)$

12. $4x - 5 = 2(2x + 1)$

13. Printing Pristine Printing will print business cards for \$.10 each plus a setup charge of \$15. The Printing Place offers business cards for \$.15 each with a setup charge of \$10. What number of business cards costs the same from either printer?

Do you UNDERSTAND?

MATHEMATICAL PRACTICES

Vocabulary **Match each equation with the appropriate number of solutions.**

14. $3y - 5 = y + 2y - 9$ **A.** infinitely many

15. $2y + 4 = 2(y + 2)$ **B.** one solution

16. $2y - 4 = 3y - 5$ **C.** no solution

17. Writing A student solved an equation and found that the variable was eliminated in the process of solving the equation. How would the student know whether the equation is an identity or an equation with no solution?

More Practice and Problem-Solving Exercises

MATHEMATICAL PRACTICES

B Apply

Solve each equation. If the equation is an identity, write *identity*. If it has no solution, write *no solution*.

18. $3.2 - 4d = 2.3d + 3$

19. $3d + 4 = 2 + 3d - \frac{1}{2}$

20. $2.25(4x - 4) = -2 + 10x + 12$

21. $3a + 1 = -3.6(a - 1)$

22. $\frac{1}{2}h + \frac{1}{3}(h - 6) = \frac{5}{6}h + 2$

23. $0.5b + 4 = 2(b + 2)$

24. $-2(-c - 12) = -2c - 12$

25. $3(m + 1.5) = 1.5(2m + 3)$

26. Travel Suppose a family drives at an average rate of 60 mi/h on the way to visit relatives and then at an average rate of 40 mi/h on the way back. The return trip takes 1 h longer than the trip there.

a. Let d be the distance in miles the family traveled to visit their relatives. How many hours did it take to drive there?

b. In terms of d, how many hours did it take to make the return trip?

c. Write and solve an equation to determine the distance the family drove to see their relatives. What was the average rate for the entire trip?

27. Think About a Plan Each morning, a deli worker has to make several pies and peel a bucket of potatoes. On Monday, it took the worker 2 h to make the pies and an average of 1.5 min to peel each potato. On Tuesday, the worker finished the work in the same amount of time, but it took 2.5 h to make the pies and an average of 1 min to peel each potato. About how many potatoes are in a bucket?

- What quantities do you know and how are they related to each other?
- How can you use the known and unknown quantities to write an equation for this situation?

28. Error Analysis Describe and correct the error in finding the solution of the equation $2x = 6x$.

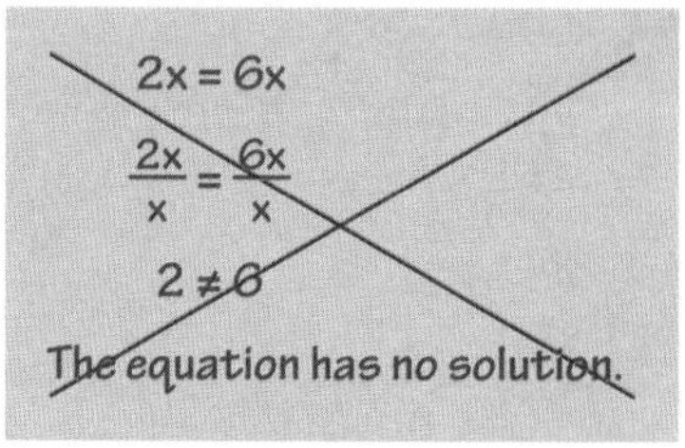

29. Skiing A skier is trying to decide whether or not to buy a season ski pass. A daily pass costs \$67. A season ski pass costs \$350. The skier would have to rent skis with either pass for \$25 per day. How many days would the skier have to go skiing in order to make the season pass less expensive than daily passes?

30. Health Clubs One health club charges a \$50 sign-up fee and \$65 per month. Another club charges a \$90 sign-up fee and \$45 per month. For what number of months is the cost of the clubs equal?

31. Geometry The perimeters of the triangles shown are equal. Find the side lengths of each triangle.

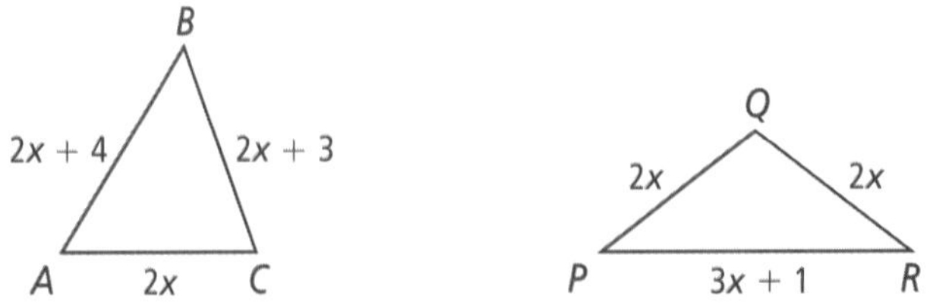

32. Business A small juice company spends \$1200 per day on business expenses plus \$1.10 per bottle of juice they make. They charge \$2.50 for each bottle of juice they produce. How many bottles of juice must the company sell in one day in order to equal its daily costs?

33. Spreadsheet You set up a spreadsheet to solve $7(x + 1) = 3(x - 1)$.

a. Does your spreadsheet show the solution of the equation?

b. Between which two values of x is the solution of the equation? How do you know?

c. For what spreadsheet values of x is $7(x + 1)$ less than $3(x - 1)$?

	A	B	C
1	x	$7(x + 1)$	$3(x - 1)$
2	−5	−28	−18
3	−3	−14	−12
4	−1	0	−6
5	1	14	0
6	3	28	6

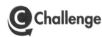

34. Reasoning Determine whether each statement is *always, sometimes,* or *never* true.

a. An equation of the form $ax + 1 = ax$ has no solution.

b. An equation in one variable has at least one solution.

c. An equation of the form $\frac{x}{a} = \frac{x}{b}$ has infinitely many solutions.

Challenge

Open-Ended Write an equation with a variable on both sides such that you get each solution.

35. $x = 5$

36. $x = 0$

37. x can be any number.

38. No values of x are solutions.

39. x is a negative number.

40. x is a fraction.

41. Suppose you have three consecutive integers. The greatest of the three integers is twice as great as the sum of the first two. What are the integers?

1-4 Literal Equations and Formulas

A.CED.4 Rearrange formulas to highlight a quantity of interest . . . Also N.Q.1, A.CED.1, A.REI.3

Objective To rewrite and use literal equations and formulas

Solve It! Write your solution to the Solve It in the space below.

In this lesson, you will learn to solve problems using equations in more than one variable. A **literal equation** is an equation that involves two or more variables.

Essential Understanding When you work with literal equations, you can use the methods you have learned in this chapter to isolate any particular variable.

Problem 1 Rewriting a Literal Equation

Got It? a. Solve the equation $4 = 2m - 5n$ for m. What are the values of m when $n = -2, 0,$ and 2?

b. **Reasoning** Solve Problem 1 by substituting $x = 3$ and $x = 6$ into the equation $10x + 5y = 80$ and then solving for y in each case. Do you prefer this method or the method shown in Problem 1? Explain.

Practice Solve each equation for y. Then find the value of y for each value of x.

1. $x - 4y = -4; x = -2, 4, 6$

2. $6x = 7 - 4y; x = -2, -1, 0$

When you rewrite literal equations, you may have to divide by a variable or variable expression. When you do so in this lesson, assume that the variable or variable expression is not equal to zero because division by zero is not defined.

Problem 2 Rewriting a Literal Equation With Only Variables

Got It? What equation do you get when you solve $-t = r + px$ for x?

Think
How can you solve a literal equation for a variable?

Practice Solve each equation for x.

3. $4(x - b) = x$

4. $A = Bxt + c$

A **formula** is an equation that states a relationship among quantities. Formulas are special types of literal equations. Some common formulas are given below. Notice that some of the formulas use the same variables, but the definitions of the variables are different.

Formula Name	Formula	Definitions of Variables
Perimeter of a rectangle	$P = 2\ell + 2w$	P = perimeter, ℓ = length, w = width
Circumference of a circle	$C = 2\pi r$	C = circumference, r = radius
Area of a rectangle	$A = \ell w$	A = area, ℓ = length, w = width
Area of a triangle	$A = \frac{1}{2}bh$	A = area, b = base, h = height
Area of a circle	$A = \pi r^2$	A = area, r = radius
Distance traveled	$d = rt$	d = distance, r = rate, t = time
Temperature	$C = \frac{5}{9}(F - 32)$	C = degrees Celsius, F = degrees Fahrenheit

ONLINE PROBLEMS

Problem 3 Rewriting a Geometric Formula

Think

How do you know which formula to use?

Got It? What is the height of a triangle that has an area of 24 in.^{2} and a base with a length of 8 in.?

A Practice **Solve the problem. Round to the nearest tenth, if necessary.**

5. A rectangle has perimeter 84 cm and length 35 cm. What is its width?

6. **Parks** A public park is in the shape of a triangle. The side of the park that forms the base of the triangle is 200 yd long, and the area of the park is 7500 yd^2. What is the length of the side of the park that forms the height of the triangle?

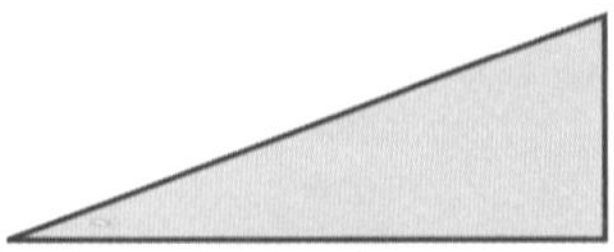

Problem 4 Rewriting a Formula

Got It? Pacific gray whales migrate annually from the waters near Alaska to the waters near Baja California, Mexico, and back. The whales travel a distance of about 5000 mi each way at an average rate of 91 mi per day. About how many days does it take the whales to migrate one way?

A Practice **Solve each problem. Round to the nearest tenth, if necessary.**

7. **Baseball** You can use the formula $a = \frac{h}{n}$ to find the batting average a of a batter who has h hits in n times at bat. Solve the formula for h. If a batter has a batting average of .290 and has been at bat 300 times, how many hits does the batter have?

STEM **8. Construction** Bricklayers use the formula $n = 7\ell h$ to estimate the number n of bricks needed to build a wall of length ℓ and height h, where ℓ and h are in feet. Solve the formula for h. Estimate the height of a wall 28 ft long that requires 1568 bricks.

Lesson Check

Do you know HOW?

Solve each equation for the given variable.

9. $-2x + 5y = 12$ for y

10. $a - 2b = -10$ for b

11. $mx + 2nx = p$ for x

12. $C = \frac{5}{9}(F - 32)$ for F

13. Gardening Jonah is planting a rectangular garden. The perimeter of the garden is 120 yd, and the width is 20 yd. What is the length of the garden?

Do you UNDERSTAND?

MATHEMATICAL PRACTICES

Vocabulary Classify each equation below as a formula, a literal equation, or both.

14. $c = 2d$

15. $y = 2x - 1$

16. $A = \frac{1}{2}bh$

17. $P = 2\ell + 2w$

18. Compare and Contrast How is the process of rewriting literal equations similar to the process of solving equations in one variable? How is it different?

More Practice and Problem-Solving Exercises

MATHEMATICAL PRACTICES

B Apply

Solve each equation for the given variable.

19. $2m - nx = x + 4$ for x

20. $\frac{x}{a} - 1 = \frac{y}{b}$ for x

21. $ax + 2xy = 14$ for y

22. $V = \frac{1}{3}\pi r^2 h$ for h

23. $A = \left(\frac{f+g}{2}\right)h$ for g

24. $2(x + a) = 4b$ for a

25. Think About a Plan The interior angles of a polygon are the angles formed inside a polygon by two adjacent sides. The sum S of the measures of the interior angles of a polygon with n sides can be found using the formula $S = 180(n - 2)$. The sum of a polygon's interior angle measures is 1260°. How many sides does the polygon have?
- What information are you given in the problem?
- What variable do you need to solve for in the formula?

STEM **26. Weather** Polar stratospheric clouds are colorful clouds that form when temperatures fall below −78°C. What is this temperature in degrees Fahrenheit?

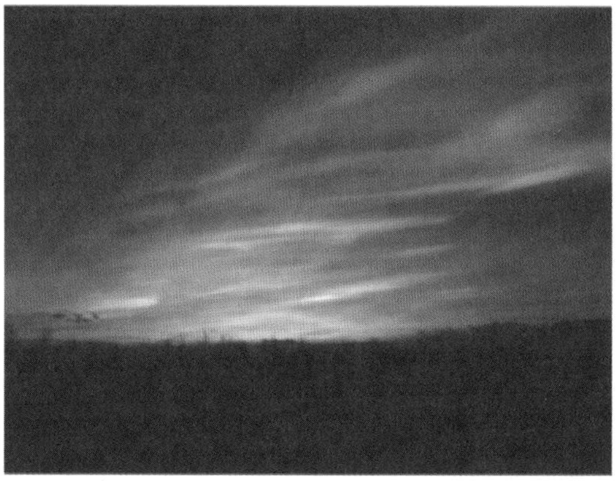

Polar stratospheric clouds

STEM **27. Science** The energy E of a moving object is called its *kinetic energy*. It is calculated using the formula $E = \frac{1}{2}mv^2$, where m is the object's mass in kilograms and v is its speed in meters per second. The units of kinetic energy are $\frac{\text{kilograms} \cdot \text{meters}^2}{\text{second}^2}$, abbreviated as $\text{kg} \cdot \text{m}^2/\text{s}^2$.

a. Solve the given formula for m.

b. What is the mass of an object moving at 10 m/s with a kinetic energy of 2500 $\text{kg} \cdot \text{m}^2/\text{s}^2$?

28. Error Analysis Describe and correct the error made in solving the literal equation at the right for n.

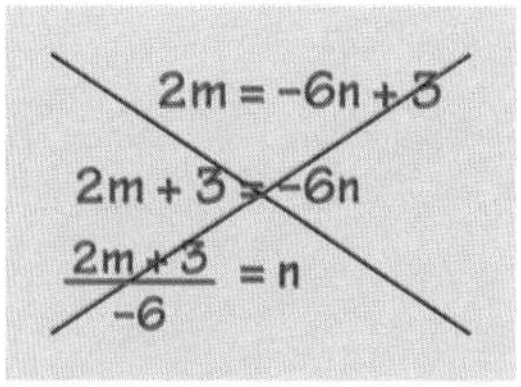

29. Geometry The formula for the volume of a cylinder is $V = \pi r^2 h$, where r is the cylinder's radius and h is its height. Solve the equation for h. What is the height of a cylinder with volume 502.4 cm³ and radius 4 cm? Use 3.14 for π.

30. Density The density of an object is calculated using the formula $D = \frac{m}{V}$, where m is the object's mass and V is its volume. Gold has a density of 19.3 g/cm³. What is the volume of an amount of gold that has a mass of 96.5 g?

31. Open-Ended Write an equation in three variables. Solve the equation for each variable. Show all your steps.

Challenge

32. Surface Area A rectangular prism with height h and with square bases with side length s is shown.

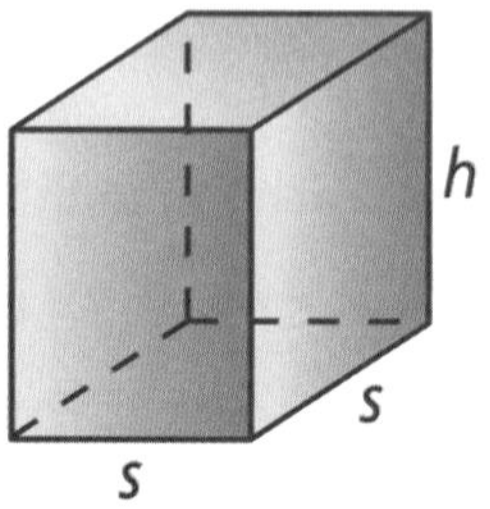

a. Write a formula for the surface area A of the prism.

b. Rewrite the formula to find h in terms of A and s. If s is 10 cm and A is 760 cm^2, what is the height of the prism?

c. Writing Suppose h is equal to s. Write a formula for A in terms of s only.

33. Midpoints Suppose a segment on a number line has endpoints with coordinates a and b. The coordinate of the segment's midpoint m is given by the formula $m = \frac{a+b}{2}$.

a. Find the midpoint of a segment with endpoints at 9.3 and 2.1.

b. Rewrite the given formula to find b in terms of a and m.

c. The midpoint of a segment is at 3.5. One endpoint is at 8.9. Find the other endpoint.

1-5 Ratios, Rates, and Conversions

N.Q.1 Use units as a way to understand problems and to guide the solution of . . . problems; choose and interpret units consistently . . . ; choose and interpret the scale and the origin in graphs and data displays. Also **N.Q.2**

Objectives To find ratios and rates
To convert units and rates

Solve It! Write your solution to the Solve It in the space below.

A **ratio** compares two numbers by division. The ratio of two numbers a and b, where $b \neq 0$, can be written in three ways: $\frac{a}{b}$, $a : b$, and a to b. For every a units of one quantity, you have b units of another quantity.

You can also think of a ratio as a multiplicative relationship. For example, if the ratio of the number of boys to the number of girls in a class is 2 : 1, then the number of boys is *two times* the number of girls.

A ratio that compares quantities measured in different units is called a **rate.** A rate with a denominator of 1 unit is a **unit rate.** In the Solve It, you can express each athlete's speed as the number of meters traveled per 1 second of time. This is an example of a unit rate.

Essential Understanding You can write ratios and find unit rates to compare quantities. You can also convert units and rates to solve problems.

Problem 1 Comparing Unit Rates

Got It? In Problem 1, if Store B lowers its price to \$42 for 4 shirts, does the solution change? Explain.

Practice **1. Running** Trisha ran 10 km in 2.5 h. Jason ran 7.5 km in 2 h. Olga ran 9.5 km in 2.25 h. Who had the fastest average speed?

2. Population Bellingham, Washington, had an area of 25.4 mi^2 and a population of 74,547 during one year. Bakersfield, California, had an area of 113.1 mi^2 and a population of 295,536 during the same year. Which city had a greater number of people per square mile?

To convert from one unit to another, such as feet to inches, you multiply the original unit by a *conversion factor* that produces the desired unit. A **conversion factor** is a ratio of two equivalent measures in different units. A conversion factor is always equal to 1, such as $\frac{1\text{ ft}}{12\text{ in.}}$.

Problem 2 Converting Units

Got It? What is 1250 cm converted to meters?

Plan
How do you choose the conversion factor?

Practice **Convert the given amount to the given unit.**

3. 63 yd; feet

4. 168 h; days

In Problem 2, notice that the units for each quantity are included in the calculations to help determine the units for the answers. This process is called **unit analysis**, or *dimensional analysis.*

Problem 3 Converting Units Between Systems

Plan

How can you convert units?

Got It? a. A building is 1450 ft tall. How many meters tall is the building? Use the fact that 1 m $\approx$ 3.28 ft.

b. Monetary exchange rates change from day to day. On a particular day, the exchange rate for dollars to euros was about 1 dollar = 0.63 euro. About how many euros could you get for $325 on that day?

Practice **Convert the given amount to the given unit.**

5. 5 kg; pounds

6. 2 ft; centimeters

You can also convert rates. For example, you can convert a speed in miles per hour to feet per second. Because rates compare measures in two different units, you must multiply by two conversion factors to change both of the units.

Problem 4 Converting Rates

Got It? a. An athlete ran a sprint of 100 ft in 3.1 s. At what speed was the athlete running in miles per hour? Round to the nearest mile per hour.

b. **Reasoning** In Problem 4, one student multiplied by the conversion factors $\frac{1\text{ mi}}{1760\text{ yd}}$, $\frac{60\text{ s}}{1\text{ min}}$, and $\frac{60\text{ min}}{1\text{ h}}$ to find the speed. Can this method work? Why or why not?

Practice 7. **Maintenance** The janitor at a school discovered a slow leak in a pipe. The janitor found that it was leaking at a rate of 4 fl oz per minute. How fast was the pipe leaking in gallons per hour?

8. Shopping Mr. Swanson bought a package of 10 disposable razors for \$6.30. He found that each razor lasted for 1 week. What was the cost per day?

Lesson Check

Do you know HOW?

9. Which is the better buy, 6 bagels for \$3.29 or 8 bagels for \$4.15?

10. What is 7 lb 4 oz converted to ounces?

11. Which is longer, 12 m or 13 yd?

12. A car is traveling at 55 mi/h. What is the car's speed in feet per second?

Do you UNDERSTAND?

MATHEMATICAL PRACTICES

Vocabulary **Tell whether each rate is a unit rate.**

13. 20 mi every 3 h

14. 2 dollars per day

15. Reasoning Does multiplying by a conversion factor change the amount of what is being measured? How do you know?

16. Reasoning If you convert pounds to ounces, will the number of ounces be greater or less than the number of pounds? Explain.

More Practice and Problem-Solving Exercises

MATHEMATICAL PRACTICES

B Apply

Copy and complete each statement.

17. 7 ft 3 in. = ___ in.

18. 2.2 kg = ___ lb

19. 2.5 h = ___ min

20. 2 qt/min = ___ gal/s

21. 75 cents/h = ___ dollars/day

22. 60 ft/s = ___ km/h

Choose a Method **Choose paper and pencil, mental math, or a calculator to tell which measurement is greater.**

23. 640 ft; 0.5 mi

24. 63 in.; 125 cm

25. 75 g; 5 oz

26. Think About a Plan A college student is considering a subscription to a social-networking Internet site that advertises its cost as "only 87 cents per day." What is the cost of membership in dollars per year?

- How many conversion factors will you need to use to solve the problem?
- How do you choose the appropriate conversion factors?

27. Recipes Recipe A makes 5 dinner rolls using 1 c of flour. Recipe B makes 24 rolls using $7\frac{1}{2}$ c of flour. Recipe C makes 45 rolls using 10 c of flour. Which recipe requires the most flour per roll?

28. Error Analysis Find the mistake in the conversion at the right. Explain the mistake and convert the units correctly.

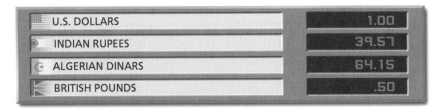

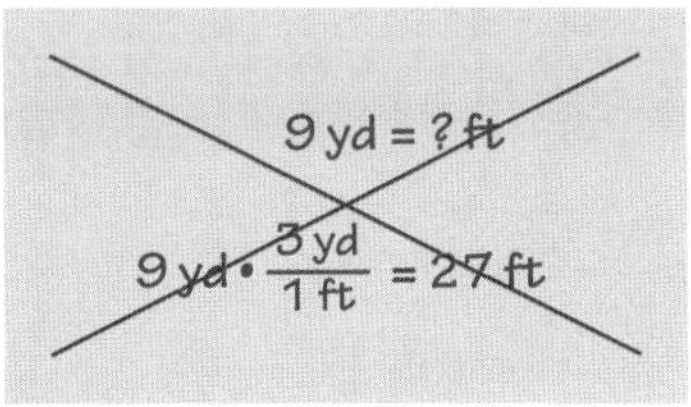

29. Writing Suppose you want to convert kilometers to miles. Which unit should be in the numerator of the conversion factor? Which unit should be in the denominator? Explain how you know.

30. Reasoning Without performing the conversion, determine whether the number of new units will be greater or less than the number of original units.

a. 3 min 20 s converted to seconds
b. 23 cm converted to inches
c. kilometers per hour converted to miles per hour

31. Exchange Rates The table below shows some exchange rates on a particular day. If a sweater sells for $39.95 in U.S. dollars, what should its price be in rupees and pounds?

U.S. DOLLARS	1.00
INDIAN RUPEES	39.57
ALGERIAN DINARS	64.15
BRITISH POUNDS	.50

32. Estimation Five mi is approximately equal to 8 km. Use mental math to estimate the distance in kilometers to a town that is 30 mi away.

33. Reasoning A carpenter is building an entertainment center. She is calculating the size of the space to leave for the television. She wants to leave about a foot of space on either side of the television. Would measuring the size of the television exactly or estimating the size to the nearest inch be more appropriate? Explain.

34. Reasoning A traveler changed $300 to euros for a trip to Germany, but the trip was canceled. Three months later, the traveler changed the euros back to dollars. Would you expect that the traveler got exactly $300 back? Explain.

Challenge

35. Measurement Dietrich draws a line on the blackboard whose length is given by the expression 1 mm + 1 cm + 1 in. + 1 ft + 1 yd + 1 m. What is the length of the line in millimeters?

36. Square Measurements There are 2.54 cm in 1 in.

a. How many square centimeters are there in 1 $in.^2$? Give your answer to the nearest hundredth of a square centimeter.
b. How many square inches are there in 129 cm^2?

ACTIVITY LAB

Use With Lesson 1-5

Unit Analysis

N.Q.1 Use units as a way to understand problems and to guide the solution of . . . problems; choose and interpret units consistently . . . ; choose and interpret the scale and the origin in graphs and data displays. Also **N.Q.2**

In Lesson 1-5, you learned that you can use unit analysis when converting units. You can also use unit analysis to help guide you to the solution of a problem.

Activity 1

The speed of light is about 3.0×10^{10} cm/s. If a rocket car of the future can travel at the speed of light, what is this rate in miles per hour?

Step 1 Make sense of the given information.

1. What units are given in the problem statement?

2. What units of measure should you have in your answer?

Step 2 Formulate a plan to solve the problem.

3. Which units need to be converted to solve the problem?

4. How do you know which conversion factors to use to solve the problem?

5. Can you use different conversion factors to solve the problem? Explain.

Step 3 **Solve the problem.**

6. Use unit analysis to write an expression by using the conversion factors you chose in Step 2.

7. Simplify the expression.

Step 4 **Check your solution.**

8. Are the units of your solution what you expected? Explain.

9. Does your answer make sense? Explain.

You can also use unit analysis to determine the reasonableness of a solution or a claim.

Activity 2

Suppose you are a gold miner in California in 1849. You have your tools in one hand. Can you use your free hand to carry a 4-liter bucket full of gold dust? The density of gold is 19.3 g/cm^3. Use unit analysis to determine whether the bucket is too heavy to carry. (*Hint:* 1 lb $\approx$ 454 g and 1000 $cm^3 = 1$ L.)

Step 1 Make sense of the given information.

10. What units are given in the problem statement?

11. Describe what you need to find in order to determine whether the bucket is too heavy to carry.

12. Will the information you need to find have units of measure? If so, what do you think those units will be?

Step 2 Formulate a plan to solve the problem.

13. Which units need to be converted to solve the problem?

14. How do you know which conversion factors to use to solve the problem?

Step 3 **Solve the problem.**

15. Use unit analysis to find what you described in Step 1.

16. Can you carry a 4-liter bucket of gold dust using one hand? Explain.

Step 4 **Check your solution.**

17. Are the units of your solution what you expected? Explain.

18. Does your answer make sense? Explain.

Exercises

19. The units mi/h and cm/s are units of distance/time. What do these units measure?

20. How can you use unit analysis to help you solve a problem?

Use unit analysis to help you solve each exercise.

21. A popular racetrack is 2.5 miles long. A race is completed in 150 laps. One year, the winner's average speed was 161 miles per hour. During cautionary lap runs, the speed was only about 80 miles per hour. If the race had 30 cautionary laps, about how long did it take the winner to complete the race?

22. Error Analysis Your gas tank holds 13.5 gallons of gas. Your fuel gauge shows that your tank is one-quarter full. Your car gets an average of 25 miles per gallon. The GPS shows that you are 85 miles from your destination. Your brother says you will make it. Is he correct? Use unit analysis to justify your response.

STEM **23. Chemistry** A metal bar in the shape of a rectangular prism with dimensions 6 cm $\times$ 8 cm $\times$ 2 cm has a mass of 53 g. The density of the metal is expressed in units of g/cm^3. Use what you have learned about unit analysis to find the density of the metal.

24. According to the directions, a 12-ounce can of lemonade concentrate makes 64 ounces of lemonade. If each serving is 8 ounces, how many 12-ounce cans of concentrate are needed to make 120 servings?

ACTIVITY LAB

Use With Lesson 1-5

Accuracy and Measurement

N.Q.3 Choose a level of accuracy appropriate to limitations on measurement . . .

Accuracy is the degree of how close a measured value is to the true value of the measurement. When making measurements, you have to be careful to take into consideration the level of accuracy of your measurements, given the tool you are using. A measurement is more accurate when it is closer to the true value of the attribute (length, weight, capacity, temperature) being measured.

Activity

You want to know the weight of three bags of sand. You weigh one bag of sand on a scale that reports weight to the nearest pound. The scale reports that the bag weighs 20 pounds.

1. What are the upper and lower bounds of the true weight of the bag?

2. What are the possible values for the true weight of the bag?

When you weigh the other two bags, the scale reads 19 pounds for one bag and 22 pounds for the other bag.

3. What is the total weight of the three bags according to the scale?

4. What are the upper and lower bounds for the total weight of the bags? What are the possible values for the true weight of the bags?

Another scale reports weights to the nearest tenth of a pound. The scale reads 20.2, 19.1, and 22.3 pounds for the same bags when weighed separately.

5. According to this scale, what are the possible values for the combined weight of the three bags?

6. Which scale is more accurate? Explain.

Exercises

You want to know the perimeter of a painting that appears to be in the shape of a rectangle. You measure the lengths of the sides with a ruler that can measure lengths to the nearest quarter-inch. The measurements are 18 in., 24 in., 24 in., and 18 in.

7. What are the upper and lower bounds for the true lengths of each side of the painting? What are the possible values for the true lengths of each side?

8. What is the perimeter of the painting according to the measured values?

9. What are the upper and lower bounds for the true perimeter of the painting? What are the possible values for the true perimeter?

You measure the lengths again with another ruler that can measure to the nearest eighth of an inch. This time you record the measurements as $18\frac{1}{8}$ in., $23\frac{7}{8}$ in., 24 in., and $18\frac{1}{8}$ in.

10. According to this ruler, what are the possible values for the true perimeter of the painting?

11. Explain why using the ruler that can measure lengths to the nearest eighth of an inch gives a more accurate measurement of the perimeter than using the ruler that can measure only to the nearest quarter-inch.

1-6 Solving Proportions

A.REI.3 Solve linear equations and inequalities in one variable . . . Also N.Q.1, A.CED.1

Objective To solve and apply proportions

Solve It! Write your solution to the Solve It in the space below.

In the Solve It, the number of red beads and the number of blue beads are quantities that have a proportional relationship. This means that the ratio of the quantities is constant even though the quantities themselves can change. For example, as you are making the necklace you will have 2 red beads and 3 blue beads, then 4 red beads and 6 blue beads, then 6 red beads and 9 blue beads, and so on. At each stage, the ratio of red beads to blue beads remains constant, 2 : 3.

A proportional relationship can produce an infinite number of equivalent ratios. Any two of these can be used to write a proportion. A **proportion** is an equation that states that two ratios are equal. For example, $\frac{a}{b} = \frac{c}{d}$, where $b \neq 0$ and $d \neq 0$, is a proportion. You read this as "*a* is to *b* as *c* is to *d*."

Essential Understanding If two ratios are equal and a quantity in one of the ratios is unknown, you can write and solve a proportion to find the unknown quantity.

Problem 1 Solving a Proportion Using the Multiplication Property

Got It? What is the solution of the proportion $\frac{x}{7} = \frac{4}{5}$?

A Practice Solve each proportion using the Multiplication Property of Equality.

1. $\frac{m}{7} = \frac{3}{5}$

2. $\frac{3}{16} = \frac{x}{12}$

In the proportion $\frac{a}{b} = \frac{c}{d}$, the products ad and bc are called **cross products**. You can use the following property of cross products to solve proportions.

take note

Property Cross Products Property of a Proportion

Words The cross products of a proportion are equal.

Algebra If $\frac{a}{b} = \frac{c}{d}$, where $b \neq 0$ and $d \neq 0$, then $ad = bc$.

Example $\frac{3}{4} = \frac{9}{12}$, so $3(12) = 4(9)$, or $36 = 36$.

Here's Why It Works You can use the Multiplication Property of Equality to prove the Cross Products Property.

$\frac{a}{b} = \frac{c}{d}$	Assume this equation is true.
$bd \cdot \frac{a}{b} = bd \cdot \frac{c}{d}$	Multiplication Property of Equality
$\cancel{b}d \cdot \frac{a}{\cancel{b}} = b\cancel{d} \cdot \frac{c}{\cancel{d}}$	Divide the common factors.
$da = bc$	Simplify.
$ad = bc$	Commutative Property of Multiplication

For this proportion, a and d are called the *extremes* of the proportion and b and c are called the *means*. Notice that in the Cross Products Property the product of the means equals the product of the extremes.

Problem 2 Solving a Proportion Using the Cross Products Property

Got It? **a.** What is the solution of the proportion $\frac{y}{3} = \frac{3}{5}$?

b. Reasoning Would you rather use the Cross Products Property or the Multiplication Property of Equality to solve $\frac{3}{5} = \frac{13}{b}$? Explain.

Practice Solve each proportion using the Cross Products Property.

3. $\frac{-3}{4} = \frac{m}{22}$

4. $\frac{2}{-5} = \frac{6}{t}$

Problem 3 Solving a Multi-Step Proportion

Got It? What is the solution of the proportion $\frac{n}{5} = \frac{2n + 4}{6}$?

Think
What property can you use to rewrite the equation?

Practice Solve each proportion using any method.

5. $\frac{q+2}{5} = \frac{2q-11}{7}$

6. $\frac{c+1}{c-2} = \frac{4}{7}$

When you model a real-world situation with a proportion, you must write the proportion carefully. You can write the proportion so that the numerators have the same units and the denominators have the same units.

Correct: $\frac{100 \text{ mi}}{2 \text{ h}} = \frac{x \text{ mi}}{5 \text{ h}}$ **Incorrect:** $\frac{100 \text{ mi}}{2 \text{ h}} = \frac{5 \text{ h}}{x \text{ mi}}$

Problem 4 Using a Proportion to Solve a Problem

Got It? An 8-oz can of orange juice contains about 97 mg of vitamin C. About how many milligrams of vitamin C are there in a 12-oz can of orange juice?

Think
How can you set up a proportion to solve this problem?

Practice

7. **Gardening** A gardener is transplanting flowers into a flower bed. She has been working for an hour and has transplanted 14 flowers. She has 35 more flowers to transplant. If she works at the same rate, how many more hours will it take her?

8. **Florists** A florist is making centerpieces. He uses 2 dozen roses for every 5 centerpieces. How many dozens of roses will he need to make 20 centerpieces?

Lesson Check

Do you know HOW?

Solve each proportion.

9. $\frac{b}{6} = \frac{4}{5}$

10. $\frac{5}{9} = \frac{15}{x}$

11. $\frac{w+3}{4} = \frac{w}{2}$

12. $\frac{3}{x+1} = \frac{1}{2}$

13. Music A band went to a recording studio and recorded 4 songs in 3 h. How long would it take the band to record 9 songs if they record at the same rate?

Do you UNDERSTAND?

MATHEMATICAL PRACTICES

Vocabulary Use the proportion $\frac{m}{n} = \frac{p}{q}$. Identify the following.

14. the extremes

15. the means

16. the cross products

17. Reasoning When solving $\frac{x}{5} = \frac{3}{4}$, Lisa's first step was to write $4x = 5(3)$. Jen's first step was to write $20\left(\frac{x}{5}\right) = 20\left(\frac{3}{4}\right)$. Will both methods work? Explain.

More Practice and Problem-Solving Exercises

MATHEMATICAL PRACTICES

B Apply

18. **Statistics** Approximately 3 people out of every 30 are left-handed. About how many left-handed people would you expect in a group of 140 people?

19. **Think About a Plan** Maya runs 100 m in 13.4 s. Amy can run 100 m in 14.1 s. If Amy were to finish a 100-m race at the same time as Maya, how much of a head start, in meters, would Amy need?
    - What information do you know? What information is unknown?
    - What proportion can you write that will help you solve the problem?

20. **Electricity** The electric bill for Ferguson's Furniture is shown at the right. The cost of electricity per kilowatt-hour and the total charges for one month are given. How many kilowatt-hours of electricity did Ferguson's Furniture use in that month?

Centerville Electric

Account Name: Ferguson's Furniture
Account Number: 34-14567-89

Cost per kilowatt-hour	$.07
Total charges	$143.32
Previous balance	$.00
Total Amount Due	$143.32

21. **Video Downloads** A particular computer takes 15 min to download a 45-min TV show. How long will it take the computer to download a 2-h movie?

22. **Schedules** You want to meet your friend at a park 4 mi away from your house. You are going to bike to the park at an average rate of 10 mi/h. Your friend lives 1.2 mi away from the park and walks at an average rate of 3 mi/h. How many minutes ahead of you should your friend start out so that you meet at the park at the same time?

Solve each proportion. Tell whether you used the Multiplication Property of Equality or the Cross Products Property for your first step. Explain your choice.

23. $\frac{p}{4} = \frac{7}{8}$

24. $\frac{m}{4.5} = \frac{2}{5}$

25. $\frac{3}{10} = \frac{b}{7}$

26. $\frac{r}{2.1} = \frac{3.6}{2.8}$

27. $\frac{9}{14} = \frac{3}{n}$

28. $\frac{1.5}{y} = \frac{2.5}{7}$

29. $\frac{b + 13}{2} = \frac{-5b}{3}$

30. $\frac{3b}{b - 4} = \frac{3}{7}$

31. $\frac{x + 2}{2x - 6} = \frac{3}{8}$

32. **Error Analysis** Describe and correct the error in solving the proportion at the right.

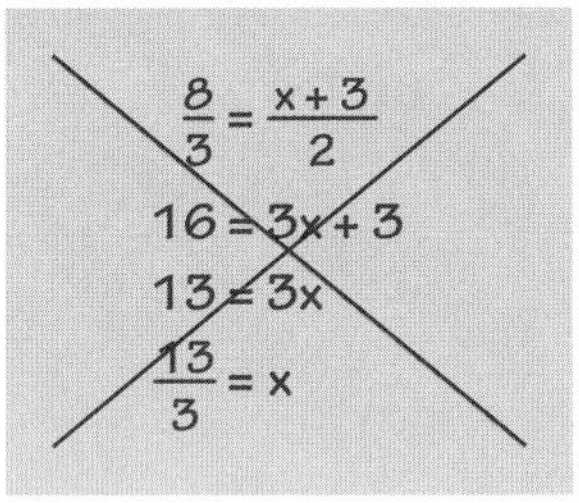

33. **Bakery** A bakery sells packages of 10 bagels for $3.69. If the bakery starts selling the bagels in packages of 12, how much would you expect a package of 12 to cost?

    (A) $3.08
    (B) $4.32
    (C) $4.43
    (D) $4.69

34. **Open-Ended** Write a proportion that contains a variable. Name the extremes, the means, and the cross products. Solve the proportion. Tell whether you used the Multiplication Property of Equality or the Cross Products Property to solve the proportion. Explain your choice.

STEM 35. **Biology** Many trees have concentric rings that can be counted to determine the tree's age. Each ring represents one year's growth. A maple tree with a diameter of 12 in. has 32 rings. If the tree continues to grow at about the same rate, how many rings will the tree have when its diameter is 20 in.?

Challenge

Solve each proportion.

36. $\frac{4y - 3}{y^2 + 1} = \frac{4}{y}$

37. $\frac{w^2 + 3}{2w + 2} = \frac{w}{2}$

38. $\frac{5x}{x^3 + 5} = \frac{5}{x^2 - 7}$

39. **Parade Floats** A group of high school students is making a parade float by stuffing pieces of tissue paper into a wire frame. They use 150 tissues to fill an area 3 ft long and 2 ft wide. The total area they want to fill is 8 ft long and 7 ft wide. What is the total number of tissues they will need?

40. **Insects** It takes an insect 15 s to crawl 1 ft. How many hours would it take the insect to crawl 1 mi if the insect crawls at the same rate?

1-7 Solving Multi-Step Inequalities

A.REI.3 Solve linear equations and inequalities in one variable . . . Also **A.CED.1**

Objective To solve multi-step inequalities

Solve It! Write your solution to the Solve It in the space below.

You can model the situation in the Solve It with the inequality $337.50 + 7.50x \geq 500$. In this lesson, you will learn how to write and solve multi-step inequalities like this one.

Essential Understanding You solve a multi-step inequality in the same way you solve a one-step inequality. You use the properties of inequality to transform the original inequality into a series of simpler, equivalent inequalities.

Problem 1 Using More Than One Step

Plan

How can you check the solutions of each inequality?

Got It? What are the solutions of the inequality? Check your solutions.

a. $-6a - 7 \leq 17$

b. $-4 < 5 - 3n$

c. $50 > 0.8x + 30$

Practice **Solve each inequality. Check your solutions.**

1. $-5y - 2 < 8$

2. $6 \leq 12 + 4j$

You can adapt familiar formulas to write inequalities. You use the real-world situation to determine which inequality symbol to use.

Problem 2 Writing and Solving a Multi-Step Inequality

Got It? You want to make a rectangular banner that is 18 ft long with a trim that goes around the entire border of the banner. You have no more than 48 ft of trim for the banner. What are the possible widths of the banner?

Practice **Write and solve an inequality.**

3. Family Trip On a trip from Buffalo, New York, to St. Augustine, Florida, a family wants to travel at least 250 mi in the first 5 h of driving. What should their average speed be in order to meet this goal?

4. Geometry An isosceles triangle has at least two congruent sides. The perimeter of a certain isosceles triangle is at most 12 in. The length of each of the two congruent sides is 5 in. What are the possible lengths of the remaining side?

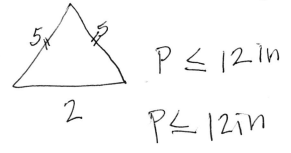

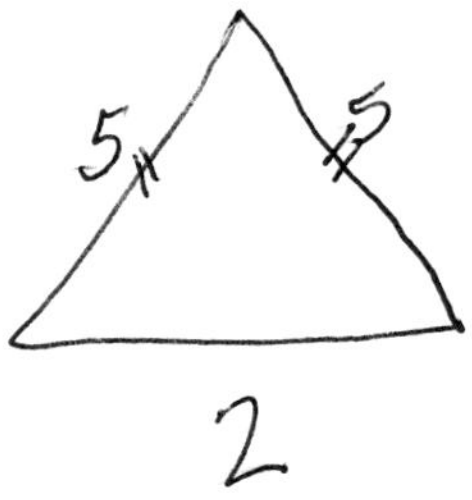

$P \leq 12$ in

$P \leq 12$ in

Problem 3 Using the Distributive Property

Got It? What are the solutions of $15 \leq 5 - 2(4m + 7)$? Check your solutions.

Practice Solve each inequality.

5. $-3(j + 3) + 9j < -15$

6. $-4 \leq 4(6y - 12) - 2y$

Some inequalities have variables on both sides of the inequality symbol. You need to gather the variable terms on one side of the inequality and the constant terms on the other side.

Problem 4 Solving an Inequality With Variables on Both Sides

Got It? **a.** What are the solutions of $3b + 12 > 27 - 2b$? Check your solutions.

b. Reasoning The first step in solving Problem 4 was to subtract $3n$ from each side of the inequality. What else could have been the first step in solving the inequality? Explain.

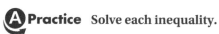

Practice Solve each inequality.

7. $3m - 4 \leq 6m + 11$

8. $4t + 17 > 7 + 5t$

Sometimes solving an inequality gives a statement that is *always* true, such as $4 > 1$. In that case, the solutions are all real numbers. If the statement is *never* true, as is $9 \leq -5$, then the inequality has no solution.

Problem 5 Inequalities With Special Solutions

Got It? What are the solutions of each inequality?

a. $9 + 5n \leq 5n - 1$

Think
Without solving, how can you tell that this inequality has no solution?

b. $8 + 6x \geq 7x + 2 - x$

Practice **Solve each inequality, if possible. If the inequality has no solution, write *no solution.* If the solutions are all real numbers, write *all real numbers.***

9. $-5r + 6 \leq -5(r - 2)$

10. $9 + 2x < 7 + 2(x - 3)$

Lesson Check

Do you know HOW?

In Exercises 11–14, solve each inequality, if possible. If the inequality has no solution, write *no solution.* If the solutions are all real numbers, write *all real numbers.*

11. $7 + 6a > 19$

$-7 \quad -7$

$\frac{6a}{6} > \frac{12}{6}$ anything greater then 2

$a > 2$ $2 < 9$

12. $2(t + 2) - 3t \geq -1$

$2t + 4 - 3t \geq -1$

$-3t$

$-t + 4 \geq -1$

$-4 \quad -4$

$t \leq \cdot 5$

13. $6z - 15 < 4z + 11$

$z < 13$

14. $18x - 5 \leq 3(6x - 2)$

$18x - 5 \leq 18x - 6$

$+6 \leq$

$18x + 1 \leq 18x$

$-18x$

$-5 \leq -6$ $\varnothing$

15. The perimeter of a rectangle is at most 24 cm. Two opposite sides are both 4 cm long. What are the possible lengths of the other two sides?

Do you UNDERSTAND?

MATHEMATICAL PRACTICES

16. Reasoning How can you tell that the inequality $3t + 1 > 3t + 2$ has no solution just by looking at the terms in the inequality?

17. **Reasoning** Can you solve the inequality $2(x - 3) \leq 10$ *without* using the Distributive Property? Explain.

18. **Error Analysis** Your friend says that the solutions of the inequality $-2(3 - x) > 2x - 6$ are all real numbers. Do you agree with your friend? Explain. What if the inequality symbol were $\geq$?

More Practice and Problem-Solving Exercises

MATHEMATICAL PRACTICES

B Apply

Solve each inequality, if possible. If the inequality has no solution, write *no solution*. If the solutions are all real numbers, write *all real numbers*.

19. $-3(x - 3) \geq 5 - 4x$
20. $3s + 6 \leq -5(s + 2)$
21. $3(2 + t) \geq 15 - 2t$
22. $\frac{4}{3}s - 3 < s + \frac{2}{3} - \frac{1}{3}s$
23. $4 - 2n \leq 5 - n + 1$
24. $-2(0.5 - 4t) \geq -3(4 - 3.5t)$
25. $4(a - 2) - 6a \leq -9$
26. $4(3n - 1) \geq 2(n + 3)$
27. $17 - (4k - 2) \geq 2(k + 3)$

28. **Think About a Plan** Your cell phone plan costs \$39.99 per month plus \$.15 for each text message you send or receive. You have at most \$45 to spend on your cell phone bill. What is the maximum number of text messages that you can send or receive next month?
    - What information do you know? What information do you need?
    - What inequality can you use to find the maximum number of text messages that you can send or receive?
    - What are the solutions of the inequality? Are they reasonable?

29. **Rental Rates** The student council wants to rent a ballroom for the junior prom. The ballroom's rental rate is \$1500 for 3 h and \$125 for each additional half hour. Suppose the student council raises \$2125. What is the maximum number of hours for which they can rent the ballroom?

30. **Writing** Suppose a friend is having difficulty solving $3.75(q - 5) > 4(q + 3)$. Explain how to solve the inequality, showing all the necessary steps and identifying the properties you would use.

STEM 31. **Biology** The average normal body temperature for humans is 98.6°F. An abnormal increase in body temperature is classified as hyperthermia, or fever. Which inequality represents the body temperature in degrees Celsius of a person with hyperthermia? (*Hint*: To convert from degrees Celsius C to degrees Fahrenheit F, use the formula $F = \frac{9}{5}C + 32$.)

(A) $\frac{9}{5}C + 32 \geq 98.6$

(B) $\frac{9}{5}C + 32 \leq 98.6$

(C) $\frac{9}{5}C + 32 < 98.6$

(D) $\frac{9}{5}C + 32 > 98.6$

32. **Open-Ended** Write two different inequalities that you can solve by subtracting 3 from each side and then dividing each side by -5. Solve each inequality.

33. a. Solve $6v + 5 \leq 9v - 7$ by gathering the variable terms on the left side and the constant terms on the right side of the inequality.
b. Solve $6v + 5 \leq 9v - 7$ by gathering the constant terms on the left side and the variable terms on the right side of the inequality.
c. Compare the results of parts (a) and (b).
d. Which method do you prefer? Explain.

34. **Mental Math** Determine whether each inequality is *always true* or *never true.*
a. $5s + 7 \geq 7 + 5s$
b. $4t + 6 > 4t - 3$
c. $5(m + 2) < 5m - 4$

35. **Commission** A sales associate in a shoe store earns \$325 per week, plus a commission equal to 4% of her sales. This week her goal is to earn at least \$475. At least how many dollars' worth of shoes must she sell in order to reach her goal?

36. A student uses the table below to help solve $7y + 2 < 6(4 - y)$.

y	$7y + 2$	$<$	$6(4 - y)$
0.5	$7(0.5) + 2 = 5.5$	True	$6(4 - 0.5) = 21$
1	$7(1) + 2 = 9$	True	$6(4 - 1) = 18$
1.5	$7(1.5) + 2 = 12.5$	True	$6(4 - 1.5) = 15$
2	$7(2) + 2 = 16$	False	$6(4 - 2) = 12$

a. Reasoning Based on the table, would you expect the solution of $7y + 2 < 6(4 - y)$ to be of the form $y < c$ or $y > c$, where c is a real number? Explain.

b. Estimate Based on the table, estimate the value of c.

c. Solve the inequality. Compare the actual solution to your estimated solution.

Error Analysis **Describe and correct the error in each solution.**

37.

$4y + 4 \leq -3y + 6$

$4y \leq -3y + 2$

$y \leq 2$

38.

$5(p + 3) > 4p + 2$

$5p + 3 > 4p + 2$

$5p > 4p - 1$

$p > -1$

Challenge

39. Geometry The base of a triangle is 12 in. Its height is $(x + 6)$ in. Its area is no more than 72 in.^{2}. What are the possible integer values of x?

40. Part-Time Jobs You can earn money by tutoring for \$8 per hour and by walking dogs for \$7.50 per hour. You have 15 h available to work. What is the greatest number of hours you can spend walking dogs and still make at least \$115?

41. Freight Handling The elevator of a building can safely carry no more than 4000 lb. A worker moves supplies in 50-lb boxes from the loading dock to the fourth floor of the building. The worker weighs 210 lb. The cart he uses weighs 95 lb.

a. What is the greatest number of boxes he can move in one trip?

b. The worker needs to deliver 275 boxes. How many trips must he make?

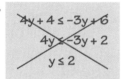

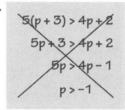

1-8 Compound Inequalities

A.REI.3 Solve linear equations and inequalities in one variable . . . Also **A.CED.1**

Objectives To solve and graph inequalities containing the word *and*
To solve and graph inequalities containing the word *or*

Solve It! Write your solution to the Solve It in the space below.

The Solve It involves a value that is between two numbers. You can use a compound inequality to represent this relationship. A **compound inequality** consists of two distinct inequalities joined by the word *and* or the word *or*.

Essential Understanding You find the solutions of a compound inequality either by identifying where the solution sets of the distinct inequalities overlap or by combining the solution sets to form a larger solution set.

The graph of a compound inequality with the word *and* contains the *overlap* of the graphs of the two inequalities that form the compound inequality.

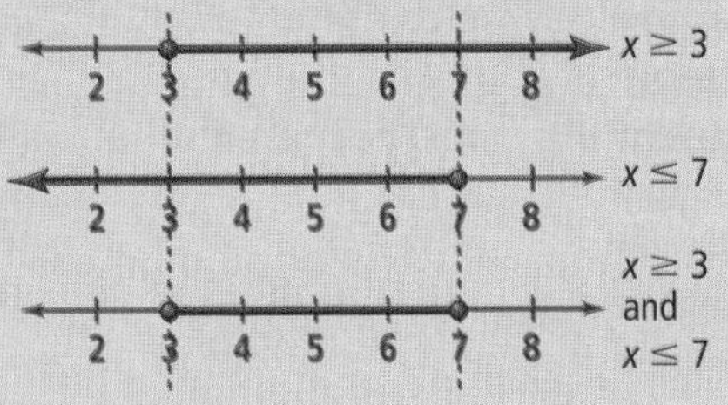

The graph of a compound inequality with the word *or* contains *each* graph of the two inequalities that form the compound inequality.

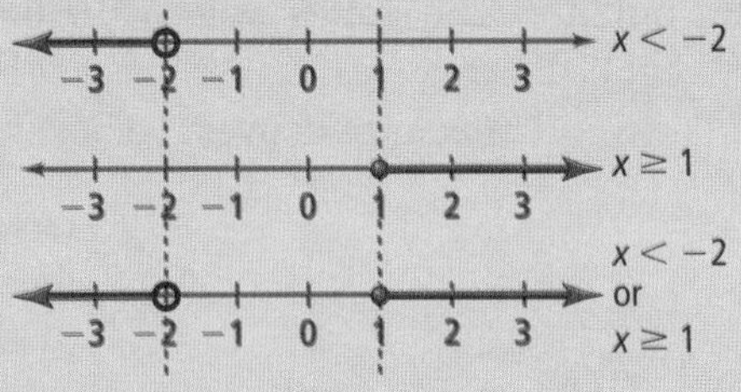

You can rewrite a compound inequality involving *and* as a single inequality. For instance, in the inequality above, you can write $x \geq 3$ and $x \leq 7$ as $3 \leq x \leq 7$. You read this as "x is greater than or equal to 3 and less than or equal to 7." Another way to read it is "x is between 3 and 7, inclusive." In this example, *inclusive* means the solutions of the inequality include both 3 and 7.

Problem 1 Writing a Compound Inequality

Got It! For parts (a) and (b) below, write a compound inequality that represents each phrase. Graph the solutions.

Think

Why can you write an *and* inequality without the word *and*?

a. all real numbers that are greater than or equal to -4 and less than 6

b. all real numbers that are less than or equal to $2\frac{1}{2}$ or greater than 6

c. Reasoning What is the difference between "x is between -5 and 7" and "x is between -5 and 7, inclusive"?

Practice **Write a compound inequality that represents each phrase. Graph the solutions.**

1. all real numbers that are between -5 and 7

2. The circumference of a women's basketball must be between 28.5 in. and 29 in., inclusive.

A solution of a compound inequality involving *and* is any number that makes *both* inequalities true. One way you can solve a compound inequality is by separating it into two inequalities.

Problem 2 Solving a Compound Inequality Involving *And*

Got It? What are the solutions of $-2 < 3y - 4 < 14$? Graph the solutions.

Practice **Solve each compound inequality. Graph your solutions.**

3. $-4 < k + 3 < 8$

4. $5 \leq y + 2 \leq 11$

You can also solve an inequality like $-3 \leq m - 4 < -1$ by working on all three parts of the inequality at the same time. You work to isolate the variable between the inequality symbols. This method is used in Problem 3.

Problem 3 Writing and Solving a Compound Inequality

Got It? Reasoning Suppose you scored 78, 78, and 79 on the first three tests. Is it possible for you to earn a B in the course? Assume that 100 is the maximum grade you can earn in the course and on the test. Explain.

Practice **Solve each compound inequality. Graph your solutions.**

5. $\frac{1}{4} < \frac{2x-7}{2} < 5$

6. $-3 \le \frac{6-q}{9} \le 3$

A solution of a compound inequality involving *or* is any number that makes *either* inequality true. To solve a compound inequality involving *or*, you must solve separately the two inequalities that form the compound inequality.

Problem 4 Solving a Compound Inequality Involving *Or*

Got It? What are the solutions of $-2y + 7 < 1$ or $4y + 3 \le -5$? Graph the solutions.

Think
What does the graph of an inequality involving *or* look like?

Practice **Solve each compound inequality. Graph your solutions.**

7. $5y + 7 \leq -3$ or $3y - 2 \geq 13$

8. $5z - 3 > 7$ or $4z - 6 < -10$

You can use an inequality such as $x \leq -3$ to describe a portion of the number line called an *interval.* You can also use *interval notation* to describe an interval on the number line. **Interval notation** includes the use of three special symbols. These symbols include

parentheses: Use (or) when a $<$ or $>$ symbol indicates that the interval's endpoints are *not* included.

brackets: Use [or] when a $\leq$ or $\geq$ symbol indicates that the interval's endpoints *are* included.

infinity: Use ∞ when the interval continues forever in a *positive* direction. Use $-\infty$ when the interval continues forever in a *negative* direction.

Inequality	Graph	Interval Notation
$x \geq 2$	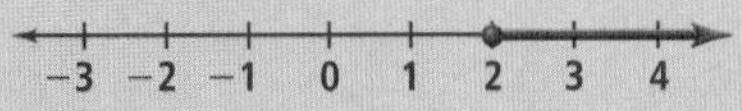	$[2, \infty)$
$x < 2$		$(-\infty, 2)$
$1 < x \leq 5$	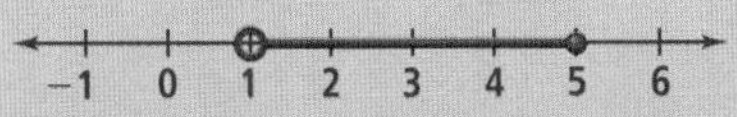	$(1, 5]$
$x < -3$ or $x \geq 4$	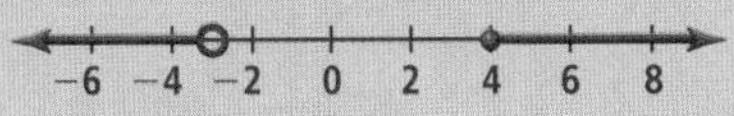	$(-\infty, -3)$ or $[4, \infty)$

Problem 5 Using Interval Notation

Got It? **a.** What is the graph of $(-2, 7]$? How do you write $(-2, 7]$ as an inequality?

b. What is the graph of $y > 7$? How do you write $y > 7$ in interval notation?

Practice **9.** Write the interval $(-\infty, -1]$ or $(3, \infty)$ as an inequality. Then graph the solution.

10. Write the inequality $x < -2$ or $x \geq 1$ in interval notation. The graph the interval.

Lesson Check

Do you know HOW?

11. What compound inequality represents the phrase "all real numbers that are greater than or equal to 0 and less than 8"? Graph the solutions.

12. What are the solutions of $-4 \leq r - 5 < -1$? Graph the solutions.

13. Your test scores in science are 83 and 87. What possible scores can you earn on your next test to have a test average between 85 and 90, inclusive?

14. Write the interval represented on the number line below as an inequality and in interval notation.

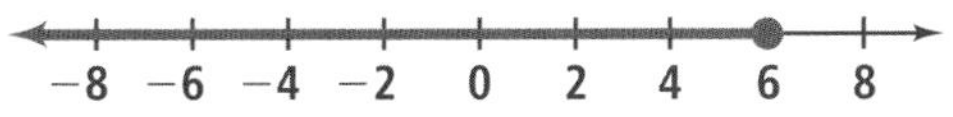

Do you UNDERSTAND?

MATHEMATICAL PRACTICES

15. Vocabulary Which of the following are compound inequalities?

(A) $x > 4$ or $x < -4$

(B) $x \geq 6$

(C) $8 \leq 5x < 30$

D. $7x > 42$ or $-5x \leq 10$

16. Error Analysis A student writes the inequality $x \geq 17$ in interval notation as $[17, \infty]$. Explain why this is incorrect.

17. Reasoning What are the solutions of $3x - 7 \leq 14$ or $4x - 8 > 20$? Write your solutions as a compound inequality and in interval notation.

18. Writing Compare the graph of a compound inequality involving *and* with the graph of a compound inequality involving *or*.

More Practice and Problem-Solving Exercises

MATHEMATICAL PRACTICES

B Apply

Solve each inequality. Write each set in interval notation.

19. $7 < x + 6 \leq 12$

20. $-9 < 3m + 6 \leq 18$

21. $f + 14 < 9$ or $-9f \leq -45$

22. $12h - 3 \geq 15h$ or $5 > -0.2h + 10$

Write a compound inequality that each graph could represent.

23. 

24. 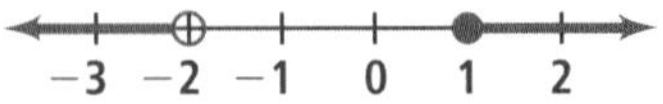

25. 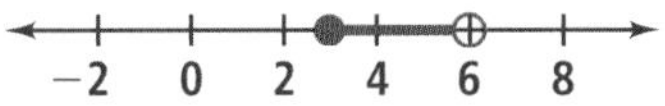

Solve each compound inequality. Justify each step.

26. $4r - 3 > 11$ or $4r - 3 \leq -11$

27. $2 \leq 0.75v \leq 4.5$

28. $\frac{4y + 2}{5} - 5 > 3$ or $\frac{4 - 3y}{6} > 4$

29. $-\frac{4}{3} \leq \frac{1}{7}w - \frac{3}{4} < 1$

STEM **30. Chemistry** The acidity of the water in a swimming pool is considered normal if the average of three pH readings is between 7.2 and 7.8, inclusive. The first two readings for a swimming pool are 7.4 and 7.9. What possible values for the third reading p will make the average pH normal?

31. Think About a Plan The Triangle Inequality Theorem states that the sum of the lengths of any two sides of a triangle is greater than the length of the third side. The lengths of two sides of a triangle are given. What are the possible lengths x of the third side of the triangle?

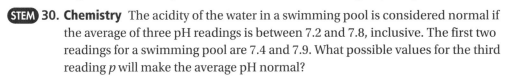

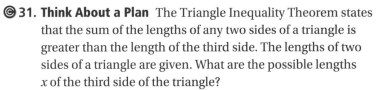

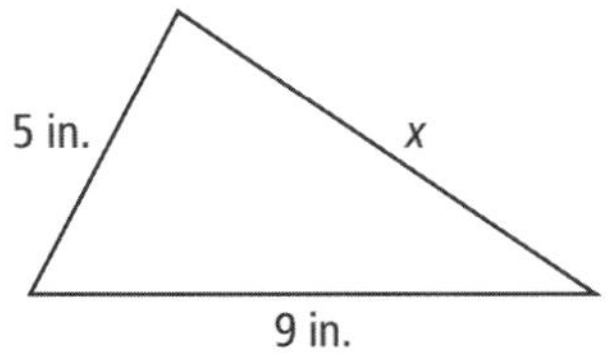

- Is there an upper limit on the value of x? Is there a lower limit?
- How can you use your answers to the previous question to write one or more inequalities involving x?

Use your answers to Exercise 31 to answer Exercises 32–35. The lengths of two sides of a triangle are given. Find the possible lengths of the third side.

32. 3.75 in., 7 in.

33. 15 ft, 21 ft

34. 14 mm, 35 mm

35. 6 m, 17 m

STEM **36. Physics** The force exerted on a spring is proportional to the distance the spring is stretched from its relaxed position. Suppose you stretch a spring a distance of d inches by applying a force of F pounds. For your spring, $\frac{d}{F} = 0.8$. You apply forces between 25 lb and 40 lb, inclusive. What inequality describes the distances the spring is stretched?

37. **Reasoning** Describe the solutions of $4x - 9 < 7$ or $3x - 10 > 2$.

38. **Nutrition** A sedentary 15-year-old male should consume no more than 2200 Calories per day. A moderately active 15-year-old male should consume between 2400 and 2800 Calories per day. An active 15-year-old male should consume between 2800 and 3200 Calories per day. Model these ranges on a number line. Represent each range of Calories using interval notation.

Challenge

39. **Heart Rates** Recommended heart rates during exercise vary with age and physical condition. For a healthy person doing moderate to intense exercise, such as hiking, the inequality $0.5(220 - a) \leq R \leq 0.9(220 - a)$ gives a target range for the heart rate R (in beats per minute), based on age a (in years).
   a. What is the target range for heart rates for a person 15 years old?
   b. How old is a person whose target range is between 99 and 178.2 beats per minute?

STEM 40. **Chemistry** Matter is in a liquid state when its temperature is between its melting point and its boiling point. The melting point of the element mercury is −38.87°C, and its boiling point is 356.58°C. What is the range of temperatures in degrees Fahrenheit for which mercury is *not* in a liquid state? (*Hint:* $C = \frac{5}{9}(F - 32)$) Express the range as an inequality and in interval notation.

1-9 Absolute Value Equations and Inequalities

A.CED.1 Create equations and inequalities in one variable and . . . solve problems . . . Also **A.SSE.1, A.SSE.1.b**

Objective To solve equations and inequalities involving absolute value

Solve It! Write your solution to the Solve It in the space below.

In the Solve It, Serena's distance from Darius decreases and then increases. You can use absolute value to model such changes. The absolute value of a number is its distance from 0 on a number line. Absolute value is always nonnegative since distance is always nonnegative.

Essential Understanding You can solve absolute value equations and inequalities by first isolating the absolute value expression, if necessary. Then write an equivalent pair of linear equations or inequalities.

Problem 1 Solving an Absolute Value Equation

Think

How many solutions does the equation have?

Got It? What are the solutions of $|n| - 5 = -2$? Graph and check the solutions.

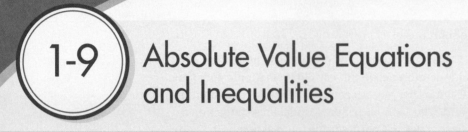

Practice **Solve each equation. Graph and check your solutions.**

1. $|n| + 3 = 7$

2. $-3|m| = -9$

Some equations, such as $|2x - 5| = 13$, have variable expressions within absolute value symbols. The equation $|2x - 5| = 13$ means that the distance on a number line from $2x - 5$ to 0 is 13 units. There are two points that are 13 units from 0: 13 and -13. So to find the values of x, solve the equations $2x - 5 = 13$ and $2x - 5 = -13$. You can generalize this process as follows.

take note

Key Concept Solving Absolute Value Equations

To solve an equation in the form $|A| = b$, where A represents a variable expression and $b > 0$, solve $A = b$ and $A = -b$.

ONLINE PROBLEMS

Problem 2 Solving an Absolute Value Equation

Got It? Another friend's distance d from you (in feet) after t seconds is given by $d = |80 - 5t|$. What does the 80 in the equation represent? What does the 5 in the equation represent? At what times is she 60 ft from you?

Practice Solve each equation.

3. $|r - 8| = 5$

4. $2 = |g + 3|$

Recall that absolute value represents distance from 0 on a number line. Distance is always nonnegative. So any equation that states that the absolute value of an expression is negative has no solutions.

Problem 3 Solving an Absolute Value Equation With No Solution

Got It? What are the solutions of $|3x - 6| - 5 = -7$?

Plan

How can you make the equation look like one you've solved before?

Practice Solve each equation. If there is no solution, write *no solution.*

5. $-2|7d| = 14$

6. $3|v - 3| = 9$

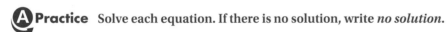

You can write absolute value inequalities as compound inequalities. The graphs below show two absolute value inequalities.

$|n-1| < 2$

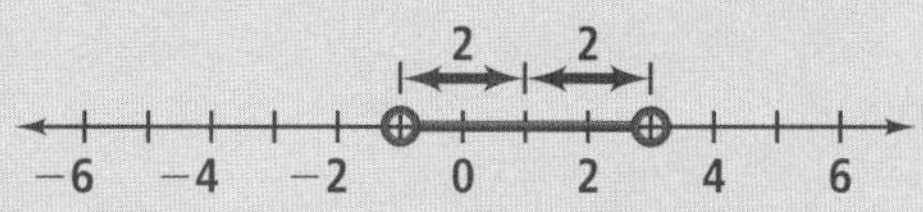

$|n-1| < 2$ represents all numbers with a distance from 1 that is less than 2 units. So $|n-1| < 2$ means $-2 < n-1 < 2$.

$|n-1| > 2$

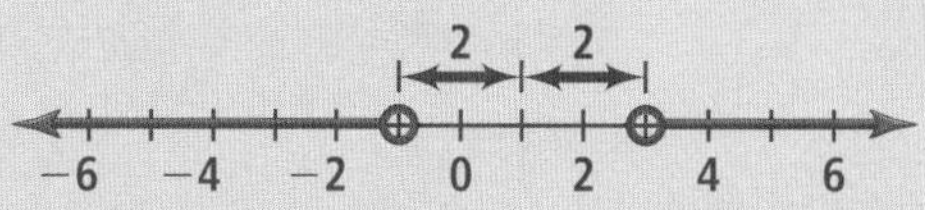

$|n-1| > 2$ represents all numbers with a distance from 1 that is greater than 2 units. So $|n-1| > 2$ means $n-1 < -2$ or $n-1 > 2$.

take note

Key Concept Solving Absolute Value Inequalities

To solve an inequality in the form $|A| < b$, where A is a variable expression and $b > 0$, solve the compound inequality $-b < A < b$.

To solve an inequality in the form $|A| > b$, where A is a variable expression and $b > 0$, solve the compound inequality $A < -b$ or $A > b$.

Similar rules are true for $|A| \leq b$ or $|A| \geq b$.

ONLINE PROBLEMS

Problem 4 Solving an Absolute Value Inequality Involving ≥

Got It? What are the solutions of $|2x+4| \geq 5$? Graph the solutions.

Practice Solve and graph each inequality.

7. $|y + 8| \geq 3$

8. $|5m - 9| \geq 24$

Problem 5 Solving an Absolute Value Inequality Involving ≤

Got It?

a. A food manufacturer makes 32-oz boxes of pasta. Not every box weighs exactly 32 oz. The allowable difference from the ideal weight is at most 0.05 oz. Write and solve an absolute value inequality to find the range of allowable weights.

b. Reasoning In Problem 5, could you have solved the inequality $|w - 213| \leq 5$ by first adding 213 to each side? Explain your reasoning.

Practice **9.** Solve and graph the inequality $|2f + 9| \leq 13$.

10. Quality Control The ideal length of one type of model airplane is 90 cm. The actual length may vary from ideal by at most 0.05 cm. What are the acceptable lengths for the model airplane?

Lesson Check

Do you know HOW?

Solve and graph each equation or inequality.

11. $|x| = 5$

12. $|n| - 3 = 4$

13. $|2t| = 6$

14. $|h - 3| < 5$

15. $|x + 2| \geq 1$

Do you UNDERSTAND?

MATHEMATICAL PRACTICES

16. Reasoning How many solutions do you expect to get when you solve an absolute value equation? Explain.

17. **Writing** Explain why the absolute value equation $|3x| + 8 = 5$ has no solution.

18. **Compare and Contrast** Explain the similarities and differences in solving the equation $|x - 1| = 2$ with solving the inequalities $|x - 1| \leq 2$ and $|x - 1| \geq 2$.

More Practice and Problem-Solving Exercises

MATHEMATICAL PRACTICES

B Apply

Solve each equation or inequality. If there is no solution, write *no solution*.

19. $|2d| + 3 = 21$
20. $1.2|5p| = 3.6$
21. $\left|d + \frac{1}{2}\right| + \frac{3}{4} = 0$
22. $|f| - \frac{2}{3} = \frac{5}{6}$
23. $3|5y - 7| - 6 = 24$
24. $|t| + 2.7 = 4.5$
25. $-2|c - 4| = -8.4$
26. $\frac{|y|}{-3} = 5$
27. $|n| - \frac{5}{4} < 5$
28. $\frac{7}{8} < |c + 7|$
29. $4 - 3|m + 2| > -14$
30. $|-3d| \geq 6.3$

31. **Think About a Plan** The monthly average temperature T for San Francisco, California, is usually within 7.5°F of 56.5°F, inclusive. What is the monthly average temperature in San Francisco?
    - Should you model this situation with an equation or an inequality?
    - How can you use the given information to write the equation or inequality?

STEM 32. Biology A horse's body temperature T is considered to be normal if it is within at least 0.9°F of 99.9°F. Find the range of normal body temperatures for a horse.

33. Biking Your friend rides his bike toward you and then passes by you at a constant speed. His distance d (in feet) from you t seconds after he started riding his bike is given by $d = |200 - 18t|$. What does the 200 in the equation represent? What does the 18 in the equation represent? At what time(s) is he 120 ft from you?

Error Analysis Find and correct the mistake in solving each equation or inequality.

34.

$|x - 3| = -2$

$x - 3 = -2$ or $x - 3 = 2$

$x = 1$ or $x = 5$

35.

$|y + 7| \le 1$

$y + 7 \le -1$ or $y + 7 \ge 1$

$y \le -8$ or $y \ge -6$

36. Open-Ended Write an absolute value equation that has 2 and 6 as solutions.

37. Reasoning Explain why you can rewrite $|x + 5| > 1$ as a compound inequality involving *or*.

38. Polling According to a poll for an upcoming school board election, 40% of voters are likely to vote for the incumbent. The poll shows a margin of error of ± 3 percentage points. Write and solve an absolute value equation to find the least and the greatest percents of voters v likely to vote for the incumbent.

39. Banking The official weight of a nickel is 5 g, but the actual weight can vary from this amount by up to 0.194 g. Suppose a bank weighs a roll of 40 nickels. The wrapper weighs 1.5 g.

a. What is the range of possible weights for the roll of nickels?

b. **Reasoning** If all of the nickels in the roll each weigh the official amount, then the roll's weight is $40(5) + 1.5 = 201.5$ g. Is it possible for a roll to weigh 201.5 g and contain nickels that do not weigh the official amount? Explain.

STEM 40. Oil Production An oil refinery aims to process 900,000 barrels of oil per day. The daily production varies by up to 50,000 barrels from this goal, inclusive. What are the minimum and maximum numbers of barrels of oil processed each day?

Write an absolute value inequality that represents each set of numbers.

41. all real numbers less than 4 units from 0

42. all real numbers at most 7 units from 0

43. all real numbers more than 2 units from 6

44. all real numbers at least 2 units from -1

STEM 45. Manufacturing The ideal diameter of a piston for one type of car engine is 90.000 mm. The actual diameter can vary from the ideal by at most 0.008 mm. What is the range of acceptable diameters for the piston?

46. Farm Maintenance For safety, the recommended height of a horse fence is 5 ft. Because of uneven ground surfaces, the actual height of the fence can vary from this recommendation by up to 3 in. Write and solve an absolute value equation to find the maximum and minimum heights of the fence.

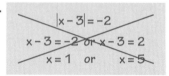

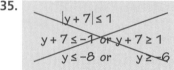

Challenge

Solve each equation. Check your solutions.

47. $|x + 4| = 3x$

48. $|4t - 5| = 2t + 1$

49. $\frac{4}{3}|2y + 3| = 4y$

Determine whether each statement is *always, sometimes,* or *never* true for real numbers *a* and *b*.

50. $|ab| = |a| \cdot |b|$

51. $\left|\frac{a}{b}\right| = \frac{|a|}{|b|}, b \neq 0$

52. $|a + b| = |a| + |b|$

1 Chapter Review

MathXL® for School
Go to pearsonsuccessnet.com

1-1 The Distributive Property

Quick Review

Terms with exactly the same variable factors are **like terms.** You can combine like terms and use the Distributive Property to simplify expressions.

Distributive Property $a(b + c) = ab + ac$

$a(b - c) = ab - ac$

Example

Simplify $7t + (3 - 4t)$.

$7t + (3 - 4t) = 7t + (-4t + 3)$	Commutative Property
$= (7t + (-4t)) + 3$	Associative Property
$= (7 + (-4))t + 3$	Distributive Property
$= 3t + 3$	Simplify.

Exercises

Simplify each expression.

1. $5(2x - 3)$

2. $-2(7 - a)$

3. $(-j + 8)\frac{1}{2}$

4. $3v^2 - 2v^2$

5. $2(3y - 3)$

6. $(6y - 1)\frac{1}{4}$

7. $(24 - 24y)\frac{1}{4}$

8. $6y - 3 - 5y$

9. $\frac{1}{3}y + 6 - \frac{2}{3}y$

10. $-ab^2 - ab^2$

11. Music All 95 members of the jazz club pay \$30 each to go see a jazz performance. What is the total cost of tickets? Use mental math.

12. Reasoning Are $8x^2y$ and $-5yx^2$ like terms? Explain.

1-2 Solving Multi-Step Equations

Quick Review

To solve some equations, you may need to combine like terms or use the Distributive Property to clear fractions or decimals.

Example

What is the solution of $12 = 2x + \frac{4}{3} - \frac{2x}{3}$?

$3 \cdot 12 = 3\left(2x + \frac{4}{3} - \frac{2x}{3}\right)$	Multiply by 3.
$36 = 6x + 4 - 2x$	Simplify.
$36 = 4x + 4$	Combine like terms.
$36 - 4 = 4x + 4 - 4$	Subtract 4.
$32 = 4x$	Combine like terms.
$\frac{32}{4} = \frac{4x}{4}$	Divide each side by 4.
$8 = x$	Simplify.

Exercises

Solve each equation. Check your answer.

13. $7(s - 5) = 42$

14. $3a + 2 - 5a = -14$

15. $-4b - 5 + 2b = 10$

16. $3.4t + 0.08 = 11$

17. $10 = \frac{c}{3} - 4 + \frac{c}{6}$

18. $\frac{2x}{7} + \frac{4}{5} = 5$

Write an equation to model each situation. Then solve the equation.

19. Earnings You work for 4 h on Saturday and 8 h on Sunday. You also receive a \$50 bonus. You earn \$164. How much did you earn per hour?

20. Entertainment Online concert tickets cost \$37 each, plus a service charge of \$8.50 per ticket. The Web site also charges a transaction fee of \$14.99 for the purchase. You paid \$242.49. How many tickets did you buy?

1-3 Solving Equations With Variables on Both Sides

Quick Review

When an equation has variables on both sides, you can use properties of equality to isolate the variable on one side. An equation has no solution if no value of the variable makes it true. An equation is an **identity** if every value of the variable makes it true.

Example

What is the solution of $3x - 7 = 5x + 19$?

$3x - 7 - 3x = 5x + 19 - 3x$	Subtract 3*x*.
$-7 = 2x + 19$	Simplify.
$-7 - 19 = 2x + 19 - 19$	Subtract 19.
$-26 = 2x$	Simplify.
$\frac{-26}{2} = \frac{2x}{2}$	Divide each side by 2.
$-13 = x$	Simplify.

Exercises

Solve each equation. If the equation is an identity, write *identity*. If it has no solution, write *no solution*.

21. $\frac{2}{3}x + 4 = \frac{3}{5}x - 2$

22. $6 - 0.25f = f - 3$

23. $3(h - 4) = -\frac{1}{2}(24 - 6h)$

24. $5n = 20(4 + 0.25n)$

25. Architecture Two buildings have the same total height. One building has 8 floors each with height h. The other building has a ground floor of 16 ft and 6 other floors each with height h. Write and solve an equation to find the height h of these floors.

26. Travel A train makes a trip at 65 mi/h. A plane traveling 130 mi/h makes the same trip in 3 fewer hours. Write and solve an equation to find the distance of the trip.

1-4 Literal Equations and Formulas

Quick Review

A **literal equation** is an equation that involves two or more variables. A **formula** is an equation that states a relationship among quantities. You can use properties of equality to solve a literal equation for one variable in terms of the others.

Example

What is the width of a rectangle with area 91 ft^2 and length 7 ft?

$A = \ell w$	Write the appropriate formula.
$\frac{A}{\ell} = w$	Divide each side by ℓ.
$\frac{91}{7} = w$	Substitute 91 for *A* and 7 for ℓ.
$13 = w$	Simplify.

The width of the rectangle is 13 ft.

Exercises

Solve each equation for *x*.

27. $ax + bx = -c$

28. $\frac{x + r}{t} + 1 = 0$

29. $m - 3x = 2x + p$

30. $\frac{x}{p} + \frac{x}{q} = s$

Solve each problem. Round to the nearest tenth, if necessary. Use 3.14 for π.

31. What is the width of a rectangle with length 5.5 cm and area 220 cm^2?

32. What is the radius of a circle with circumference 94.2 mm?

33. A triangle has height 15 in. and area 120 in.^{2}. What is the length of its base?

1-5 and 1-6 Ratios, Rates, and Conversions and Solving Proportions

Quick Review

A ratio between numbers measured in different units is called a **rate.** A **conversion factor** is a ratio of two equivalent measures in different units such as $\frac{1\text{ h}}{60\text{ min}}$, and is always equal to 1. To convert from one unit to another, multiply the original unit by a conversion factor that has the original units in the denominator and the desired units in the numerator.

The **cross products** of a proportion are equal. If $\frac{a}{b} = \frac{c}{d}$, where $b \neq 0$ and $d \neq 0$, then $ad = bc$.

Example

A painting is 17.5 in. wide. What is its width in centimeters? Recall that 1 in. = 2.54 cm.

$$17.5\cancel{\text{ in.}} \cdot \frac{2.54\text{ cm}}{1\cancel{\text{ in.}}} = 44.45\text{ cm}$$

The painting is 44.45 cm wide.

Exercises

Convert the given amount to the given unit.

34. $6\frac{1}{2}$ ft; in.

35. 4 lb 7 oz; oz

36. 135 s; min

37. 2.25 mi; yd

38. Production A bread slicer runs 20 h per day for 30 days and slices 144,000 loaves of bread. How many loaves per hour are sliced?

Solve each proportion.

39. $\frac{3}{7} = \frac{9}{x}$

40. $\frac{-8}{10} = \frac{y}{5}$

41. $\frac{6}{15} = \frac{a}{4}$

42. $\frac{3}{-7} = \frac{-9}{t}$

43. $\frac{b+3}{7} = \frac{b-3}{6}$

44. $\frac{5}{2c-3} = \frac{3}{7c+4}$

1-7 Solving Multi-Step Inequalities

Quick Review

When you solve inequalities, sometimes you need to use more than one step. You need to gather the variable terms on one side of the inequality and the constant terms on the other side.

Example

What are the solutions of $3x + 5 > -1$?

$3x + 5 > -1$

$3x > -6$ Subtract 5 from each side.

$x > -2$ Divide each side by 3.

Exercises

Solve each inequality.

45. $4k - 1 \geq -3$

46. $6(c - 1) < -18$

47. $3t > 5t + 12$

48. $-\frac{6}{7}y - 6 \geq 42$

49. $4 + \frac{x}{2} > 2x$

50. $3x + 5 \leq 2x - 8$

51. $13.5a + 7.4 \leq 85.7$

52. $42w > 2(w + 7)$

53. Commission A salesperson earns \$200 per week plus a commission equal to 4% of her sales. This week her goal is to earn no less than \$450. Write and solve an inequality to find the amount of sales she must have to reach her goal.

1-8 Compound Inequalities

Quick Review

Two inequalities that are joined by the word *and* or the word *or* are called **compound inequalities.** A solution of a compound inequality involving *and* makes both inequalities true. A solution of an inequality involving *or* makes either inequality true.

Example

What are the solutions of $-3 \leq z - 1 < 3$?

$-3 \leq z - 1 < 3$

$-2 \leq z < 4$ — Add 1 to each part of the inequality.

Exercises

Solve each compound inequality.

54. $-2 \leq d + \frac{1}{2} < 4\frac{1}{2}$

55. $0 < -8b \leq 12$

56. $2t \leq -4$ or $7t \geq 49$

57. $5m < -10$ or $3m > 9$

58. $-1 \leq a - 3 \leq 2$

59. $9.1 > 1.4p \geq -6.3$

60. Climate A town's high temperature for a given month is 88°F and the low temperature is 65°F. Write a compound inequality to represent the range of temperatures for the given month.

1-9 Absolute Value Equations and Inequalities

Quick Review

Solving an equation or inequality that contains an absolute value expression is similar to solving other equations and inequalities. You will need to write two equations or inequalities using positive and negative values. Then solve.

Example

What is the solution of $|x| - 7 = 3$?

$|x| - 7 = 3$

$|x| = 10$ — Add 7 to each side.

$x = 10$ or $x = -10$ — Definition of absolute value

Exercises

Solve each equation or inequality. If there is no solution, write *no solution*.

61. $|y| = 3$

62. $|n + 2| = 4$

63. $4 + |r + 2| = 7$

64. $|x + 3| = -2$

65. $|5x| \leq 15$

66. $|3d + 5| < -2$

67. $|2x - 7| - 1 > 0$

68. $4|k + 5| > 8$

69. Manufacturing The ideal length of a certain nail is 20 mm. The actual length can vary from the ideal by at most 0.4 mm. Find the range of acceptable lengths of the nail.

1 *Pull It* All Together

PERFORMANCE TASK

ASSESSMENT

Planning for a Fundraiser

Some students are planning to sell gourmet popcorn at a school fundraiser. They plan to offer cheese popcorn and peanut butter popcorn. The table shows the cost of the ingredients for each type of popcorn and the prices at which the students plan to sell the popcorn.

Gourmet Popcorn

Type of Popcorn	Cost of Ingredients per Container	Price per Container at Fundraiser
Cheese	$.65	$5.00
Peanut butter	$.40	$3.50

The students want to make and sell 100 containers of popcorn. They can spend at most $50 for the ingredients. Their goal is to take in at least $400 from selling the popcorn at the fundraiser.

Task Description

Find a range for the number of containers of each type of popcorn the students should make.

a. Let $c =$ the number of containers of cheese popcorn the students make. Write an expression that represents the number of containers of peanut butter popcorn the students make.

b. Write and solve an inequality involving c that compares the total cost of the ingredients to the students' spending limit for the ingredients.

c. Write and solve an inequality involving c that compares the total amount of money the students will take in from selling the popcorn to the students' sales goal. (*Hint:* When you solve your inequality, remember that c must be a whole number of containers.)

d. Write a compound inequality for the number of containers of cheese popcorn c the students should make. Then write a compound inequality for the number of containers of peanut butter popcorn p the students should make.

CHAPTER 2

Get Ready!

Evaluating Expressions

Evaluate each expression for the given value(s) of the variable(s).

1. $3x - 2y; x = -1, y = 2$

2. $-w^2 + 3w; w = -3$

3. $\frac{3 + k}{k}; k = 3$

4. $h - (h^2 - 1) \div 2; h = -1$

Graphing in the Coordinate Plane

Graph the ordered pairs in the same coordinate plane.

5. $(3, -3)$

6. $(0, -5)$

7. $(-2, 2)$

8. $(-2, 0)$

Solving Two-Step Equations

Solve each equation. Check your answer.

9. $5x + 3 = -12$

10. $\frac{n}{6} - 1 = 10$

11. $7 = \frac{x + 8}{2}$

12. $\frac{x - 1}{4} = \frac{3}{4}$

Solving Absolute Value Equations

Solve each equation. If there is no solution, write *no solution*.

13. $|r + 2| = 2$

14. $-3|d - 5| = -6$

15. $-3.2 = |8p|$

16. $5|2x - 7| = 20$

Looking Ahead Vocabulary

17. The amount of money you earn from a summer job is *dependent* upon the number of hours you work. What do you think it means when a variable is *dependent* upon another variable?

18. A *relation* is a person to whom you are related. If (1, 2), (3, 4), and (5, 6) form a mathematical *relation*, to which number is 3 related?

19. When a furnace runs *continuously*, there are no breaks or interruptions in its operation. What do you think a *continuous* graph looks like?

CHAPTER 2

An Introduction to Functions

Big Ideas

1 Functions

Essential Question How can you represent and describe functions?

2 Modeling

Essential Question Can functions describe real-world situations?

Domains

- Interpreting Functions
- Building Functions

Chapter Preview

Interactive Digital Path

Log in to **pearsonsuccessnet.com** and click on Interactive Digital Path to access the Solve Its and animated Problems.

Vocabulary

English/Spanish Vocabulary Audio Online:

English	Spanish
continuous graph, *p. 119*	gráfica continua
dependent variable, *p. 103*	variable dependiente
discrete graph, *p. 119*	gráfica discreta
domain, *p. 135*	dominio
function, *p. 105*	función
independent variable, *p. 103*	variable independiente
linear function, *p. 105*	función lineal
nonlinear function, *p. 110*	función no lineal
range, *p. 135*	rango
recursive formula, *p. 149*	fórmula recursiva
relation, *p. 135*	relación
sequence, *p. 146*	progresión

2-1 Using Graphs to Relate Two Quantities

F.IF.4 For a function that models a relationship between two quantities, interpret key features of graphs and tables in terms of the quantities, and sketch graphs showing key features given a verbal description . . .

Objective To represent mathematical relationships using graphs

Solve It! Write your solution to the Solve It in the space below.

As you may have noticed in the Solve It, the change in the height of the water as the volume increases is related to the shape of the container.

Essential Understanding You can use graphs to visually represent the relationship between two variable quantities as they both change.

Problem 1 Analyzing a Graph

Got It? What are the variables in each graph? Describe how the variables are related at various points on the graph.

a.

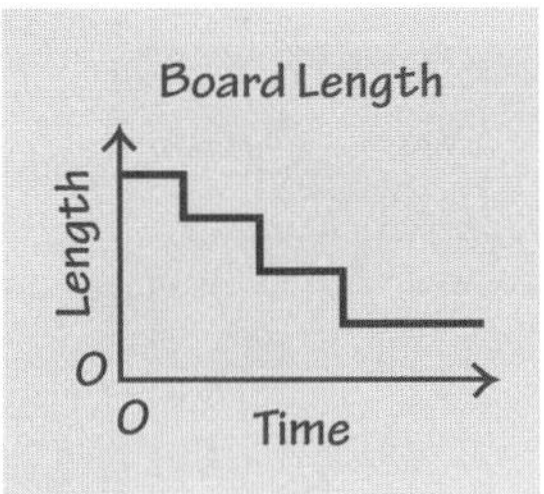

b.

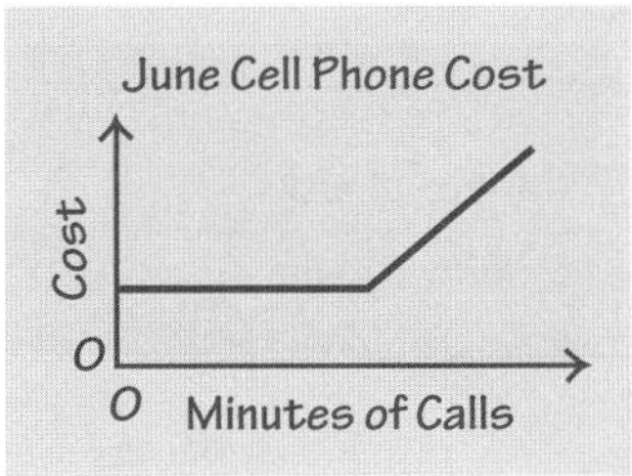

Think
How can you analyze the relationship in a graph?

Practice **What are the variables in each graph? Describe how the variables are related at various points on the graph.**

1.

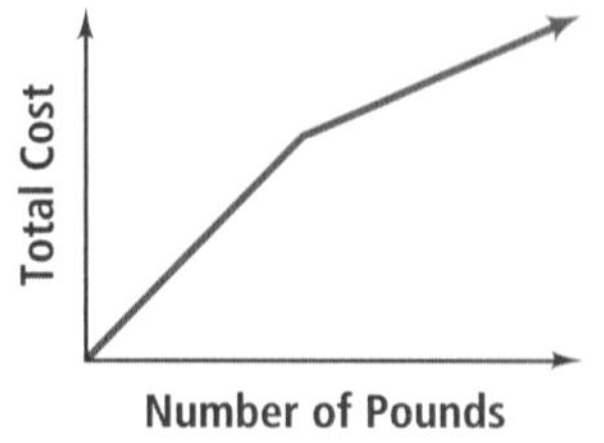

2.

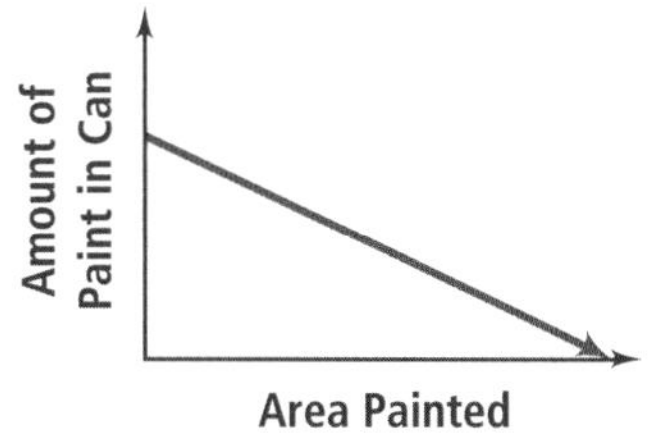

Tables and graphs can both show relationships between variables. Data from a table are often displayed using a graph to visually represent the relationship.

Problem 2 Matching a Table and a Graph

Got It? The table shows the amount of sunscreen left in a can based on the number of times the sunscreen has been used. Which graph could represent the data shown in the table?

Sunscreen				
Number of Uses	0	1	2	3
Amount of Sunscreen (oz)	5	4.8	4.6	4.4

A.

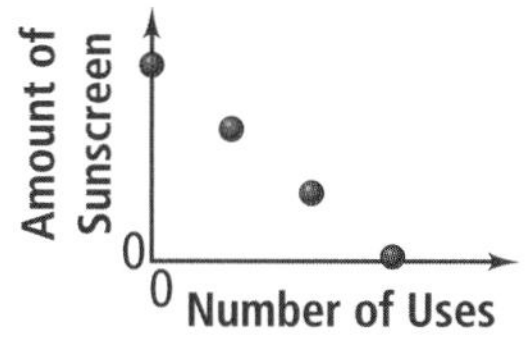

B.

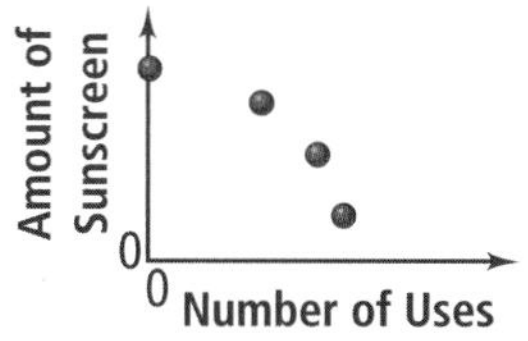

C.

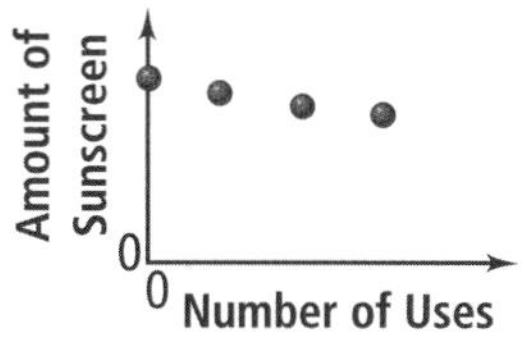

Practice Match each graph with its related table. Explain your answers.

3.

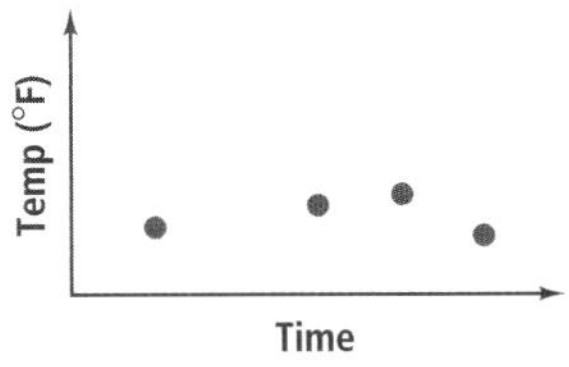

4.

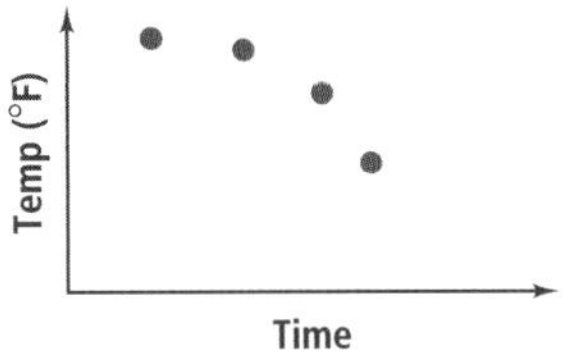

5.

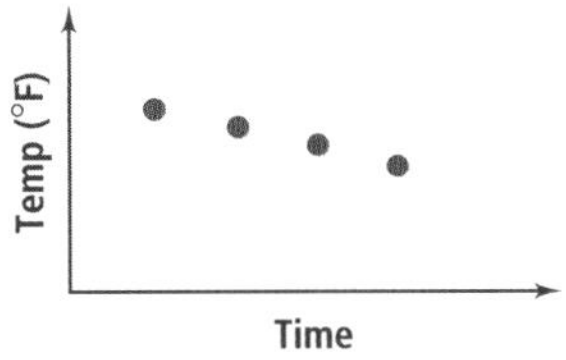

A.

Time	Temperature (F)
1 P.M.	91°
3 P.M.	89°
5 P.M.	81°
7 P.M.	64°

B.

Time	Temperature (F)
1 P.M.	61°
3 P.M.	60°
5 P.M.	59°
7 P.M.	58°

C.

Time	Temperature (F)
1 P.M.	24°
3 P.M.	26°
5 P.M.	27°
7 P.M.	21°

In Problem 2, the number of downloads, which is on the vertical axis of each graph, depends on the day, which is on the horizontal axis. When one quantity depends on another, show the independent quantity on the horizontal axis and the dependent quantity on the vertical axis.

ONLINE PROBLEMS

Problem 3 Sketching a Graph

Think

How can you get started?

Got It? **a.** Suppose you start to swing yourself on a playground swing. You move back and forth and swing higher in the air. Then you slowly swing to a stop. What sketch of a graph could represent how your height from the ground might change over time? Label each section.

b. Reasoning If you jumped from the swing instead of slowly swinging to a stop, how would the graph in part (a) be different? Explain.

Practice **Sketch a graph to represent each situation. Label each section.**

6. hours of daylight each day over the course of one year

7. your distance from the ground as you ride a Ferris wheel

Lesson Check

Do you know HOW?

8. What are the variables in the graph at the right? Use the graph to describe how the variables are related.

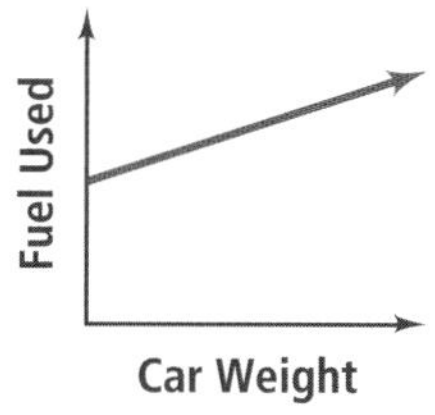

9. Describe the relationship between time and temperature in the table at the right.

Time (number of hours after noon)	1	3	5	7
Temperature (°F)	61	62	58	51

Do you UNDERSTAND?

MATHEMATICAL PRACTICES

10. Match one of the labeled segments in the graph at the right with each of the following verbal descriptions: *rising slowly, constant,* and *falling quickly.*

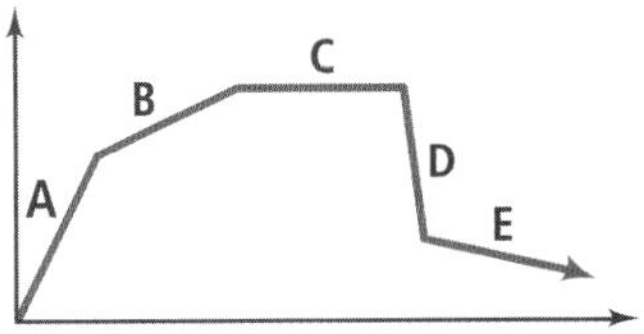

11. Reasoning Describe a real-world relationship that could be represented by the graph sketched above in Exercise 10.

More Practice and Problem-Solving Exercises

MATHEMATICAL PRACTICES

B Apply

12. Think About a Plan The *shishi-odoshi,* a popular Japanese garden ornament, was originally designed to frighten away deer. Using water, it makes a sharp rap each time a bamboo tube rises. Sketch a graph that could represent the volume of water in the bamboo tube as it operates.

Tube begins filling.

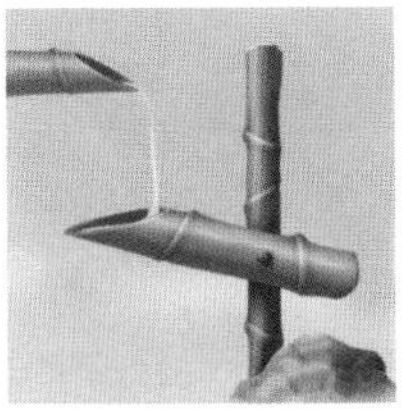

Full tube begins falling.

Tube falls and empties water.

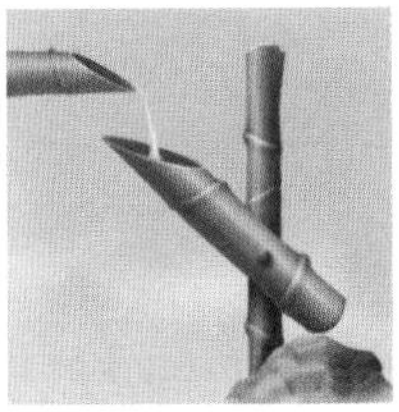

Tube rises and hits rock, making noise.

- What quantities vary in this situation?
- How are these quantities related?

13. Error Analysis T-shirts cost $12.99 each for the first 5 shirts purchased. Each additional T-shirt costs $4.99. Describe and correct the error in the graph at the right that represents the relationship between total cost and number of shirts purchased.

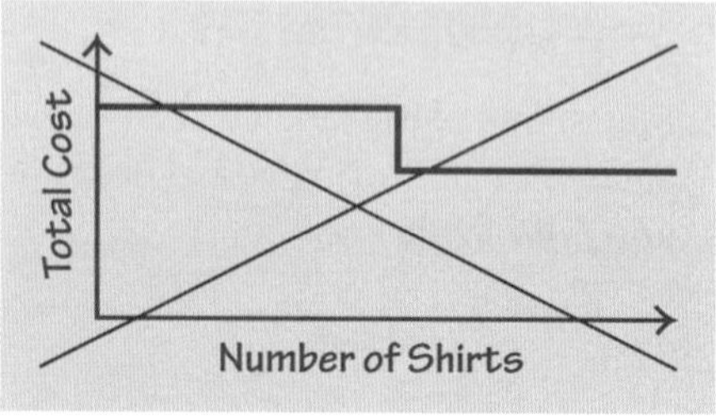

14. Open-Ended Describe a real-world relationship between the area of a rectangle and its width, as the width varies and the length stays the same. Sketch a graph to show this relationship.

15. Skiing Sketch a graph of each situation. Are the graphs the same? Explain.

a. your speed as you travel on a ski lift from the bottom of a ski slope to the top

b. your speed as you ski from the top of a ski slope to the bottom

16. Reasoning The diagram at the left below shows a portion of a bike trail.

a. Explain whether the graph at the right is a reasonable representation of how the speed might change for the blue biker.

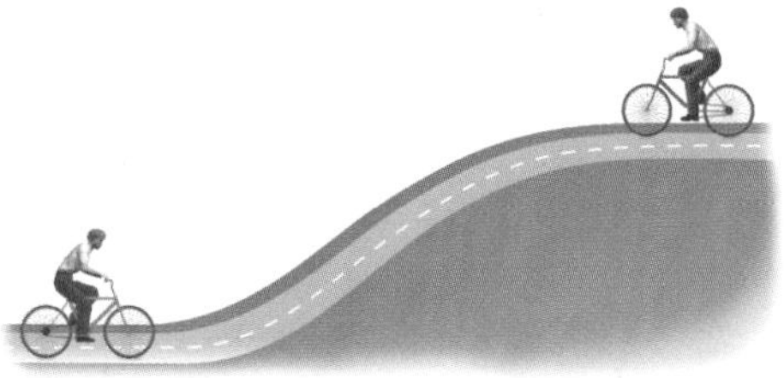

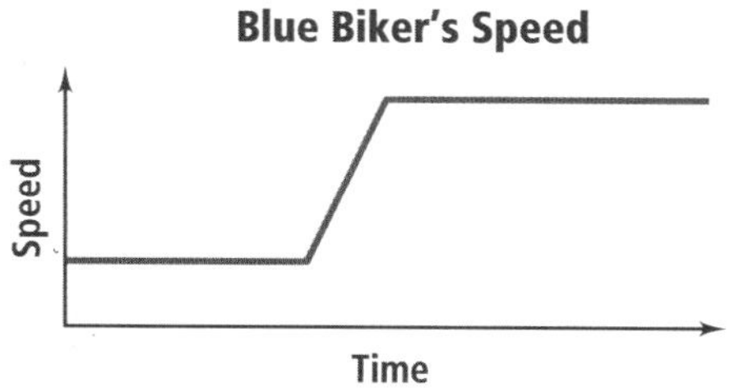

b. Sketch two graphs that could represent a biker's speed over time. Sketch one graph for the blue biker, and the other for the red biker.

Challenge

17. Track The sketch at the right shows the distance three runners travel during a race. Describe what occurs at times A, B, C, and D. In what order do the runners finish? Explain.

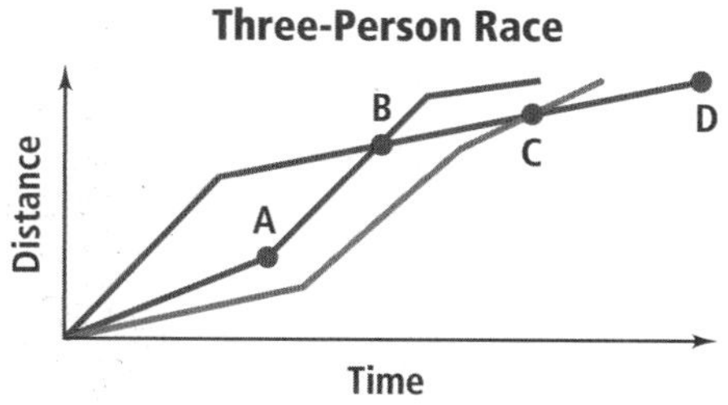

18. Reasoning The graph at the right shows the vertical distance traveled as Person A walks up a set of stairs and Person B walks up the steps of a moving escalator next to the stairs. Copy the graph. Then draw a line that could represent the vertical distance traveled as Person C rides the moving escalator while standing still. Explain your reasoning.

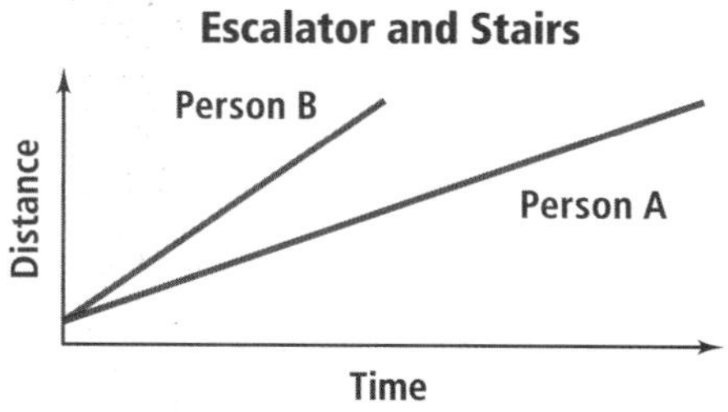

2-2 Patterns and Linear Functions

F.IF.4 For a function that models a relationship between two quantities, interpret key features of graphs and tables in terms of the quantities, and sketch graphs showing key features . . . Also **A.CED.2**

Objective To identify and represent patterns that describe linear functions

Solve It! Write your solution to the Solve It in the space below.

In the Solve It, you identified variables whose value *depends* on the value of another variable. In a relationship between variables, the **dependent variable** changes in response to another variable, the **independent variable.** Values of the independent variable are called **inputs.** Values of the dependent variable are called **outputs.**

Essential Understanding The value of one variable may be uniquely determined by the value of another variable. Such relationships may be represented using tables, words, equations, sets of ordered pairs, and graphs.

Problem 1 Representing a Geometric Relationship

Got It? **a.** In the diagram below, what is the relationship between the number of triangles and the perimeter of the figure they form? Represent this relationship using a table, words, an equation, and a graph.

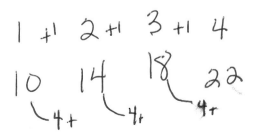

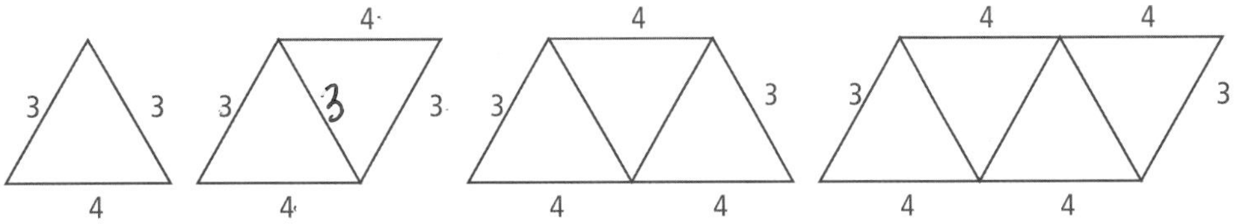

1 triangle 2 triangles 3 triangles 4 triangles

1 +1 2 +1 3 +1 4

10 14 18 22

4+ 4+ 4+

Total cost depends on how many we buy

b. Reasoning Suppose you know the perimeter of n triangles. What would you do to find the perimeter of $n + 1$ triangles?

Think
How can you use a pattern to answer this question?

c. How does your answer to part (b) relate to the equation you wrote in part (a)?

Practice **For each diagram, find the relationship between the number of shapes and the perimeter of the figures they form. Represent this relationship using a table, words, an equation, and a graph.**

1. 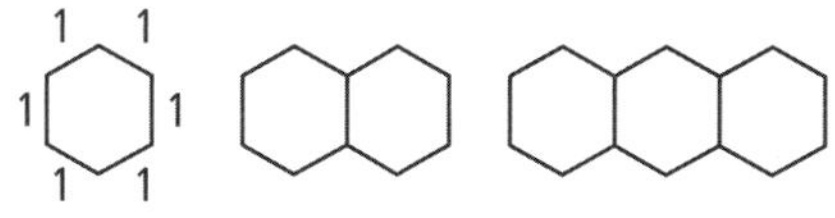

1 hexagon **2 hexagons** **3 hexagons**

2. 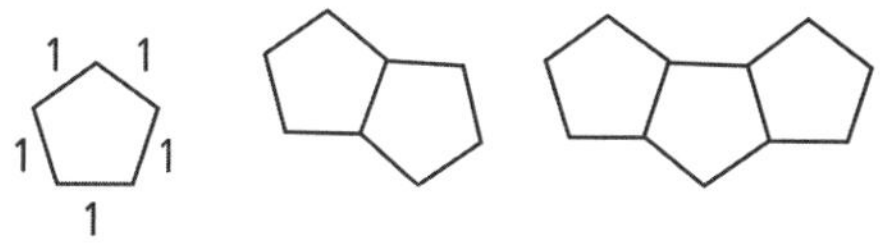

1 pentagon **2 pentagons** **3 pentagons**

You can describe the relationship in Problem 1 by saying that the perimeter is a function of the number of rectangles. A **function** is a relationship that pairs each input value with exactly one output value.

You have seen that one way to represent a function is with a graph. A **linear function** is a function whose graph is a nonvertical line or part of a nonvertical line.

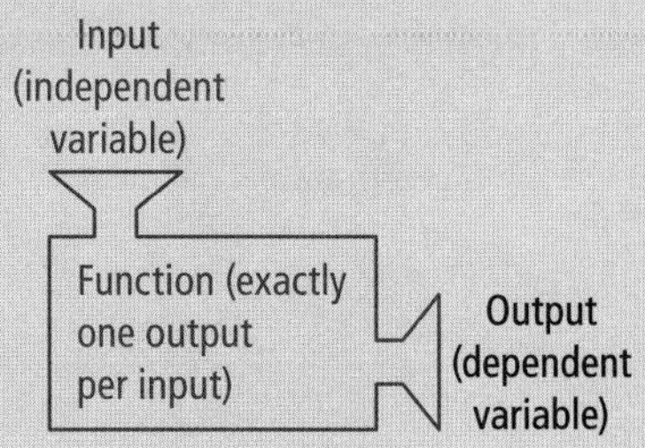

Problem 2 Representing a Linear Function

Think

How can you tell whether a relationship in a table is a function?

Got It? **a.** Is the relationship in the table below a linear function? Describe the relationship using words, an equation, and a graph.

Input, *x*	0	1	2	3
Output, *y*	8	10	12	14

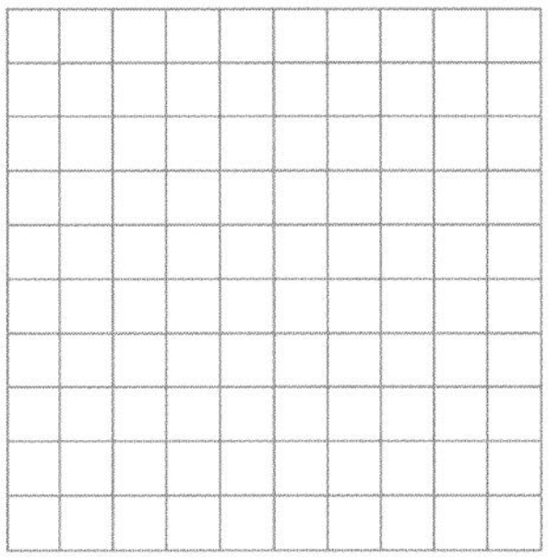

b. Reasoning Does the set of ordered pairs (0, 2), (1, 4), (3, 5), and (1, 8) represent a linear function? Explain.

Practice For each table, determine whether the relationship is a linear function. Then represent the relationship using words, an equation, and a graph.

3.

x	y
0	5
1	8
2	11
3	14

4.

x	y
0	43
1	32
2	21
3	10

Lesson Check

Do you know HOW?

5. Graph each set of ordered pairs. Use words to describe the pattern shown in the graph.

a. (0, 0), (1, 1), (2, 2), (3, 3), (4, 4)

b. (0, 8), (1, 6), (2, 4), (3, 2), (4, 0)

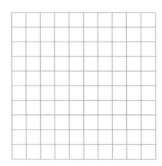

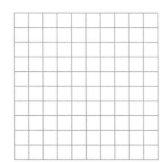

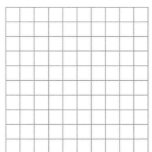

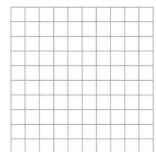

c. (3, 0), (3, 1), (3, 2), (3, 3), (3, 4)

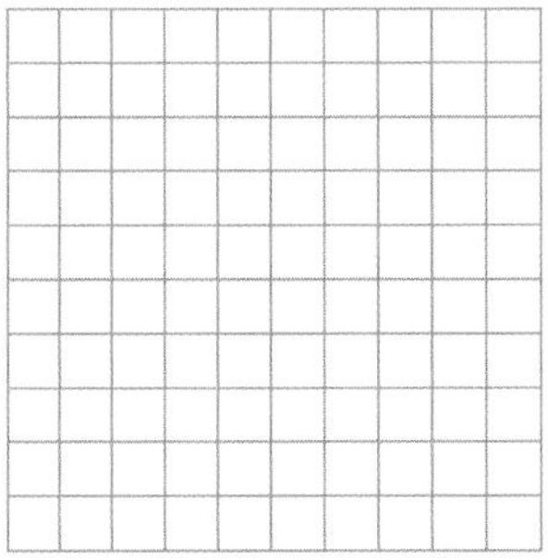

6. Use the diagram below. Complete the table showing the relationship between the number of squares and the perimeter of the figures they form.

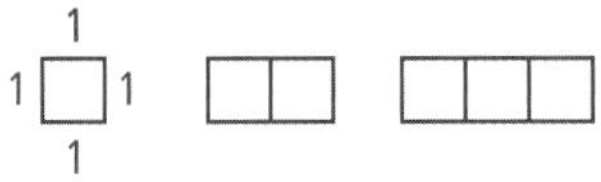

1 square **2 squares** **3 squares**

Number of Squares	Perimeter
1	4
2	6
3	
4	
10	
	62
n	

Do you UNDERSTAND?

MATHEMATICAL PRACTICES

7. Vocabulary The amount of toothpaste in a tube decreases each time you brush your teeth. Identify the independent and dependent variables in this relationship.

8. Reasoning Tell whether each set of ordered pairs in Exercise 5 represents a function. Justify your answers.

9. **Reasoning** Does the graph at the right represent a linear function? Explain.

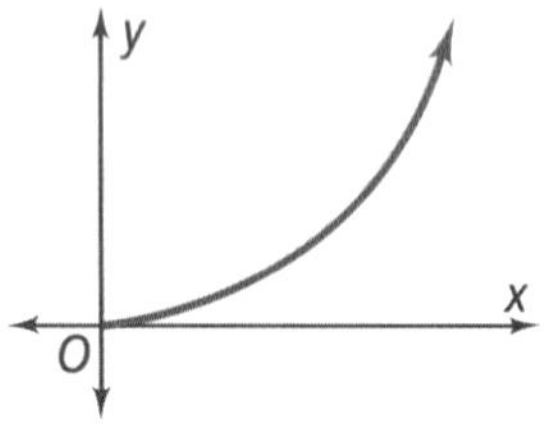

More Practice and Problem-Solving Exercises

MATHEMATICAL PRACTICES

B Apply

10. **Gardening** You can make 5 gal of liquid fertilizer by mixing 8 tsp of powdered fertilizer with water. Represent the relationship between the teaspoons of powder used and the gallons of fertilizer made using a table, an equation, and a graph. Is the amount of fertilizer made a function of the amount of powder used? Explain.

11. **Reasoning** Graph the set of ordered pairs $(-2, -3)$, $(0, -1)$, $(1, 0)$, $(3, 2)$, and $(4, 4)$. Determine whether the relationship is a linear function. Explain how you know.

12. **Think About a Plan** Gears are common parts in many types of machinery. In the diagram below, Gear A turns in response to the cranking of Gear B. Describe the relationship between the number of turns of Gear B and the number of turns of Gear A. Use words, an equation, and a graph.

- What are the independent and dependent variables?
- How much must you turn Gear B to get Gear A to go around once?

STEM 13. **Electric Car** An automaker makes a car that can travel 40 mi on its charged battery before it begins to use gas. Then the car travels 50 mi per gallon of gas used. Represent the relationship between the amount of gas used and the distance traveled using a table, an equation, and a graph. Is total distance traveled a function of the amount of gas used? What are the independent and dependent variables? Explain.

14. **Reasoning** Suppose you know the perimeter of n octagons arranged as shown. What would you do to find the perimeter if 1 more octagon was added?

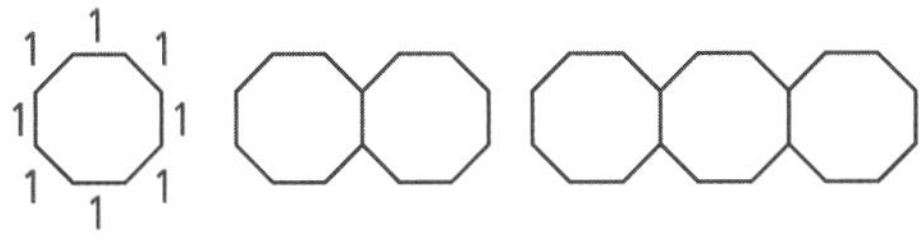

Challenge

15. **Athletics** The graph at the right shows the distance a runner has traveled as a function of the amount of time (in minutes) she has been running. Draw a graph that shows the time she has been running as a function of the distance she has traveled.

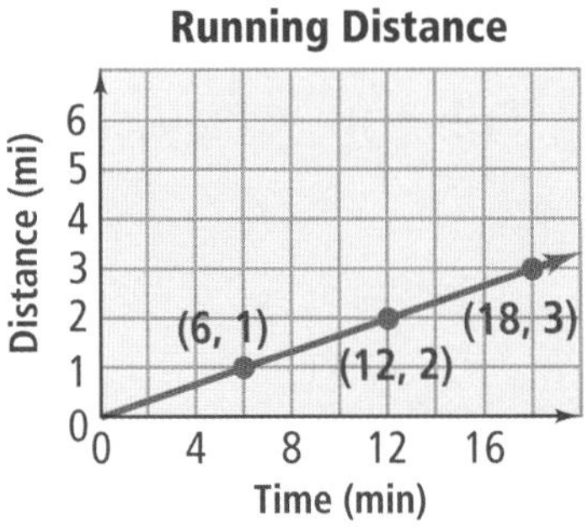

16. **Movies** When a movie on film is projected, a certain number of frames pass through the projector per minute. You say that the length of the movie in minutes is a function of the number of frames. Someone else says that the number of frames is a function of the length of the movie. Can you both be right? Explain.

2-3 Patterns and Nonlinear Functions

F.IF.4 For a function that models a relationship between two quantities, interpret key features of graphs and tables in terms of the quantities, and sketch graphs showing key features . . . Also **A.CED.2**

Objective To identify and represent patterns that describe nonlinear functions

Solve It! Write your solution to the Solve It in the space below.

The relationship in the Solve It is an example of a nonlinear function. A **nonlinear function** is a function whose graph is not a line or part of a line.

Essential Understanding Just like linear functions, nonlinear functions can be represented using words, tables, equations, sets of ordered pairs, and graphs.

take note

Concept Summary Linear and Nonlinear Functions

Linear Function

A linear function is a function whose graph is a nonvertical line or part of a nonvertical line.

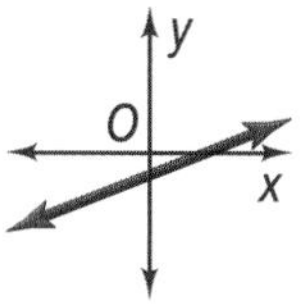

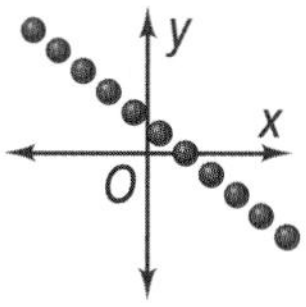

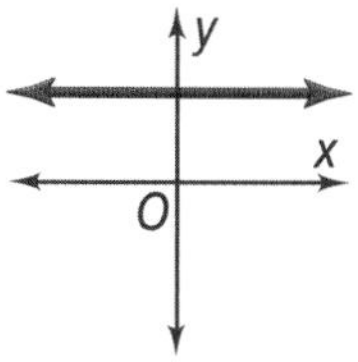

Nonlinear Function

A nonlinear function is a function whose graph is not a line or part of a line.

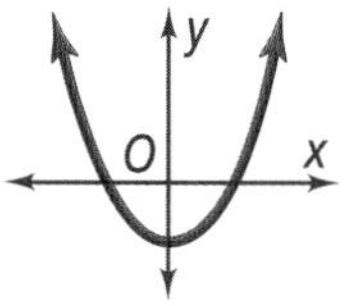

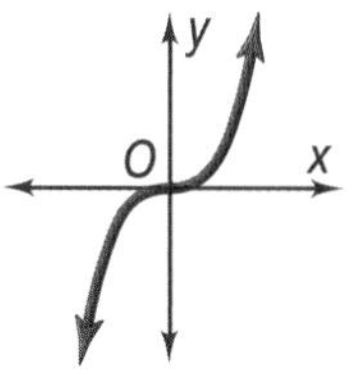

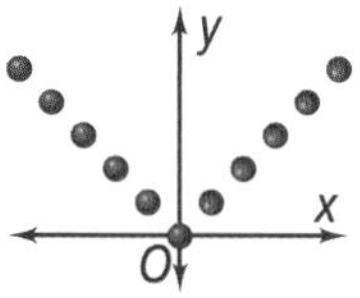

Problem 1 Classifying Functions as Linear or Nonlinear

Think

How can a graph tell you if a function is linear or nonlinear?

Got It? **a.** The table below shows the fraction A of the original area of a piece of paper that remains after the paper has been cut in half n times. Graph the function represented by the table. Is the function *linear* or *nonlinear*?

Cutting Paper				
Number of Cuts, n	1	2	3	4
Fraction of Original Area Remaining, A	$\frac{1}{2}$	$\frac{1}{4}$	$\frac{1}{8}$	$\frac{1}{16}$

b. Reasoning Will the area A in part (a) ever reach zero? Explain.

Practice **The cost C, in dollars, for pencils is a function of the number of pencils purchased, n. The length L of a pencil, in inches, is a function of the time t, in seconds, it has been sharpened. Graph the function shown by each table. Tell whether the function is *linear* or *nonlinear*.**

1.

Pencil Cost					
Number of Pencils, n	6	12	18	24	30
Cost, C	\$1	\$2	\$3	\$4	\$5

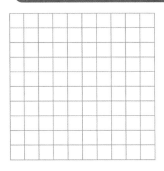

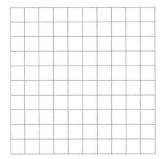

2.

Pencil Sharpening						
Time (s), *t*	0	3	6	9	12	15
Length (in.), *L*	7.5	7.5	7.5	7.5	7.4	7.3

Problem 2 Representing Patterns and Nonlinear Functions

Got It? The table shows the number of new branches in each figure of the pattern below. What is a pattern you can use to complete the table? Represent the relationship using words, an equation, and a graph.

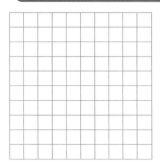

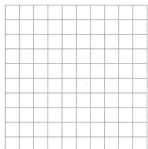

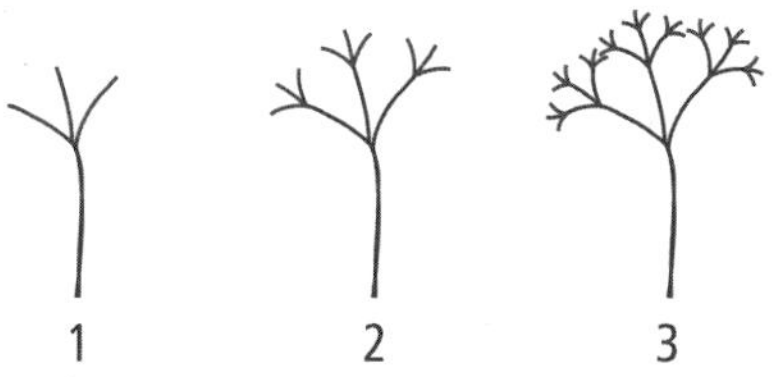

Number of Figure, *x*	1	2	3	4	5
Number of New Branches, *y*	3	9	27		

A Practice **3.** For the diagram below, the table gives the total number of small triangles y in figure number x. What pattern can you use to complete the table? Represent the relationship using words, an equation, and a graph.

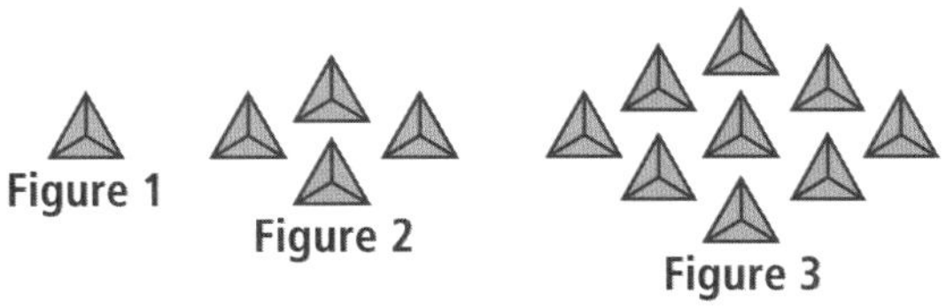

Figure Number, x	Total Small Triangles, y	Ordered Pair (x, y)
1	3	(1, 3)
2	12	(2, 12)
3	27	(3, 27)
4		
5		

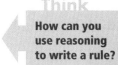

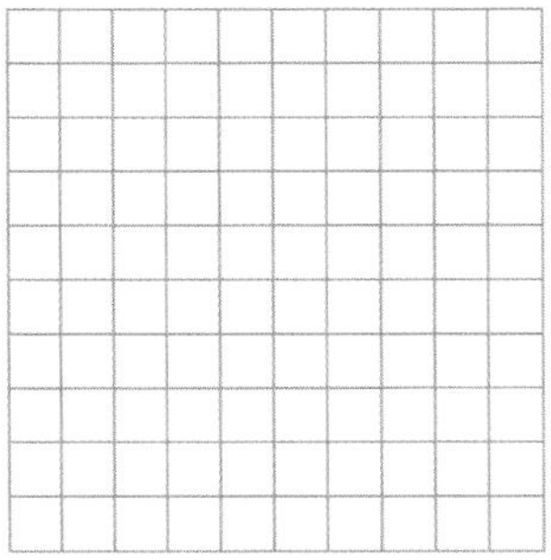

A function can be thought of as a rule that you apply to the input in order to get the output. You can describe a nonlinear function with words or with an equation, just as you did with linear functions.

Problem 3 Writing a Rule to Describe a Nonlinear Function

Think

How can you use reasoning to write a rule?

Got It? What is a rule for the function represented by the ordered pairs (1, 1), (2, 4), (3, 9), (4, 16), and (5, 25)?

Practice **Each set of ordered pairs represents a function. Write a rule that represents the function.**

4. (0, 0), (1, 4), (2, 16), (3, 36), (4, 64)

5. (0, 0), (1, 0.5), (2, 2), (3, 4.5), (4, 8)

Lesson Check

Do you know HOW?

6. Graph the function represented by the table below. Is the function *linear* or *nonlinear*?

x	0	1	2	3	4
y	12	13	14	15	16

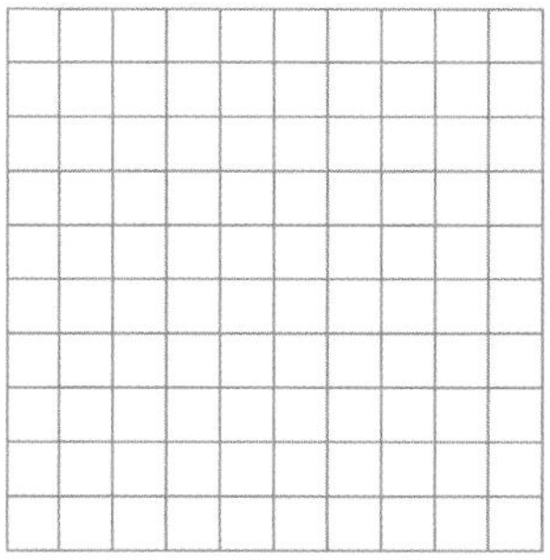

7. The ordered pairs (0, −2), (1, 1), (2, 4), (3, 7), and (4, 10) represent a function. What is a rule that represents this function?

8. Which rule could represent the function shown by the table below?

x	0	1	2	3	4
y	0	−1	−4	−9	−16

Ⓐ $y = x^2$ Ⓑ $y = -x^3$ Ⓒ $y = -x^2$

Do you UNDERSTAND?

MATHEMATICAL PRACTICES

9. Vocabulary Does each graph represent a *linear function* or a *nonlinear function*? Explain.

a.

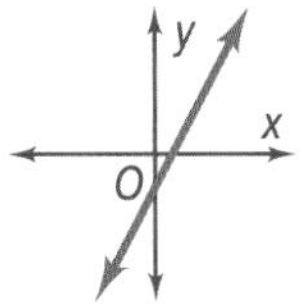

b.

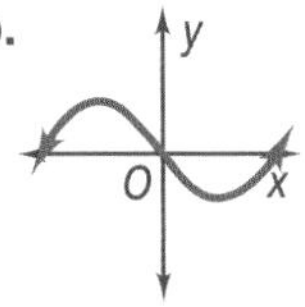

10. Error Analysis A classmate says that the function shown by the table at the right can be represented by the rule $y = x + 1$. Describe and correct your classmate's error.

x	y
0	1
1	2
2	5
3	10
4	17

More Practice and Problem-Solving Exercises

MATHEMATICAL PRACTICES

B Apply

11. Writing The rule $V = \frac{4}{3}\pi r^3$ gives the volume V of a sphere as a function of its radius r. Identify the independent and dependent variables in this relationship. Explain your reasoning.

12. Open-Ended Write a rule for a nonlinear function such that y is negative when $x = 1$, positive when $x = 2$, negative when $x = 3$, positive when $x = 4$, and so on.

13. Think About a Plan Concrete forming tubes are used as molds for cylindrical concrete supports. The volume V of a tube is the product of its length ℓ and the area A of its circular base. You can make $\frac{2}{3}$ ft^3 of cement per bag. Write a rule to find the number of bags of cement needed to fill a tube 4 ft long as a function of its radius r. How many bags are needed to fill a tube with a 4-in. radius? A 5-in. radius? A 6-in. radius?

- What is a rule for the volume V of any tube?
- What operation do you use to find the number of bags needed for a given volume?

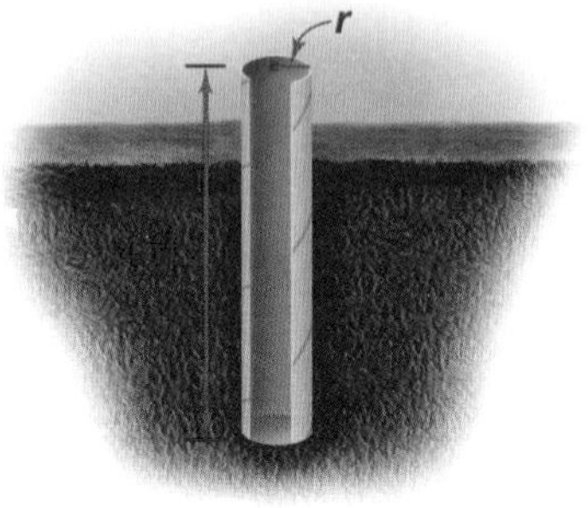

14. Fountain A designer wants to make a circular fountain inside a square of grass as shown at the right. What is a rule for the area A of the grass as a function of r?

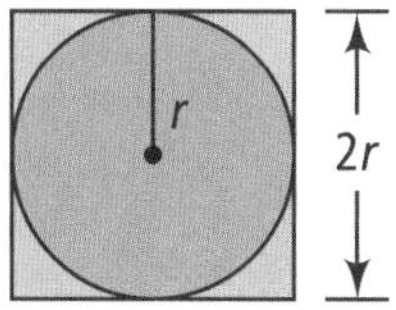

C Challenge

15. Reasoning What is a rule for the function represented by $\left(0, \frac{2}{19}\right), \left(1, 1\frac{2}{19}\right), \left(2, 4\frac{2}{19}\right), \left(3, 9\frac{2}{19}\right), \left(4, 16\frac{2}{19}\right)$, and $\left(5, 25\frac{2}{19}\right)$? Explain your reasoning.

16. Reasoning A certain function fits the following description: As the value of x increases by 1 each time, the value of y continually decreases by a smaller amount each time, and never reaches a value as low as 1. Is this function *linear* or *nonlinear*? Explain your reasoning.

2-4 Graphing a Function Rule

A.REI.10 Understand that the graph of an equation in two variables is the set of all its solutions plotted in the coordinate plane . . . Also **N.Q.1, F.IF.4**

Objective To graph equations that represent functions

Solve It! Write your solution to the Solve It in the space below.

You can use a table of values to help you make a graph in the Solve It.

Essential Understanding The set of all solutions of an equation forms the equation's graph. A graph may include solutions that do not appear in a table. A real-world graph should only show points that make sense in the given situation.

Problem 1 Graphing a Function Rule

Got It? What is the graph of the function rule $y = \frac{1}{2}x - 1$?

Think

How can a table of values help you draw the graph?

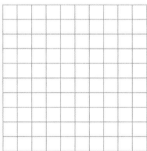

Practice Graph each function rule.

1. $y = \frac{3}{4}x + 2$

2. $y = -\frac{1}{2}x + \frac{1}{2}$

When you graph a real-world function rule, choose appropriate intervals for the units on the axes. Every interval on an axis should represent the same change in value. If all the data are nonnegative, show only the first quadrant.

Problem 2 Graphing a Real-World Function Rule

Got It? **a.** The function rule $W = 8g + 700$ represents the total weight W, in pounds, of a spa that contains g gallons of water. What is a reasonable graph of the function rule, given that the capacity of the spa is 250 gal?

b. Reasoning What is the weight of the spa when empty? Explain.

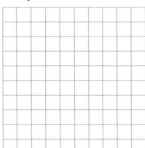

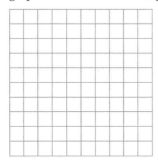

Practice 3. **Beverages** The height h, in inches, of the juice in a 20-oz bottle depends on the amount of juice j, in ounces, that you drink. This situation is represented by the function rule $h = 6 - 0.3j$. Graph the function rule. Explain your choice of intervals on the axes of the graph.

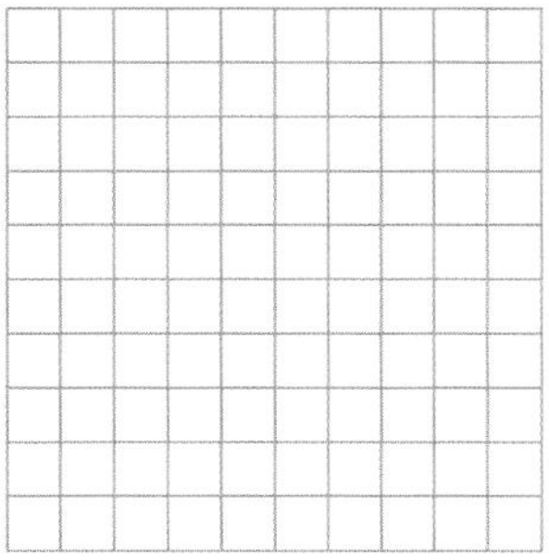

In Problem 2, the truck could contain any amount of concrete from 0 to 200 ft^3, such as 27.3 ft^3 or $105\frac{2}{3}\,ft^3$. You can connect the data points from the table because any point between the data points has meaning.

Some graphs may be composed of isolated points. For example, in the Solve It you graphed only points that represent printing whole numbers of photos.

take note

Key Concept Continuous and Discrete Graphs

Continuous Graph

A **continuous graph** is a graph that is unbroken.

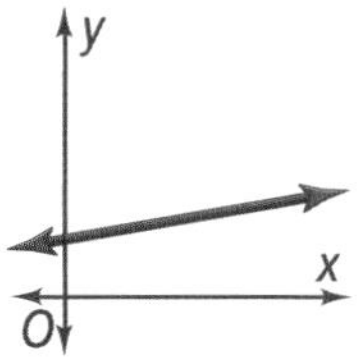

Discrete Graph

A **discrete graph** is composed of distinct, isolated points.

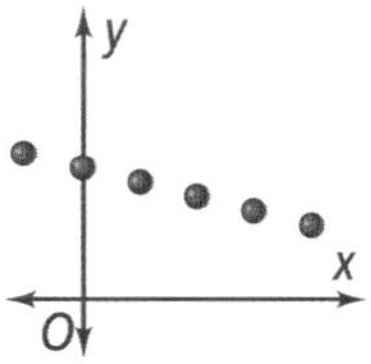

Problem 3 Identifying Continuous and Discrete Graphs

Got It? Graph each function rule. Is the graph *continuous* or *discrete*? Justify your answer.

a. The amount of water w in a wading pool, in gallons, depends on the amount of time t, in minutes, the wading pool has been filling, as related by the function rule $W = 3t$.

Think

How can you decide if a graph is continuous or discrete?

b. The cost C for baseball tickets, in dollars, depends on the number n of tickets bought, as related by the function rule $C = 16n$.

Practice **Graph each function rule. Explain your choice of intervals on the axes of the graph. Tell whether the graph is *continuous* or *discrete*.**

4. Trucking The total weight w, in pounds, of a tractor-trailer capable of carrying 8 cars depends on the number of cars c on the trailer. This situation is represented by the function rule $w = 37{,}000 + 4200c$.

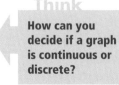

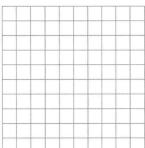

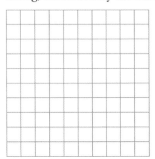

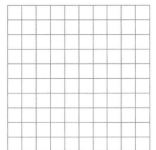

5. Food Delivery The cost C, in dollars, for delivered pizza depends on the number of pizzas ordered, p. This situation is represented by the function rule $C = 5 + 9p$.

The function rules graphed in Problems 1–3 represent linear functions. You can also graph a nonlinear function rule. When a function rule does not represent a real-world situation, graph it as a continuous function.

Problem 4 Graphing Nonlinear Function Rules

Got It? What is the graph of the function rule $y = x^3 + 1$?

Practice Graph each function rule.

6. $y = -x^3$

7. $y = |x - 3| - 1$

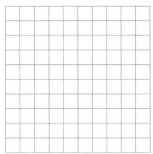

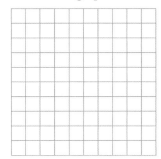

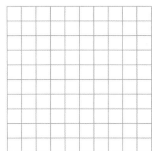

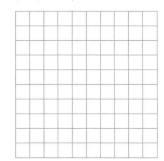

Lesson Check

Do you know HOW?

In Exercises 8–11, graph each function rule.

8. $y = 2x + 4$

9. $y = \frac{1}{2}x - 7$

10. $y = 9 - x$

11. $y = -x^2 + 2$

12. The function rule $h = 18 + 1.5n$ represents the height h, in inches, of a stack of traffic cones.

a. Make a table for the function rule.

b. Suppose the stack of cones can be no taller than 30 in. What is a reasonable graph of the function rule?

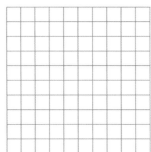

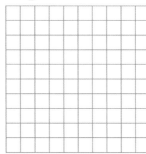

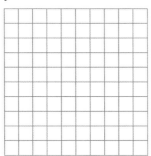

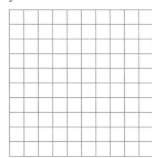

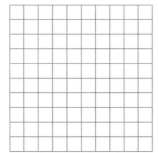

Do you UNDERSTAND?

MATHEMATICAL PRACTICES

Vocabulary **Tell whether each relationship should be represented by a continuous or a discrete graph.**

13. The number of bagels b remaining in a dozen depends on the number s that have been sold.

14. The amount of gas g remaining in the tank of a gas grill depends on the amount of time t the grill has been used.

15. Error Analysis Your friend graphs $y = x + 3$ at the right. Describe and correct your friend's error.

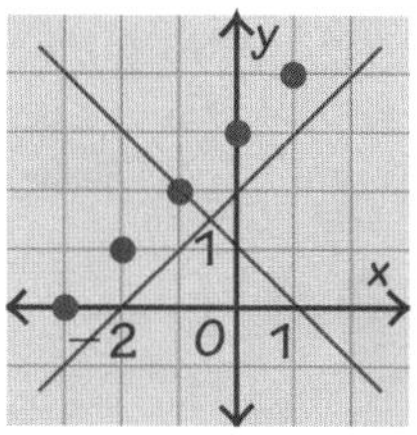

More Practice and Problem-Solving Exercises

MATHEMATICAL PRACTICES

B Apply

16. Error Analysis The graph at the right shows the distance d you run, in miles, as a function of time t, in minutes, during a 5-mi run. Your friend says that the graph is not continuous because it stops at $d = 5$, so the graph is discrete. Do you agree? Explain.

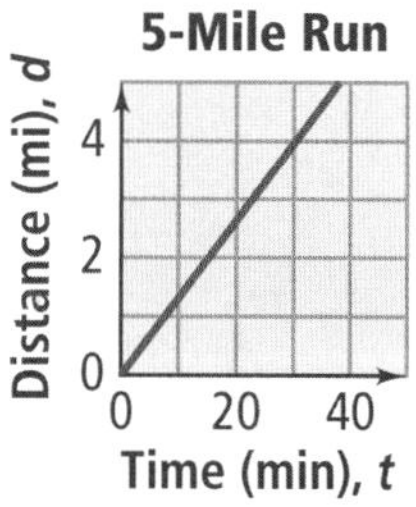

17. Writing Is the point $\left(2, 2\frac{1}{2}\right)$ on the graph of $y = x + 2$? How do you know?

18. Geometry The area A of an isosceles right triangle depends on the length ℓ of each leg of the triangle. This is represented by the rule $A = \frac{1}{2}\ell^2$. Graph the function rule. Is the graph *continuous* or *discrete*? How do you know?

19. Which function rule is graphed at the right?

Ⓐ $y = -\frac{1}{2}x + 1$

Ⓑ $y = \frac{1}{2}x - 1$

Ⓒ $y = \left|\frac{1}{2}x\right| - 1$

Ⓓ $y = \frac{1}{2}x + 1$

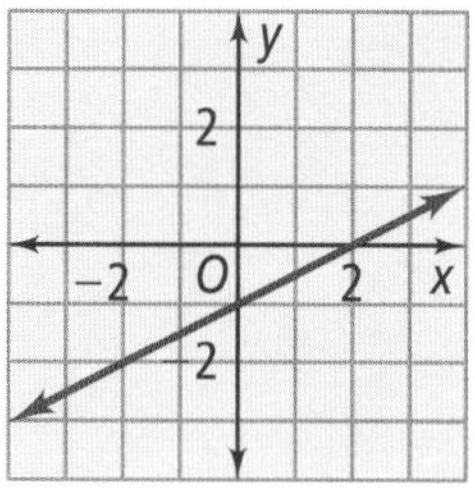

20. Sporting Goods The amount a basketball coach spends at a sporting goods store depends on the number of basketballs the coach buys. The situation is represented by the function rule $a = 15b$.

a. Make a table of values and graph the function rule. Is the graph *continuous* or *discrete*? Explain.

b. Suppose the coach spent \$120. How many basketballs did she buy?

21. Think About a Plan The height h, in inches, of the vinegar in the jars of pickle chips shown at the right depends on the number of chips p you eat. About how many chips must you eat to lower the level of the vinegar in the jar on the left to the level of the jar on the right? Use a graph to find the answer.

- What should the maximum value of p be on the horizontal axis?
- What are reasonable values of p in this situation?

STEM **22. Falling Objects** The height h, in feet, of an acorn that falls from a branch 100 ft above the ground depends on the time t, in seconds, since it has fallen. This is represented by the rule $h = 100 - 16t^2$. About how much time does it take for the acorn to hit the ground? Use a graph and give an answer between two consecutive whole-number values of t.

Challenge

23. Reasoning Graph the function rules below in the same coordinate plane.

$y = |x| + 1$ $\qquad$ $y = |x| + 4$ $\qquad$ $y = |x| - 3$

In the function rule $y = |x| + k$, how does changing the value of k affect the graph?

24. Reasoning Make a table of values and a graph for the function rules $y = 2x$ and $y = 2x^2$. How does the value of y change when you double the value of x for each function rule?

Graphing Functions and Solving Equations

A.REI.11 Explain why the x-coordinates of the points where . . . $y = f(x)$ and $y = g(x)$ intersect are the solutions of the equation $f(x) = g(x)$; find the solutions approximately . . .

MATHEMATICAL PRACTICES

You have learned to graph function rules by making a table of values. You can also use a graphing calculator to graph function rules.

Example 1

Graph $y = \frac{1}{2}x - 4$ using a graphing calculator.

Step 1 Press the 【y=】 key. To the right of **Y₁ =**, enter $\frac{1}{2}x - 4$ by pressing 【(】 1 【÷】 2 【)】 【x,t,θ,n】 【−】 4.

```
Plot1  Plot2  Plot3
\Y1 ■ (1/2)X − 4
\Y2 = ■
\Y3 =
\Y4 =
\Y5 =
\Y6 =
\Y7 =
```

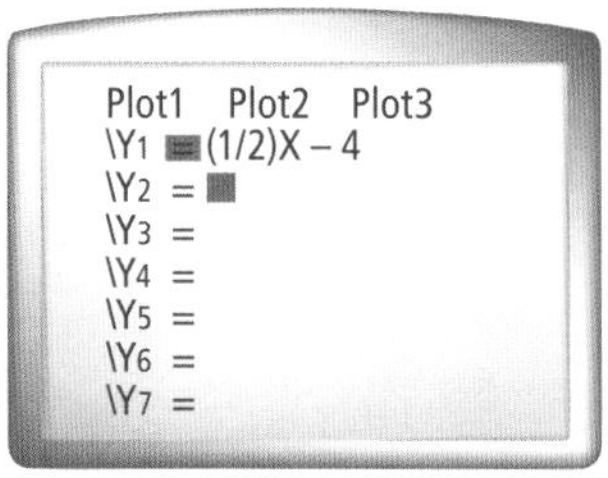

Step 2 The screen on the graphing calculator is a "window" that lets you look at only part of the graph. Press the 【window】 key to set the borders of the graph. A good window for this function rule is the standard viewing window, $-10 \le x \le 10$ and $-10 \le y \le 10$.

You can have the axes show 1 unit between tick marks by setting **Xscl** and **Yscl** to 1, as shown.

```
WINDOW
 Xmin  = −10
 Xmax  = 10
 Xscl  = 1
 Ymin  = −10
 Ymax  = 10
 Yscl  = 1
 Xres  = 1
```

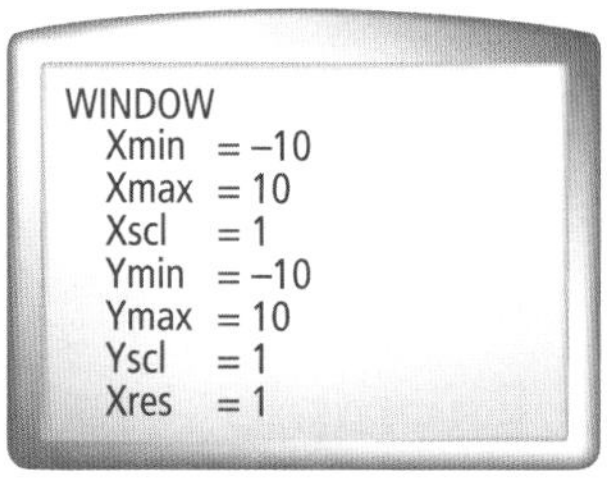

Step 3 Press the 【graph】 key. The graph of the function rule is shown.

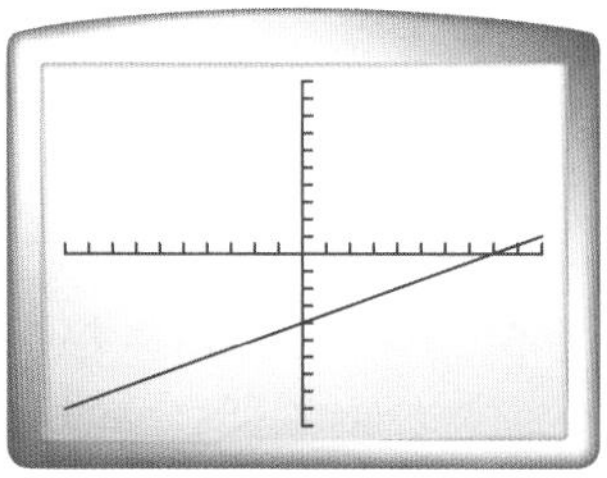

In Chapter 1 you learned how to solve equations in one variable. You can also solve equations by using a graphing calculator to graph each side of the equation as a function rule. The x-coordinate of the point where the graphs intersect is the solution of the equation.

Example 2

Solve $7 = -\frac{3}{4}k + 3$ using a graphing calculator.

Step 1 Press [y=]. Clear any equations. Then enter each side of the given equation. For **Y_1 =**, enter 7. For **Y_2 =**, enter $-\frac{3}{4}x + 3$ by pressing [(] [(-)] 3 [÷] 4 [)] [x,t,θ,n] [+] 3. Notice that you must replace the variable k with x.

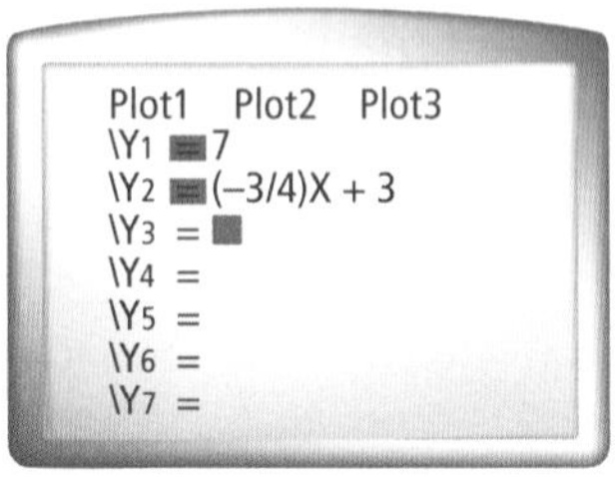

Step 2 Graph the function rules. Use a standard graphing window by pressing [zoom] 6. This gives a window defined by $-10 \le x \le 10$ and $-10 \le y \le 10$.

Step 3 Use the [calc] feature. Select **INTERSECT** and press [enter] to select the first line, then press [enter] to select the second line. Move the cursor near the point of intersection and press [enter] a third time.

The calculator's value for the x-coordinate of the point of intersection is -5.333333. The actual x-coordinate is $-5\frac{1}{3}$.

The solution of the equation $7 = -\frac{3}{4}k + 3$ is $-5\frac{1}{3}$.

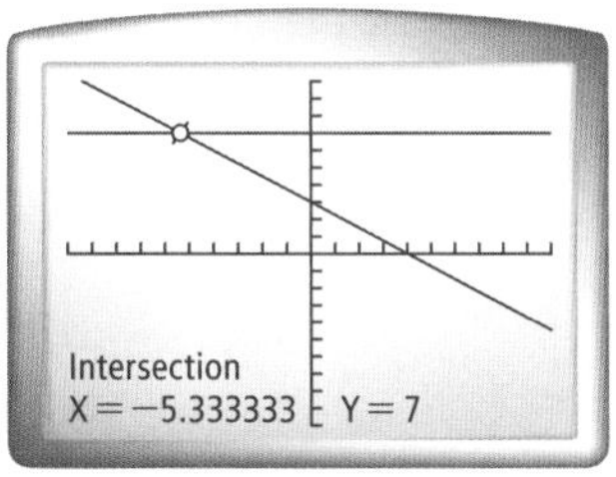

You cannot solve all equations using the methods of Chapter 1. In those cases, you can find approximate solutions by graphing.

Example 3

Solve $-x^2 + 6 = \frac{x + 4}{x + 2}$ using a graphing calculator.

Step 1 Press [y=]. Clear any equations. Then enter each side of the given equation. For **Y_1 =**, enter $-x^2 + 6$. For **Y_2 =**, enter $\frac{(x + 4)}{(x + 2)}$.

Step 2 Use the [calc] feature. Select **INTERSECT** and press [enter] to select the first curve, then press [enter] to select the second curve. Move the cursor near a point of intersection and press [enter] a third time.

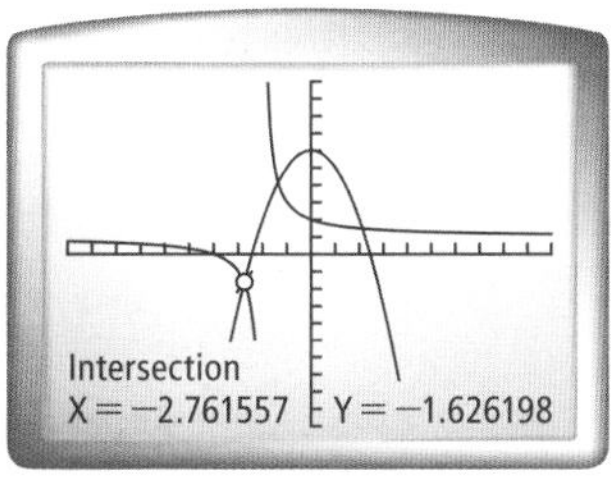

Step 3 Find the other points of intersection in a similar way.

The calculator's values for the x-coordinates of the points of intersection are -2.761557, -1.363328, and 2.1248854. These are the approximate solutions to the equation $-x^2 + 6 = \frac{x+4}{x+2}$.

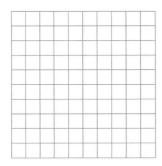

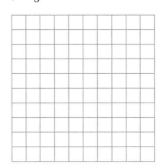

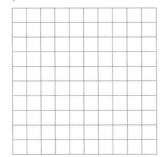

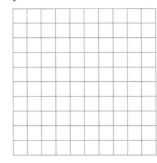

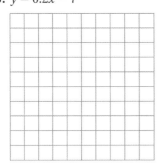

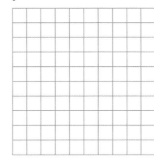

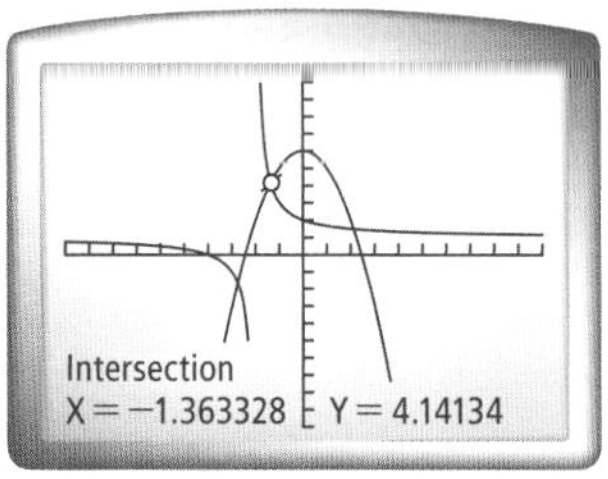

Exercises

Graph each function rule using a graphing calculator.

1. $y = 6x + 3$

2. $y = -3x + 8$

3. $y = 0.2x - 7$

4. $y = -1.8x - 6$

5. $y = -\frac{1}{3}x + 5$

6. $y = \frac{8}{3}x - 5$

7. Open-Ended Graph $y = -0.4x + 8$. Using the **window** screen, experiment with values for **Xmin, Xmax, Ymin,** and **Ymax** until you can see the graph crossing both axes. What values did you use for **Xmin, Xmax, Ymin,** and **Ymax**?

8. Reasoning How can you graph the equation $2x + 3y = 6$ on a graphing calculator?

Use a graphing calculator to solve each equation.

9. $8a - 12 = 6$

10. $-4 = -3t + 2$

11. $-5 = -0.5x - 2$

12. $4 + \frac{3}{2}n = -7$

13. $\frac{5}{4}d - \frac{1}{2} = 6$

14. $-3y - 1 = 3.5$

15. $4 = |x - 2|$

16. $x^2 - 4 = |x|$

17. $x^2 - 5 = (x - 1)^3 + 4$

2-5 Writing a Function Rule

A.CED.2 Create equations in two or more variables . . .; graph equations on coordinate axes with labels and scales. Also **N.Q.2., A.SSE.1.a, F.BF.1.a**

Objective To write equations that represent functions

Solve It! Write your solution to the Solve It in the space below.

In the Solve It, you can see how the value of one variable depends on another. Once you see a pattern in a relationship, you can write a rule.

Essential Understanding Many real-world functional relationships can be represented by equations. You can use an equation to find the solution of a given real-world problem.

Problem 1 Writing a Function Rule

Got It? A landfill has 50,000 tons of waste in it. Each month it accumulates an average of 420 more tons of waste. What is a function rule that represents the total amount of waste after m months?

Think
How can a model help you visualize this real-world situation?

Practice **Write a function rule that represents each situation.**

1. **Wages** A worker's earnings e are a function of the number of hours n worked at a rate of $8.75 per hour.

2. Baking The almond extract a remaining in an 8-oz bottle decreases by $\frac{1}{6}$ oz for each batch b of waffle cookies made.

Problem 2 Writing and Evaluating a Function Rule

Got It? **a.** A kennel charges $15 per day to board a dog. Upon arrival, each dog must have a flea bath that costs $12. Write a function rule for the total cost for n days of boarding plus a bath. How much does a 10-day stay cost?

b. Reasoning Does a 5-day stay cost half as much as a 10-day stay? Explain.

Practice **3. Aviation** A helicopter hovers 40 ft above the ground. Then the helicopter climbs at a rate of 21 ft/s. Write a rule that represents the helicopter's height h above the ground as a function of time t. What is the helicopter's height after 45 s?

4. **Diving** A team of divers assembles at an elevation of −10 ft relative to the surface of the water. Then the team dives at a rate of −50 ft/min. Write a rule that represents the team's depth d as a function of time t. What is the team's depth after 3 min?

Problem 3 Writing a Nonlinear Function Rule

Think

How can *drawing a diagram* help you write the rule?

Got It? a. Write a function rule for the area of a triangle whose height is 4 in. more than twice the length of its base. What is the area of the triangle when the length of its base is 16 in.?

b. **Reasoning** Graph the function rule from part (a). How do you know the rule is nonlinear?

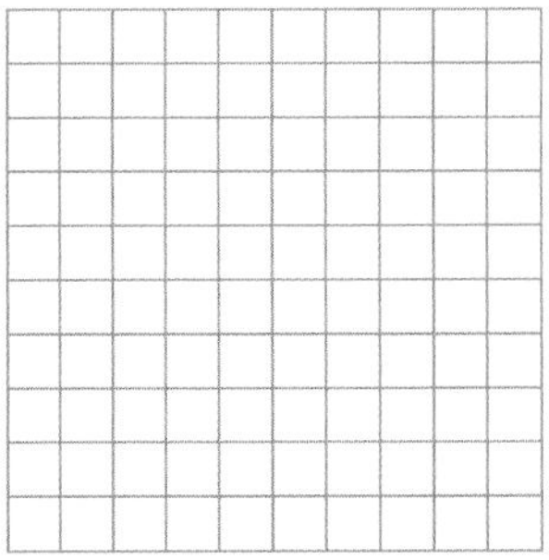

Practice 5. Write a function rule for the area of a triangle with a base 3 cm greater than 5 times its height. What is the area of the triangle when its height is 6 cm?

6. Write a function rule for the volume of the cylinder shown at the right with a height 3 in. more than 4 times the radius of the cylinder's base. What is the volume of the cylinder when it has a radius of 2 in.?

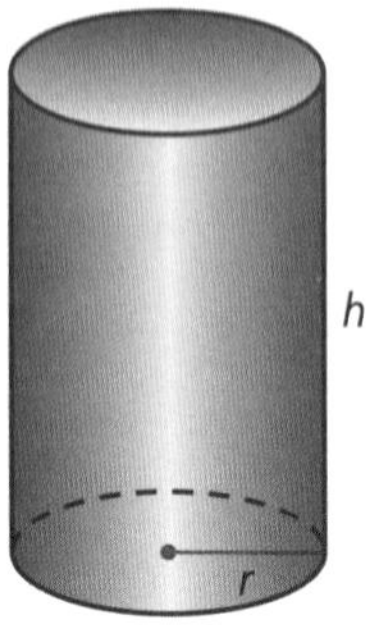

$V = \pi r^2 h$

Lesson Check

Do you know HOW?

Write a function rule to represent each situation.

7. the total cost C for p pounds of copper if each pound costs \$3.57

8. the height f, in feet, of an object when you know the object's height h in inches

9. the amount y of your friend's allowance if the amount she receives is \$2 more than the amount x you receive

10. the volume V of a cube-shaped box whose edge lengths are 1 in. greater than the diameter d of the ball that the box will hold

Do you UNDERSTAND?

MATHEMATICAL PRACTICES

11. Vocabulary Suppose you write an equation that gives a as a function of b. Which is the dependent variable and which is the independent variable?

12. Error Analysis A worker has dug 3 holes for fence posts. It will take 15 min to dig each additional hole. Your friend writes the rule $t = 15n + 3$ for the time t, in minutes, required to dig n additional holes. Describe and correct your friend's error.

13. Reasoning Is the graph of a function rule that relates a square's area to its side length *continuous* or *discrete*? Explain.

More Practice and Problem-Solving Exercises

MATHEMATICAL PRACTICES

B Apply

14. Open-Ended Write a function rule that models a real-world situation. Evaluate your function for an input value and explain what the output represents.

15. Writing What advantage(s) can you see of having a rule instead of a table of values to represent a function?

16. History of Math The golden ratio has been studied and used by mathematicians and artists for more than 2000 years. A golden rectangle, constructed using the golden ratio, has a length about 1.6 times its width. Write a rule for the area of a golden rectangle as a function of its width.

17. Whales From an elevation of 3.5 m below the surface of the water, a northern bottlenose whale dives at a rate of 1.8 m/s. Write a rule that gives the whale's depth d as a function of time in minutes. What is the whale's depth after 4 min?

18. **Think About a Plan** The height h, in inches, of the juice in the pitcher shown at the right is a function of the amount of juice j, in ounces, that has been poured out of the pitcher. Write a function rule that represents this situation. What is the height of the juice after 47 oz have been poured out?
   - What is the height of the juice when half of it has been poured out?
   - What fraction of the juice would you pour out to make the height decrease by 1 in.?

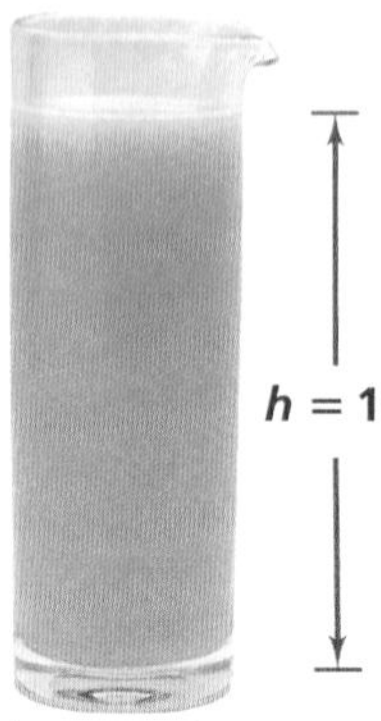

19. **Tips** You go to dinner and decide to leave a 15% tip for the server. You had \$55 when you entered the restaurant.
   a. Make a table showing how much money you would have left after buying a meal that costs \$15, \$21, \$24, or \$30.
   b. Write a function rule for the amount of money m you would have left if the meal costs c dollars before the tip.
   c. Graph the function rule.

20. **Car Rental** A car rental agency charges \$29 per day to rent a car and \$13.95 per day for a global positioning system (GPS). Customers are charged for their full tank of gas at \$3.80 per gallon.
   a. A car has a 12-gal tank and a GPS. Write a rule for the total bill b as a function of the number of days d the car is rented.
   b. What is the bill for a 9-day rental?

21. **Projectors** You consult your new projector's instruction manual before mounting it on the wall. The manual says to multiply the desired image width by 1.8 to find the correct distance of the projector lens from the wall.
   a. Write a rule to describe the distance of the lens from the wall as a function of desired image width.
   b. The diagram shows the room in which the projector will be installed. Will you be able to project an image 7 ft wide? Explain.
   c. What is the maximum image width you can project in the room?

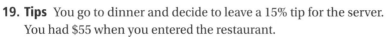

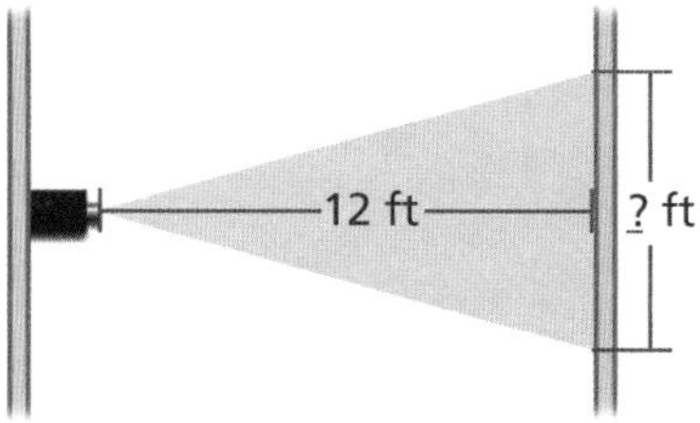

22. **Reasoning** Write a rule that is an example of a nonlinear function that fits the following description.

    When d is 4, r is 9, and r is a function of d.

Challenge

Make a table and a graph of each set of ordered pairs (x, y). Then write a function rule to represent the relationship between x and y.

23. $(-4, 7), (-3, 6), (-2, 5), (-1, 4), (0, 3), (1, 2), (2, 1), (3, 0), (4, -1)$

24. $(-4, 15), (-3, 8), (-2, 3), (-1, 0), (0, -1), (1, 0), (2, 3), (3, 8), (4, 15)$

2-6 Formalizing Relations and Functions

F.IF.1 Understand that a function from one set (called the domain) to another set (called the range) assigns each element of the domain exactly one element of the range . . . Also **F.IF.2, F.IF.5**

Objectives To determine whether a relation is a function
To find domain and range and use function notation

Solve It! Write your solution to the Solve It in the space below.

A **relation** is a pairing of numbers in one set, called the **domain**, with numbers in another set, called the **range**. A relation is often represented as a set of ordered pairs (x, y). In this case, the domain is the set of x-values and the range is the set of y-values.

Essential Understanding A function is a special type of relation in which each value in the domain is paired with exactly one value in the range.

Problem 1 Identifying Functions Using Mapping Diagrams

Got It? Identify the domain and range of each relation. Represent the relation with a mapping diagram. Is the relation a function?

Think
When is a relation *not* a function?

a. $\{(4.2, 1.5), (5, 2.2), (7, 4.8), (4.2, 0)\}$

b. $\{(-1, 1), (-2, 2), (4, -4), (7, -7)\}$

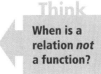

A Practice **Identify the domain and range of each relation. Use a mapping diagram to determine whether the relation is a function.**

1. $\{(3, 7), (3, 8), (3, -2), (3, 4), (3, 1)\}$

2. $\{(0.04, 0.2), (0.2, 1), (1, 5), (5, -5)\}$

Another way to decide if a relation is a function is to analyze the graph of the relation using the **vertical line test**. If any vertical line passes through more than one point of the graph, then for some domain value there is more than one range value. So the relation is not a function.

Problem 2 Identifying Functions Using the Vertical Line Test

Got It? Is the relation a function? Use the vertical line test.

a. $\{(4, 2), (1, 2), (0, 1), (-2, 2), (3, 3)\}$

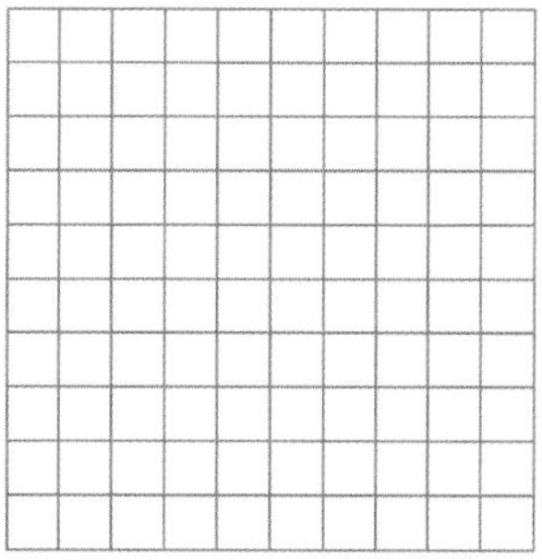

Think

How can you use a pencil to apply the vertical line test?

b. $\{(0, 2), (1, -1), (-1, 4), (0, -3), (2, 1)\}$

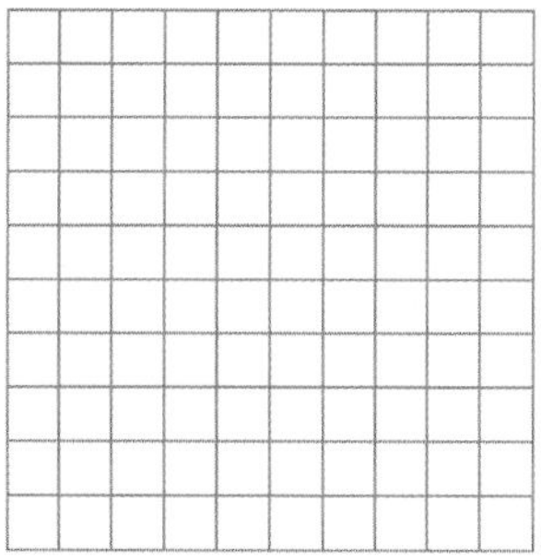

A Practice **Use the vertical line test to determine whether the relation is a function.**

3. 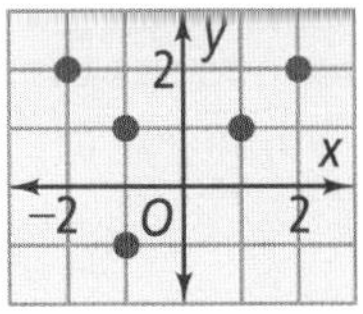

4. 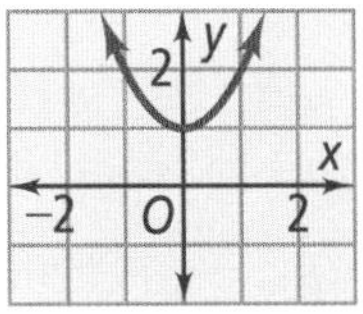

You have seen functions represented as equations involving x and y, such as $y = -3x + 1$. Below is the same equation written using **function notation.**

$$f(x) = -3x + 1$$

Notice that $f(x)$ replaces y. It is read "f of x." The letter f is the name of the function, not a variable. Function notation is used to emphasize that the function value $f(x)$ depends on the independent variable x. Other letters besides f can also be used, such as g and h.

Problem 3 Evaluating a Function

Got It? Use the function $w(x) = 250x$ from Problem 3, which represents the number of words you can read in x minutes. How many words can you read in 6 min?

Practice **5. Shopping** You are buying orange juice for \$4.50 per container and have a gift card worth \$7. The function $f(x) = 4.50x - 7$ represents your total cost $f(x)$ if you buy x containers of orange juice and use the gift card. How much do you pay to buy 4 containers of orange juice?

STEM **6. Physics** Light travels about 186,000 mi/s. The function $d(t) = 186{,}000t$ gives the distance $d(t)$, in miles, that light travels in t seconds. How far does light travel in 30 s?

Problem 4 Finding the Range of a Function

Got It? The domain of $g(x) = 4x - 12$ is $\{1, 3, 5, 7\}$. What is the range?

Practice **Find the range of each function for the given domain.**

7. $h(x) = x^2; \{-1.2, 0, 0.2, 1.2, 4\}$

8. $f(x) = 8x - 3; \left\{-\frac{1}{2}, \frac{1}{4}, \frac{3}{4}, \frac{1}{8}\right\}$

Problem 5 Identifying a Reasonable Domain and Range

Got It? **a.** What domain and range are reasonable if you have 7 qt of paint instead of 3 qt in Problem 5?

b. Reasoning Why does it *not* make sense to have domain values less than 0 or greater than 3 in Problem 5?

Practice **Find a reasonable domain and range for each function. Then graph the function.**

9. Fuel A car can travel 32 mi for each gallon of gasoline. The function $d(x) = 32x$ represents the distance $d(x)$, in miles, that the car can travel with x gallons of gasoline. The car's fuel tank holds 17 gal.

10. Nutrition There are 98 International Units (IUs) of vitamin D in 1 cup of milk. The function $V(c) = 98c$ represents the amount $V(c)$ of vitamin D, in IUs, you get from c cups of milk. You have a 16-cup jug of milk.

Lesson Check

Do you know HOW?

11. Identify the domain and range of the relation $\{(-2, 3), (-1, 4), (0, 5), (1, 6)\}$. Represent the relation with a mapping diagram. Is the relation a function?

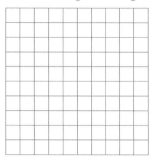

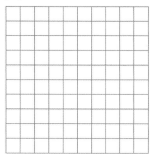

12. Is the relation in the graph shown at the right a function? Use the vertical line test.

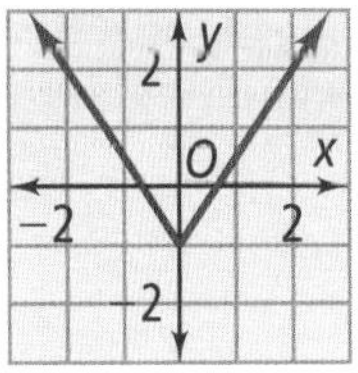

13. What is $f(2)$ for the function $f(x) = 4x + 1$?

14. The domain of $f(x) = \frac{1}{2}x$ is $\{-4, -2, 0, 2, 4\}$. What is the range?

Do you UNDERSTAND?

MATHEMATICAL PRACTICES

15. **Vocabulary** Write $y = 2x + 7$ using function notation.

16. **Compare and Contrast** You can use a mapping diagram or the vertical line test to tell if a relation is a function. Which method do you prefer? Explain.

17. Error Analysis A student drew the dashed line on the graph shown and concluded that the graph represented a function. Is the student correct? Explain.

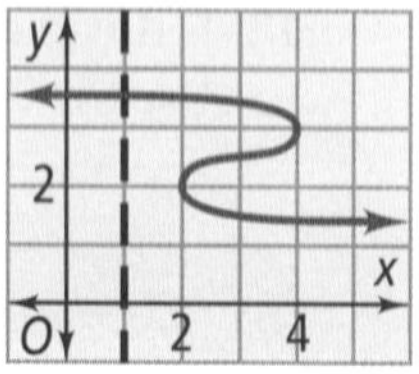

More Practice and Problem-Solving Exercises

MATHEMATICAL PRACTICES

B Apply

Determine whether the relation represented by each table is a function. If the relation is a function, state the domain and range.

18.

0	3	3	5
2	1	−1	3

19.

−4	−1	0	3
−4	−4	−4	−4

20. Open-Ended Make a table that represents a relation that is not a function. Explain why the relation is not a function.

21. Reasoning If $f(x) = 6x - 4$ and $f(a) = 26$, what is the value of a? Explain.

22. Think About a Plan In a factory, a certain machine needs 10 min to warm up. It takes 15 min for the machine to run a cycle. The machine can operate for as long as 6 h per day including warm-up time. Draw a graph showing the total time the machine operates during 1 day as a function of the number of cycles it runs.
- What domain and range are reasonable?
- Is the function a linear function?

23. Carwash A theater group is having a carwash fundraiser. The group can only spend \$34 on soap, which is enough to wash 40 cars. Each car is charged \$5.

a. If c is the total number of cars washed and p is the profit, which is the independent variable and which is the dependent variable?

b. Is the relationship between c and p a function? Explain.

c. Write an equation that shows this relationship.

d. Find a reasonable domain and range for the situation.

24. Open-Ended What value of x makes the relation $\{(1, 5), (x, 8), (-7, 9)\}$ a function?

Determine whether each relation is a function. Assume that each different variable has a different value.

25. $\{(a, b), (b, a), (c, c), (e, d)\}$

26. $\{(b, b), (c, d), (d, c), (c, a)\}$

27. $\{(c, e), (c, d), (c, b)\}$

28. $\{(a, b), (b, c), (c, d), (d, e)\}$

29. Reasoning Can the graph of a function be a horizontal line? A vertical line? Explain.

Challenge

30. To form the inverse of a relation written as a set of ordered pairs, you switch the coordinates of each ordered pair. For example, the inverse of the relation $\{(1, 8), (3, 5), (7, 9)\}$ is $\{(8, 1), (5, 3), (9, 7)\}$. Give an example of a relation that is a function, but whose inverse is *not* a function.

Use the functions $f(x) = 2x$ and $g(x) = x^2 + 1$ to find the value of each expression.

31. $f(3) + g(4)$

32. $g(3) + f(4)$

33. $f(5) - 2 \cdot g(1)$

34. $f(g(3))$

TECHNOLOGY LAB

Use With Lesson 2-6

Even and Odd Functions

F.BF.3 . . . Recognize even and odd functions from their graphs and algebraic expressions for them.

MATHEMATICAL PRACTICES

Some functions can be classified as *even* or *odd*. You can determine whether a function is even or odd by its graph or by using algebra.

An **even function** is a function f such that $f(-x) = f(x)$. The graph of an even function is symmetric across the y-axis. This means that if the point (x, y) is on the graph of the function, so is the point $(-x, y)$.

An **odd function** is a function f such that $f(-x) = -f(x)$. The graph of an odd function is symmetric about the origin. This means that if the point (x, y) is on the graph of the function, so is the point $(-x, -y)$.

Example 1

Determine whether the function $f(x) = x^2$ is *even*, *odd*, or *neither* by graphing.

Step 1 Press the y= key. To the right of $\mathbf{Y_1}$, enter x^2 by pressing X [^] 2.

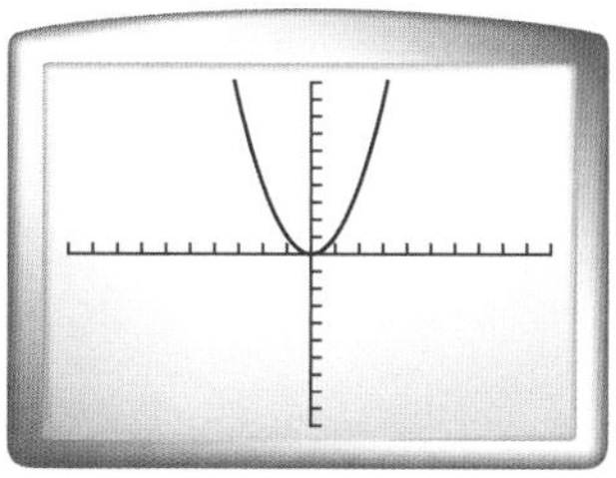

Step 2 Graph the function on your calculator. Press the window key to set the borders of the graph if needed.

The function is symmetric across the y-axis because the graph is a mirror image on each side of the y-axis. So, $f(x) = x^2$ is an even function.

Example 2

Determine whether the function $g(x) = x^3$ is *even*, *odd*, or *neither* algebraically.

$g(-x) = (-x)^3$	Evaluate $g(-x)$.
$= (-1)^3 \cdot x^3$	Raise each factor to the third power.
$= -x^3$	Simplify.
$= -g(x)$	Subsitute $g(x)$ for x^3.

Because $g(-x) = -g(x)$, the function is odd.

Exercises

Determine whether each function is *even, odd,* or *neither.*

1. $f(x) = x^2 - 3$

2. $g(x) = x^3 + 1$

3. $h(x) = |x|$

4. $g(x) = x^5$

5. $f(x) = x^5 - 2x^3 - x$

6. $h(x) = x^6 - 2x^4 - x^2 - 5$

7. Reasoning Is it possible for a function to be both even and odd? Explain.

2-7 Arithmetic Sequences

F.IF.3 Recognize that sequences are functions, sometimes defined recursively . . . **A.SSE.1.a, A.SSE.1.b, F.BF.1.a, F.BF.2, F.LE.2**

Objectives To identify and extend patterns in sequences
To represent arithmetic sequences using function notation

Solve It! Write your solution to the Solve It in the space below.

In the Solve It, the numbers of pieces of wood used for 1 section of fence, 2 sections of fence, and so on, form a pattern, or a sequence. A **sequence** is an ordered list of numbers that often form a pattern. Each number in the list is called a **term of a sequence**.

Essential Understanding When you can identify a pattern in a sequence, you can use it to extend the sequence. You can also model some sequences with a function rule that you can use to find any term of the sequence.

Problem 1 Extending Sequences

Got It? Describe a pattern in each sequence. What are the next two terms of each sequence?

a. 5, 11, 17, 23, . . .

b. 400, 200, 100, 50, . . .

c. 2, −4, 8, −16, . . .

d. −15, −11, −7, −3, . . .

Practice **Describe a pattern in each sequence. Then find the next two terms of the sequence.**

1. 10, 4, −2, −8, . . .

2. 2, 20, 200, 2000, . . .

In an **arithmetic sequence**, the difference between consecutive terms is constant. This difference is called the **common difference**.

Problem 2 Identifying an Arithmetic Sequence

Got It? Tell whether the sequence is arithmetic. If it is, what is the common difference?

Plan
How can you identify an arithmetic sequence?

a. 8, 15, 22, 30, . . .

b. 7, 9, 11, 13, . . .

c. 10, 4, −2, −8, . . .

d. 2, −2, 2, −2, . . .

Practice **Tell whether the sequence is arithmetic. If it is, identify the common difference.**

3. 10, 24, 36, 52, . . .

4. 15, 14.5, 14, 13.5, 13, . . .

A sequence is a function whose domain is the natural numbers, and whose outputs are the terms of the sequence.

You can write a sequence using a recursive formula. A **recursive formula** is a function rule that relates each term of a sequence after the first to the ones before it. Consider the sequence 7, 11, 15, 19, . . . You can use the common difference of the terms of an arithmetic sequence to write a recursive formula for the sequence. For the sequence 7, 11, 15, 19, . . . , the common difference is 4.

Let n = the term number in the sequence.

Let $A(n)$ = the value of the nth term of the sequence.

value of term 1 = $A(1) = 7$

value of term 2 = $A(2) = A(1) + 4 = 11$ (The common difference is 4.)

value of term 3 = $A(3) = A(2) + 4 = 15$

value of term 4 = $A(4) = A(3) + 4 = 19$

value of term n = $A(n) = A(n - 1) + 4$ (The value of the previous term plus 4)

The recursive formula for the arithmetic sequence above is $A(n) = A(n - 1) + 4$, where $A(1) = 7$.

Problem 3 Writing a Recursive Formula

Got It? Write a recursive formula for each arithmetic sequence. What is the 9th term of each sequence?

a. 3, 9, 15, 21, . . .

b. 23, 35, 47, 59, . . .

c. 7.3, 7.8, 8.3, 8.8, . . .

d. 97, 88, 79, 70, . . .

e. Reasoning Is a recursive formula a useful way to find the value of an arithmetic sequence? Explain.

Practice **Write a recursive formula for each sequence.**

5. 2.3, 2.8, 3.3, 3.8, . . .

6. 4.6, 4.7, 4.8, 4.9, . . .

You can find the value of any term of an arithmetic sequence using a recursive formula. You can also write a sequence using an explicit formula. An **explicit formula** is a function rule that relates each term of a sequence to the term number.

take note

Key Concept Explicit Formula For an Arithmetic Sequence

The nth term of an arithmetic sequence with first term $A(1)$ and common difference d is given by

$$A(n) = A(1) + (n - 1)d$$

nth term ↗ $A(n)$; first term ↗ $A(1)$; term number ↑ n; common difference ↖ d

Problem 4 Writing an Explicit Formula

Got It? a. A subway pass has a starting value of \$100. After one ride, the value of the pass is \$98.25. After two rides, its value is \$96.50. After three rides, its value is \$94.75. Write an explicit formula to represent the remaining value on the card as an arithmetic sequence. What is the value of the pass after 15 rides?

Plan

What information do you need to write a rule for an arithmetic sequence?

b. **Reasoning** How many rides can be taken with the \$100 pass?

Practice 7. **Garage** After one customer buys 4 new tires, a garage recycling bin has 20 tires in it. After another customer buys 4 new tires, the bin has 24 tires in it. Write an explicit formula to represent the number of tires in the bin as an arithmetic sequence. How many tires are in the bin after 9 customers buy all new tires?

8. **Cafeteria** You have a cafeteria card worth \$50. After you buy lunch on Monday, its value is \$46.75. After you buy lunch on Tuesday, its value is \$43.50. Write an explicit formula to represent the amount of money left on the card as an arithmetic sequence. What is the value of the card after you buy 12 lunches?

You can write an explicit formula from a recursive formula and vice versa.

Problem 5 Writing an Explicit Formula From a Recursive Formula

Got It? For each recursive formula, find an explicit formula that represents the same sequence.

a. $A(n) = A(n - 1) + 2; A(1) = 21$

b. $A(n) = A(n - 1) + 7; A(1) = 2$

Practice Write an explicit formula for each recursive formula.

9. $A(n) = A(n - 1) + 3; A(1) = 6$

10. $A(n) = A(n - 1) - 0.3; A(1) = 0.3$

Problem 6 Writing a Recursive Formula From an Explicit Formula

Got It? For each explicit formula, find a recursive formula that represents the same sequence.

a. $A(n) = 76 + (n - 1)(10)$

b. $A(n) = 1 + (n - 1)(3)$

Practice Write a recursive formula for each explicit formula.

11. $A(n) = -1 + (n - 1)(-2)$

12. $A(n) = 4 + (n - 1)(1)$

Lesson Check

Do you know HOW?

Describe a pattern in each sequence. Then find the next two terms of the sequence.

13. 3, 11, 19, 27, . . .

14. 3, −6, 12, −24, . . .

Tell whether the sequence is arithmetic. If it is, identify the common difference.

15. 1, −7, −14, −21, . . .

16. 11, 20, 29, 38, . . .

17. Write a recursive and an explicit formula for the arithmetic sequence.

$9, 7, 5, 3, 1, \ldots$

Do you UNDERSTAND?

MATHEMATICAL PRACTICES

18. Vocabulary Consider the following arithmetic sequence: $25, 19, 13, 7, \ldots$ Is the common difference 6 or -6? Explain.

19. Error Analysis Describe and correct the error at the right in finding the tenth term of the arithmetic sequence $4, 12, 20, 28, \ldots$

~~first term = 4~~
~~common difference = 8~~
~~tenth term = 4 + 10(8) = 84~~

20. Reasoning Can you use the explicit formula below to find the nth term of an arithmetic sequence with a first term $A(1)$ and a common difference d? Explain.

$$A(n) = A(1) + nd - d$$

More Practice and Problem-Solving Exercises

MATHEMATICAL PRACTICES

B Apply

Tell whether each sequence is arithmetic. Justify your answer. If the sequence is arithmetic, write a recursive and an explicit formula to represent it.

21. 0.3, 0.9, 1.5, 2.1, . . .

22. $-3, -7, -11, -15, \ldots$

23. 1, 8, 27, 64, . . .

24. $-5, 5, -5, 5, \ldots$

25. 46, 31, 16, 2, . . .

26. $0.2, -0.6, -1.4, -2.2, \ldots$

Using the recursive formula for each arithmetic sequence, find the second, third, and fourth terms of the sequence. Then write the explicit formula that represents the sequence.

27. $A(n) = A(n-1) - 4; A(1) = 8$

28. $A(n) = A(n-1) + 1.2; A(1) = 8.8$

29. $A(n) = A(n-1) + 3; A(1) = 13$

30. $A(n) = A(n-1) - 2; A(1) = 0$

31. Reasoning An arithmetic sequence can be represented by the explicit function $A(n) = -10 + (n-1)(4)$. Describe the relationship between the first term and the second term. Describe the relationship between the second term and the third term. Write a recursive formula to represent this sequence.

32. Open-Ended Write a function rule for a sequence that has 25 as the sixth term.

Write the first six terms in each sequence. Explain what the sixth term means in the context of the situation.

33. A cane of bamboo is 30 in. tall the first week and grows 6 in. per week thereafter.

34. You borrow $350 from a friend the first week and pay the friend back $25 each week thereafter.

35. Think About a Plan Suppose the first Friday of a new year is the fourth day of that year. Will the year have 53 Fridays regardless of whether or not it is a leap year?
- What is a rule that represents the sequence of the days in the year that are Fridays?
- How many full weeks are in a 365-day year?

36. Look For a Pattern The first five rows of Pascal's Triangle are shown at the right.
a. Predict the numbers in the seventh row.
b. Find the sum of the numbers in each of the first five rows. Predict the sum of the numbers in the seventh row.

1
1 1
1 2 1
1 3 3 1
1 4 6 4 1

37. Transportation Buses run every 9 min starting at 6:00 A.M. You get to the bus stop at 7:16 A.M. How long will you wait for a bus?

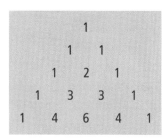

38. **Multiple Representations** Use the table at the right that shows an arithmetic sequence.

x	y
1	5
2	8
3	■
4	■

a. Copy and complete the table.
b. Graph the ordered pairs (x, y) on a coordinate plane.
c. What do you notice about the points on your graph?

39. **Number Theory** The Fibonacci sequence is 1, 1, 2, 3, 5, 8, 13, . . . After the first two numbers, each number is the sum of the two previous numbers.
a. What is the next term of the sequence? The eleventh term of the sequence?
b. **Open-Ended** Choose two other numbers to start a Fibonacci-like sequence. Write the first seven terms of your sequence.

Challenge

Find the common difference of each arithmetic sequence. Then find the next term.

40. $4, x + 4, 2x + 4, 3x + 4, \ldots$

41. $a + b + c, 4a + 3b + c, 7a + 5b + c, \ldots$

42. **a.** **Geometry** Draw the next figure in the pattern.

b. **Reasoning** What is the color of the twentieth figure? Explain.
c. How many sides does the twenty-third figure have? Explain.

LESSON LAB

Use With Lesson 2-7

The Fibonacci Sequence

F.IF.3 Recognize that sequences are functions, sometimes defined recursively . . .

One famous mathematical sequence is the Fibonacci sequence. You can find each term of the sequence using addition, but the sequence is not arithmetic.

Example

The recursive formula for the Fibonacci sequence is $F_n = F_{n-2} + F_{n-1} = 1$, with $F_1 = 1$ and $F_2 = 1$. Using the formula, what are the first five terms of the sequence?

$F_1 = 1$

$F_2 = 1$

$F_3 = F_1 + F_2 = 1 + 1 = 2$

$F_4 = F_2 + F_3 = 1 + 2 = 3$

$F_5 = F_3 + F_4 = 2 + 3 = 5$

The first five terms of the Fibonacci sequence are 1, 1, 2, 3, 5.

Exercises

1. Nature The numbers of the Fibonacci sequence are often found in other areas, especially nature. Which term of the Fibonacci sequence does each picture represent?

a. 

b. 

c. 

d. 

2. a. Generate the first ten terms of the Fibonacci sequence.

b. Find the sum of the first ten terms of the Fibonacci sequence. Divide the sum by 11. What do you notice?

c. Open-Ended Choose two numbers other than 1 and 1. Generate a Fibonacci-like sequence from them. Write the first ten terms of your sequence, find the sum, and divide the sum by 11. What do you notice?

d. Make a Conjecture What is the sum of the first ten terms of any Fibonacci-like sequence?

3. a. Study the pattern at the right. Write the next line.

$$1^2 + 1^2 = 2 = 1 \cdot 2$$
$$1^2 + 1^2 + 2^2 = 6 = 2 \cdot 3$$
$$1^2 + 1^2 + 2^2 + 3^2 = 15 = 3 \cdot 5$$
$$1^2 + 1^2 + 2^2 + 3^2 + 5^2 = 40 = 5 \cdot 8$$

b. Without calculating, use the pattern to predict the sum of the squares of the first ten terms of the Fibonacci sequence.

c. Verify the prediction you made in part (b).

2 Chapter Review

MathXL® for School
Go to pearsonsuccessnet.com

2-1 Using Graphs to Relate Two Quantities

Quick Review

You can use graphs to represent the relationship between two variables.

Example

A dog owner plays fetch with her dog. Sketch a graph to represent the distance between them and the time.

Playing Fetch

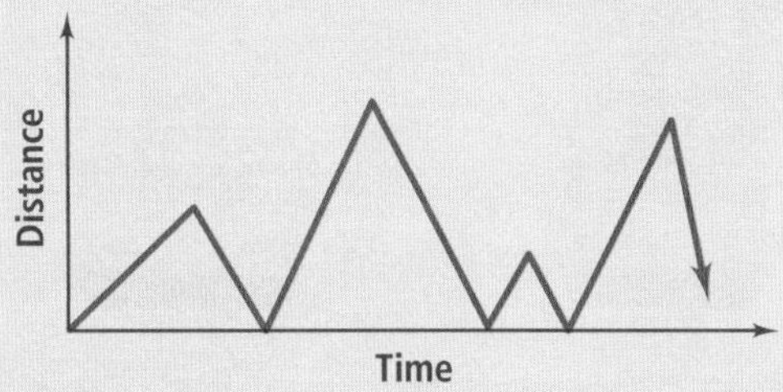

Exercises

1. **Travel** A car's speed increases as it merges onto a highway. The car travels at 65 mi/h on the highway until it slows to exit. The car then stops at two traffic lights before reaching its destination. Draw a sketch of a graph that shows the car's speed over time. Label each section.

2. **Surfing** A professional surfer paddles out past breaking waves, rides a wave, paddles back out past the breaking waves, rides another wave, and paddles back to the beach. Draw a sketch of a graph that shows the surfer's possible distance from the beach over time.

2-2 Patterns and Linear Functions

Quick Review

A **function** is a relationship that pairs each **input** value with exactly one **output** value. A **linear function** is a function whose graph is a line or part of a line.

Example

The number y of eggs left in a dozen depends on the number x of 2-egg omelets you make, as shown in the table. Represent this relationship using words, an equation, and a graph.

Number of Omelets Made, x	0	1	2	3
Number of Eggs Left, y	12	10	8	6

Look for a pattern in the table. Each time x increases by 1, y decreases by 2. The number y of eggs left is 12 minus the quantity 2 times the number x of omelets made: $y = 12 - 2x$.

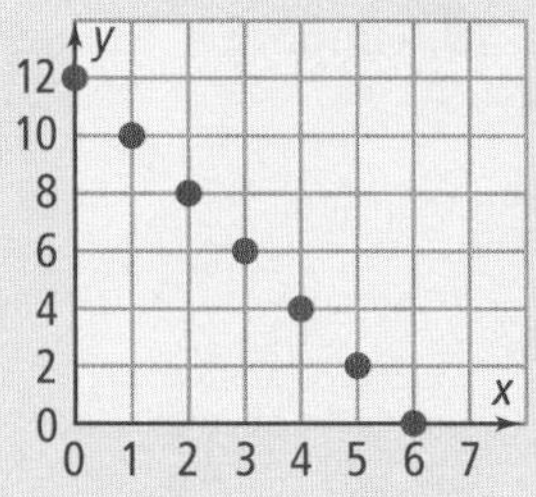

Exercises

For each table, identify the independent and dependent variables. Represent the relationship using words, an equation, and a graph.

3. **Paint in Can**

Number of Chairs Painted, p	Paint Left (oz), L
0	128
1	98
2	68
3	38

4. **Game Cost**

Number of Snacks Purchased, s	Total Cost, C
0	$18
1	$21
2	$24
3	$27

5. **Elevation**

Number of Flights of Stairs Climbed, n	0	1	2	3
Elevation (ft above sea level), E	311	326	341	356

2-3 Patterns and Nonlinear Functions

Quick Review

A **nonlinear function** is a function whose graph is *not* a line or part of a line.

Example

The area A of a square field is a function of the side length s of the field. Is the function *linear* or *nonlinear*?

Side Length (ft), s	10	15	20	25
Area (ft^2), A	100	225	400	625

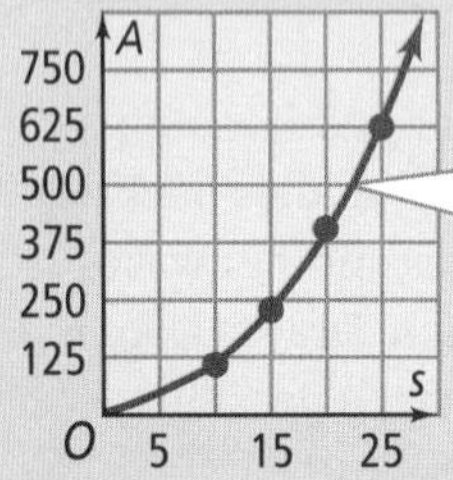

Graph the ordered pairs and connect the points. The graph is not a line, so the function is nonlinear.

Exercises

Graph the function shown by each table. Tell whether the function is *linear* or *nonlinear*.

6.

x	y
1	0
2	1
3	8
4	20

7.

x	y
1	0
2	4.5
3	9
4	13.5

8.

x	y
1	2
2	6
3	12
4	72

9.

x	y
1	−2
2	−9
3	−16
4	−23

2-4 Graphing a Function Rule

Quick Review

A **continuous graph** is a graph that is unbroken. A **discrete graph** is composed of distinct, isolated points. In a real-world graph, show only points that make sense.

Example

The total height h of a stack of cans is a function of the number n of layers of 4.5-in. cans used. This situation is represented by $h = 4.5n$. Graph the function.

n	h
0	0
1	4.5
2	9
3	13.5
4	18

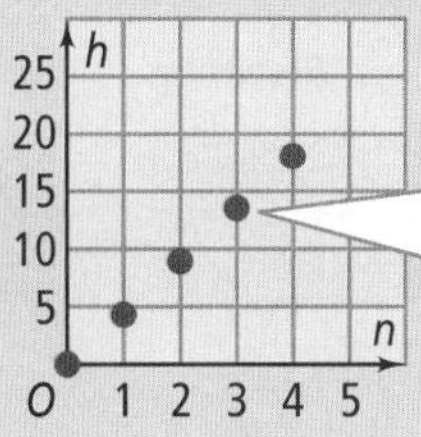

The graph is discrete because only whole numbers of layers make sense.

Exercises

Graph the function rule. Explain why the graph is *continuous* or *discrete.*

10. **Walnuts** Your cost c to buy w pounds of walnuts at \$6/lb is represented by $c = 6w$.

11. **Moving** A truck originally held 24 chairs. You remove 2 chairs at a time. The number of chairs n remaining after you make t trips is represented by $n = 24 - 2t$.

12. **Flood** A burst pipe fills a basement with 37 in. of water. A pump empties the water at a rate of 1.5 in./h. The water level ℓ, in inches, after t hours is represented by $\ell = 37 - 1.5t$.

13. Graph $y = -|x| + 2$.

2-5 Writing a Function Rule

Quick Review

To write a function rule describing a real-world situation, it is often helpful to start with a verbal model of the situation.

Example

At a bicycle motocross (BMX) track, you pay $40 for a racing license plus $15 per race. What is a function rule that represents your total cost?

total cost = license fee + fee per race • number of races

$$C \quad = \quad 40 \quad + \quad 15 \quad \cdot \quad r$$

A function rule is $C = 40 + 15 \cdot r$.

Exercises

Write a function rule to represent each situation.

14. Landscaping The volume V remaining in a 243-ft^3 pile of gravel decreases by 0.2 ft^3 with each shovelful s of gravel spread in a walkway.

15. Design Your total cost C for hiring a garden designer is $200 for an initial consultation plus $45 for each hour h the designer spends drawing plans.

2-6 Formalizing Relations and Functions

Quick Review

A **relation** pairs numbers in the **domain** with numbers in the **range**. A relation may or may not be a function.

Example

Is the relation $\{(0, 1), (3, 3), (4, 4), (0, 0)\}$ a function?

The x-values of the ordered pairs form the domain, and the y-values form the range. The domain value 0 is paired with two range values, 1 and 0. So the relation is not a function.

Exercises

Tell whether each relation is a function.

16. $\{(21, 7), (9, 4), (3, -2), (5, 3), (9, 1)\}$

17. $\{(2, 5), (3, 5), (4, -4), (5, 24), (6, 8)\}$

Evaluate each function for $x = 2$ and $x = 7$.

18. $f(x) = 2x - 8$

19. $h(x) = -4x + 61$

20. The domain of $t(x) = -3.8x - 4.2$ is $\{-3, -1.4, 0, 8\}$. What is the range?

2-7 Arithmetic Sequences

Quick Review

A **sequence** is an ordered list of numbers, called terms, that often forms a pattern. A sequence can be represented by a **recursive formula** or an **explicit formula**.

Example

Tell whether the sequence is arithmetic.

5, 2, −1, −4, ...

−3 −3 −3

The sequence has a common difference of −3, so it is arithmetic.

Exercises

For each sequence, write a recursive and an explicit formula.

21. 3, 8, 13, 18, ...

22. −2, −5, −8, −11, ...

23. 4, 6.5, 9, 11.5, ...

24. 18, 11, 4, −3, ...

For each recursive formula, find an explicit formula that represents the same sequence.

25. $A(n) = A(n - 1) + 3; A(1) = 4$

26. $A(n) = A(n - 1) + 11; A(1) = 13$

27. $A(n) = A(n - 1) - 1; A(1) = 19$

2 Pull It All Together

ASSESSMENT

Comparing the Growth of Two Blogs

Jayden and Keiko each start writing a blog at the same time. When Jayden starts his blog (Month 0), he gets 48 of his friends to subscribe. At the end of each month, he records the number of subscribers in a table. His data for the first few months are shown below.

Jayden's Blog

Number of Months	Number of Subscribers
0	48
1	56
2	64
3	72
4	80

Keiko finds that the number of subscribers K to her blog can be modeled by the function rule $K = m^2 + 10$, where m is the number of months since she started the blog.

Task Description

Determine which person's blog will be the first to have 200 subscribers.

a. Let J = the number of subscribers to Jayden's blog.
Let m = the number of months since he started the blog.

Write a function rule for the relationship in the table, assuming the number of subscribers continues to grow at the same rate.

b. Make a graph of the function rule you wrote in part (a). Did you draw a continuous graph or a discrete graph? Why?

c. Make a graph of the function rule for the number of subscribers to Keiko's blog. How is this function different from the function you wrote in part (a)?

d. Use your graphs to determine which person's blog will be the first to have 200 subscribers. About how many additional months will it take for the other blog to reach this level? Explain.

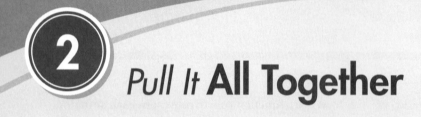

CHAPTER 3

Get Ready!

Solutions of a Two-Variable Equation

Tell whether the given ordered pair is a solution of the equation.

1. $4y + 2x = 3; (1.5, 0)$ **2.** $y = 7x - 5; (0, 5)$ **3.** $y = -2x + 5; (2, 1)$

Transforming Equations

Solve each equation for *y*.

4. $2y - x = 4$ **5.** $3x = y + 2$ **6.** $-2y - 2x = 4$

Comparing Unit Rates

7. Transportation A car traveled 360 km in 6 h. A train traveled 400 km in 8 h. A boat traveled 375 km in 5 h. Which had the fastest average speed?

8. Plants A birch tree grew 2.5 in. in 5 months. A bean plant grew 8 in. in 10 months. A rose bush grew 5 in. in 8 months. Which grew the fastest?

Graphing a Function Rule

9. Make a table of values for the function $f(x) = x + 3$. Then graph the function.

Arithmetic Sequences

Write an explicit formula for each arithmetic sequence.

10. 2, 5, 8, 11, . . . **11.** 13, 10, 7, 4, . . . **12.** −3, −0.5, 2, 4.5, . . .

VOCABULARY

Looking Ahead Vocabulary

13. A steep hill has a greater *slope* than a flat plain. What does the *slope* of a line on a graph describe?

14. Two streets are *parallel* when they go the same way and do not cross. What does it mean in math to call two lines *parallel*?

CHAPTER 3

Linear Functions

Big Ideas

1 Proportionality
Essential Question: What does the slope of a line indicate about the line?

2 Functions
Essential Question: What information does the equation of a line give you?

Domains

- Interpreting Functions
- Building Functions
- Creating Equations

Chapter Preview

Interactive Digital Path
Log in to **pearsonsuccessnet.com** and click on Interactive Digital Path to access the Solve Its and animated Problems.

Vocabulary

English/Spanish Vocabulary Audio Online:

English	Spanish
direct variation, *p. 176*	variación directa
linear equation, *p. 186*	ecuación lineal
parallel lines, *p. 212*	rectas paralelas
perpendicular lines, *p. 213*	rectas perpendiculares
point-slope form, *p. 195*	forma punto-pendiente
rate of change, *p. 167*	tasa de cambio
slope, *p. 168*	pendiente
slope-intercept form, *p. 186*	forma pendiente-intercepto
standard form, *p. 203*	forma normal
x-intercept, *p. 203*	intercepto en x
y-intercept, *p. 186*	intercepto en y

3-1 Rate of Change and Slope

F.LE.1.b Recognize situations in which one quantity changes at a constant rate . . . relative to another. F.IF.6

Objectives To find rates of change from tables
To find slope

Solve It! Write your solution to the Solve It in the space below.

Essential Understanding You can use ratios to show a relationship between changing quantities, such as vertical and horizontal change.

Rate of change shows the relationship between two changing quantities. When one quantity depends on the other, the following is true.

$$\text{rate of change} = \frac{\text{change in the dependent variable}}{\text{change in the independent variable}}$$

Problem 1 Finding Rate of Change Using a Table

Got It? In Problem 1, do you get the same rate of change if you use nonconsecutive rows of the table? Explain.

Practice Determine whether each rate of change is constant. If it is, find the rate of change and explain what it represents.

1. **Turtle Walking**

Time (min)	Distance (m)
1	6
2	12
3	15
4	21

2. **Airplane Descent**

Time (min)	Elevation (ft)
0	30,000
2	29,000
5	27,500
12	24,000

The graphs of the ordered pairs (time, distance) in Problem 1 lie on a line, as shown at the right. The relationship between time and distance is linear. When data are linear, the rate of change is constant.

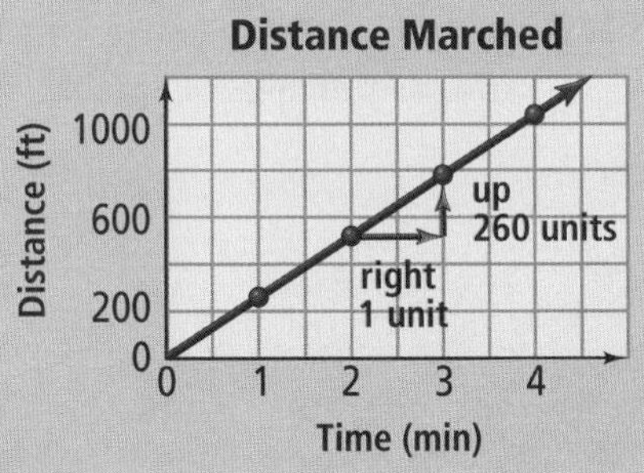

Notice also that the rate of change found in Problem 1 is just the ratio of the vertical change (or *rise*) to the horizontal change (or *run*) between two points on the line. The rate of change is called the *slope* of the line.

$$\textbf{slope} = \frac{\text{vertical change}}{\text{horizontal change}} = \frac{\text{rise}}{\text{run}}$$

Problem 2 Finding Slope Using a Graph

Plan

What do you need to find the slope?

Got It? What is the slope of each line in parts (a) and (b)?

a.

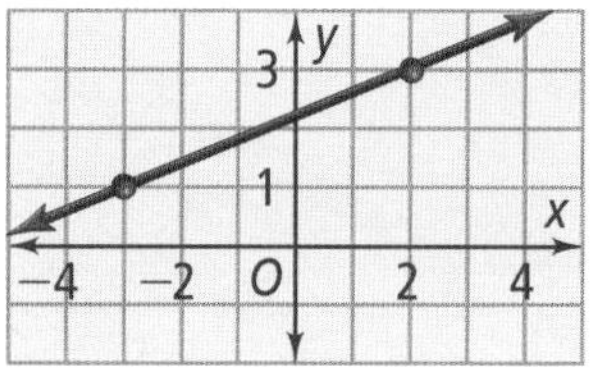

b.

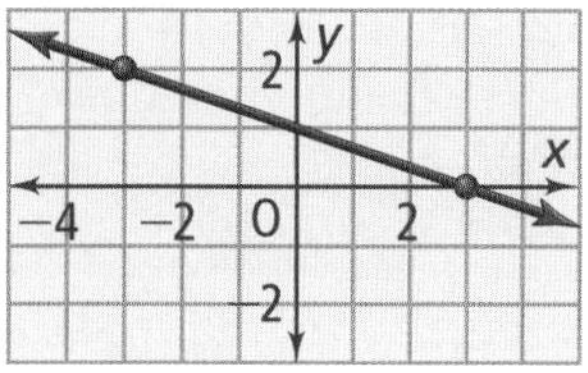

c. Reasoning In part (a) of Problem 2, pick two new points on the line to find the slope. Do you get the same slope?

A Practice Find the slope of each line.

3.

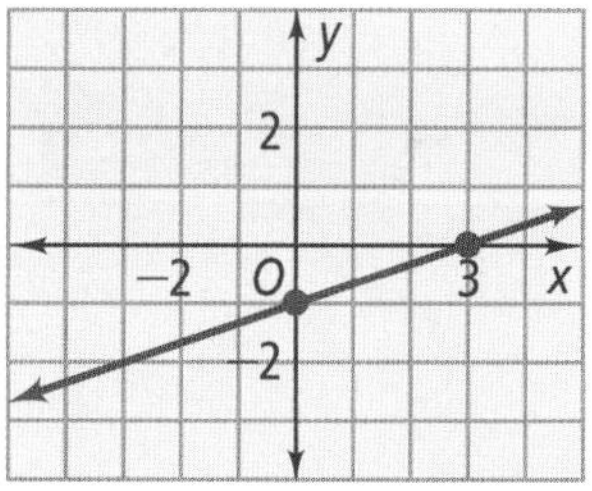

4.

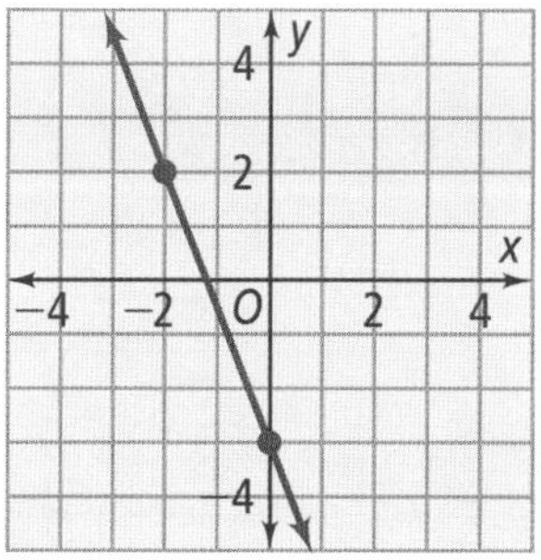

Notice that the line in part (A) of Problem 2 has a positive slope and slants upward from left to right. The line in part (B) of Problem 2 has a negative slope and slopes downward from left to right.

You can use any two points on a line to find its slope. Use subscripts to distinguish between the two points. In the diagram, (x_1, y_1) are the coordinates of point A, and (x_2, y_2) are the coordinates of point B. To find the slope of $\overleftrightarrow{AB}$, you can use the *slope formula.*

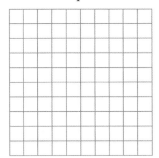

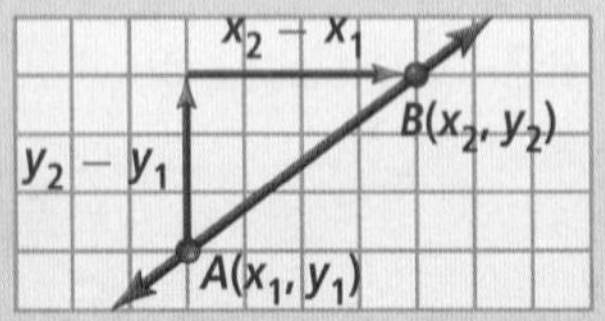

take note

Key Concept The Slope Formula

$\text{slope} = \frac{\text{rise}}{\text{run}} = \frac{y_2 - y_1}{x_2 - x_1}$, where $x_2 - x_1 \neq 0$

The x-coordinate you use first in the denominator must belong to the same ordered pair as the y-coordinate you use first in the numerator.

Problem 3 Finding Slope Using Points

Plan

Does it matter which point is (x_1, y_1) and which is (x_2, y_2)?

Got It? **a.** What is the slope of the line through (1, 3) and (4, −1)?

b. Reasoning Plot the points in part (a) and draw a line through them. Does the slope of the line look as you expected it to? Explain.

Practice **Find the slope of the line that passes through each pair of points.**

5. (−6, 1), (4, 8)

6. (2, −3), (5, −4)

Problem 4 Finding Slopes of Horizontal and Vertical Lines

Got It? What is the slope of the line through the given points?

a. $(4, -3), (4, 2)$

b. $(-1, -3), (5, -3)$

A Practice Find the slope of each line.

7.

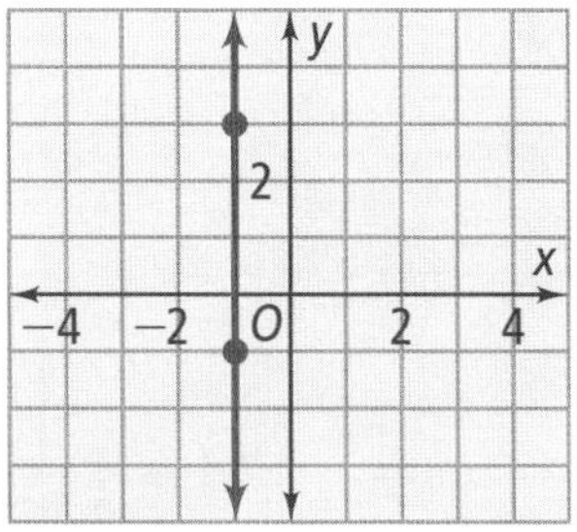

8.

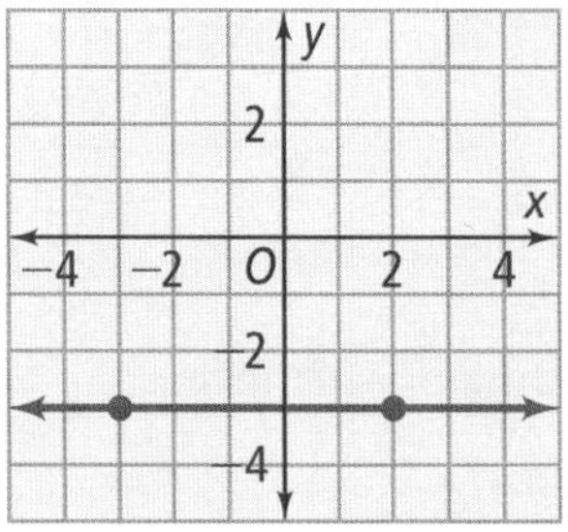

The following summarizes what you have learned about slope.

take note

Concept Summary Slopes of Lines

A line with positive slope slants upward from left to right.

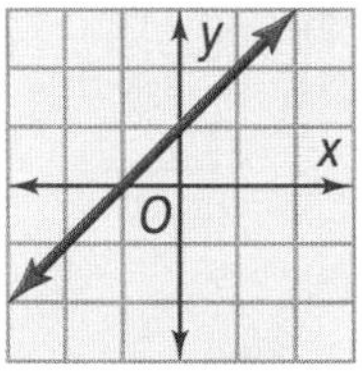

A line with negative slope slants downward from left to right.

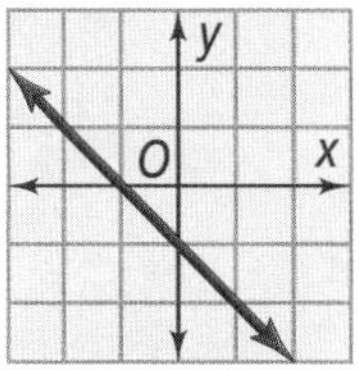

A line with an undefined slope is vertical.

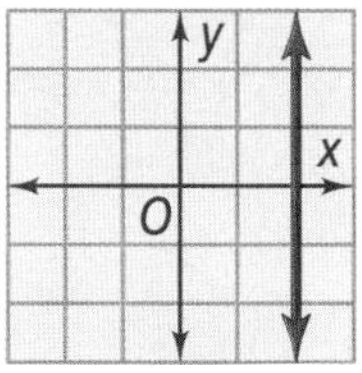

A line with a slope of 0 is horizontal.

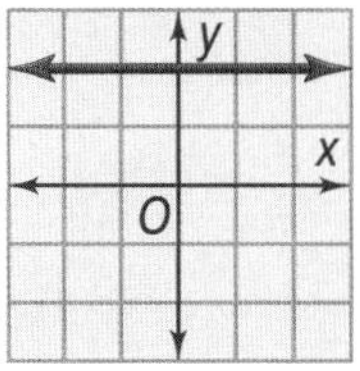

Lesson Check

Do you know HOW?

9. Is the rate of change in cost constant with respect to the number of pencils bought? Explain.

Cost of Pencils				
Number of Pencils	1	4	7	12
Cost ($)	0.25	1	1.75	3

10. What is the slope of the line?

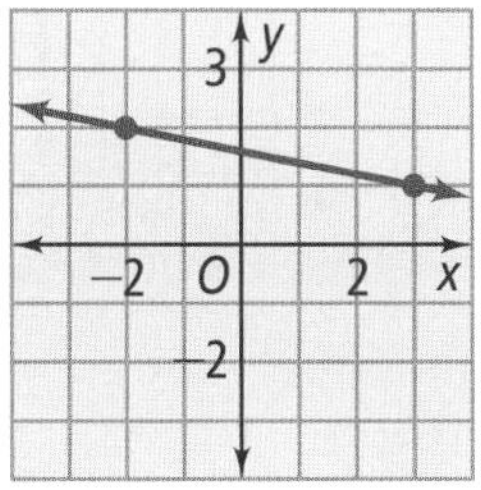

11. What is the slope of the line through $(-1, 2)$ and $(2, -3)$?

Do you UNDERSTAND?

MATHEMATICAL PRACTICES

12. Vocabulary What characteristic of a graph represents the rate of change? Explain.

13. Open-Ended Give an example of a real-world situation that you can model with a horizontal line. What is the rate of change for the situation? Explain.

14. Compare and Contrast How does finding a line's slope by counting units of vertical and horizontal change on a graph compare with finding it using the slope formula?

15. Error Analysis A student calculated the slope of the line at the right to be 2. Explain the mistake. What is the correct slope?

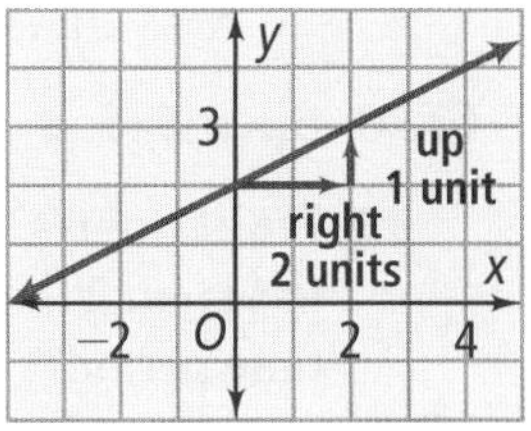

More Practice and Problem-Solving Exercises

MATHEMATICAL PRACTICES

B Apply

Without graphing, tell whether the slope of a line that models each linear relationship is positive, negative, zero, or undefined. Then find the slope.

16. The length of a bus route is 4 mi long on the sixth day and 4 mi long on the seventeenth day.

17. A babysitter earns \$9 for 1 h and \$36 for 4 h.

18. A student earns a 98 on a test for answering one question incorrectly and earns a 90 for answering five questions incorrectly.

19. The total cost, including shipping, for ordering five uniforms is \$66. The total cost, including shipping, for ordering nine uniforms is \$114.

State the independent variable and the dependent variable in each linear relationship. Then find the rate of change for each situation.

20. Snow is 0.02 m deep after 1 h and 0.06 m deep after 3 h.

21. The cost of tickets is \$36 for three people and \$84 for seven people.

22. A car is 200 km from its destination after 1 h and 80 km from its destination after 3 h.

Use the slope formula to find the slope of the line that passes through each pair of points. Then plot the points and sketch the line that passes through them. Does the slope you found using the formula match the direction of the line you sketched?

23. $(-2, 1), (7, 1)$

24. $(4.25, 0), (3.5, 3)$

25. $\left(-\frac{1}{2}, \frac{4}{7}\right), \left(8, \frac{4}{7}\right)$

26. $(-5, 0.124), (-5, -0.584)$

27. $(-42.25, 5.2), (3.25, 3)$

28. $\left(-2, \frac{2}{11}\right), \left(-2, \frac{7}{13}\right)$

29. Think About a Plan The graph shows the average growth rates for three different animals. Which animal's growth shows the fastest rate of change? The slowest rate of change?
- How can you use the graph to find the rates of change?
- Are your answers reasonable?

Rate of Growth

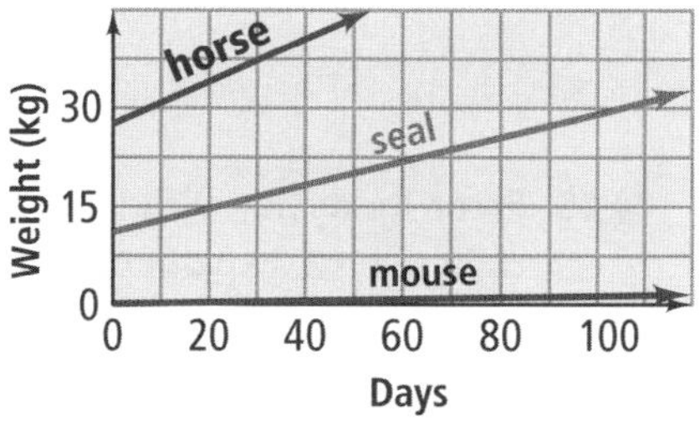

30. Open-Ended Find two points that lie on a line with slope -9.

31. Profit John's business made \$4500 in January and \$8600 in March. What is the rate of change in his profit for this time period?

Each pair of points lies on a line with the given slope. Find *x* or *y*.

32. $(2, 4), (x, 8)$; slope $= -2$

33. $(4, 3), (5, y)$; slope $= 3$

34. $(2, 4), (x, 8)$; slope $= -\frac{1}{2}$

35. $(3, y), (1, 9)$; slope $= -\frac{5}{2}$

36. $(-4, y), (2, 4y)$; slope $= 6$

37. $(3, 5), (x, 2)$; undefined slope

38. Reasoning Is it true that a line with slope 1 always passes through the origin? Explain your reasoning.

39. Arithmetic Sequences Use the arithmetic sequence 10, 15, 20, 25, ...

a. Find the common difference of the sequence.

b. Let $x =$ the term number, and let $y =$ the corresponding term of the sequence. Graph the ordered pairs (x, y) for the first eight terms of the sequence. Draw a line through the points.

c. Reasoning How is the slope of a line from part (b) related to the common difference of the sequence?

Challenge

Do the points in each set lie on the same line? Explain your answer.

40. $A(1, 3), B(4, 2), C(-2, 4)$

41. $G(3, 5), H(-1, 3), I(7, 7)$

42. $D(-2, 3), E(0, -1), F(2, 1)$

43. $P(4, 2), Q(-3, 2), R(2, 5)$

44. $G(1, -2), H(-1, -5), I(5, 4)$

45. $S(-3, 4), T(0, 2), X(-3, 0)$

Find the slope of the line that passes through each pair of points.

46. $(a, -b), (-a, -b)$

47. $(-m, n), (3m, -n)$

48. $(2a, b), (c, 2d)$

3-2 Direct Variation

A.CED.2 Create equations in two or more variables . . .; graph equations on coordinate axes with labels and scales.

Objective To write and graph an equation of a direct variation

Solve It! Write your solution to the Solve It in the space below.

The time it takes to hear thunder *varies directly with* the distance from lightning.

Essential Understanding If the ratio of two variables is constant, then the variables have a special relationship, known as a *direct variation*.

A **direct variation** is a relationship that can be represented by a function in the form $y = kx$, where $k \neq 0$. The **constant of variation for a direct variation** k is the coefficient of x. By dividing each side of $y = kx$ by x, you can see that the ratio of the variables is constant: $\frac{y}{x} = k$.

To determine whether an equation represents a direct variation, solve it for y. If you can write the equation in the form $y = kx$, where $k \neq 0$, it represents a direct variation.

Problem 1 Identifying a Direct Variation

Got It? Does $4x + 5y = 0$ represent a direct variation? If so, find the constant of variation.

Think
How do you know if an equation represents a direct variation?

Practice **Determine whether each equation represents a direct variation. If it does, find the constant of variation.**

1. $2y = 5x + 1$

2. $-4 + 7x + 4 = 3y$

To write an equation for a direct variation, first find the constant of variation k using an ordered pair, other than (0, 0), that you know is a solution of the equation.

Problem 2 Writing a Direct Variation Equation

Got It? Suppose y varies directly with x, and $y = 10$ when $x = -2$. What direct variation equation relates x and y? What is the value of y when $x = -15$?

Plan
How can you find the constant of variation?

$y = kx$

$10 = k \cdot -2$

$-2k = 10$

$y = -5(-15)$

$y = 75$

Practice **Suppose y varies directly with x. Write a direct variation equation that relates x and y. Then find the value of y when $x = 12$.**

3. $y = 10.4$ when $x = 4$.

4. $y = 9\frac{1}{3}$ when $x = -\frac{1}{2}$

Problem 3 Graphing a Direct Variation

Got It? a. Weight on the moon y varies directly with weight on Earth x. A person who weighs 100 lb on Earth weighs 16.6 lb on the moon. What is an equation that relates weight on Earth x and weight on the moon y? What is the graph of this equation?

b. **Reasoning** What is the slope of the graph of $y = 0.38x$ in Problem 3? How is the slope related to the equation?

Practice

5. **Travel Time** The distance d you bike varies directly with the amount of time t you bike. Suppose you bike 13.2 mi in 1.25 h. What is an equation that relates d and t? What is the graph of the equation?

6. **Geometry** The perimeter p of a regular hexagon varies directly with the length ℓ of one side of the hexagon. What is an equation that relates p and ℓ? What is the graph of the equation?

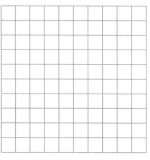

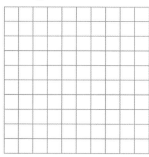

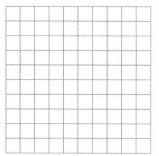

take note

Concept Summary — Graphs of Direct Variations

The graph of a direct variation equation $y = kx$ is a line with the following properties.

- The line passes through (0, 0).
- The slope of the line is k.

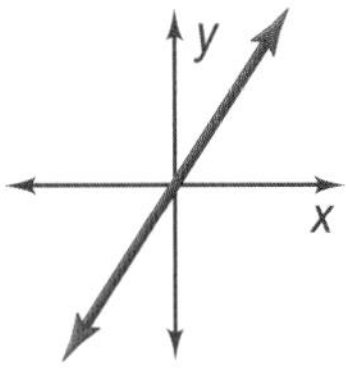

$k > 0$

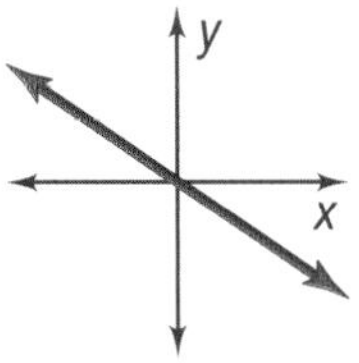

$k < 0$

You can rewrite a direct variation equation $y = kx$ as $\frac{y}{x} = k$. When a set of data pairs (x, y) vary directly, $\frac{y}{x}$ is the constant of variation. It is the same for each data pair.

Problem 4 Writing a Direct Variation From a Table

Got It? For the data in the table at the right, does y vary directly with x? If it does, write an equation for the direct variation.

x	y
−3	2.25
1	−0.75
4	−3

A Practice **For the data in each table, tell whether y varies directly with x. If it does, write an equation for the direct variation. Check your answer by plotting the points from the table and sketching the line.**

7.

x	y
3	5.4
7	12.6
12	21.6

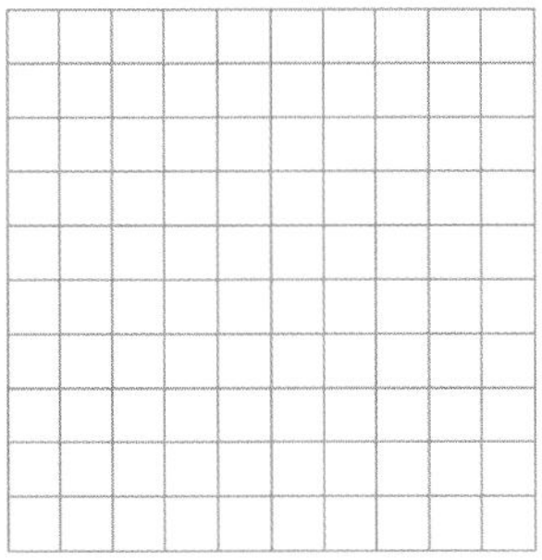

8.

x	y
−2	1
3	6
8	11

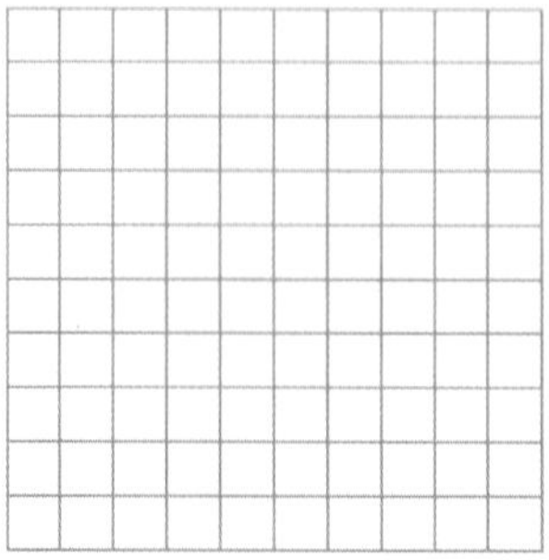

Lesson Check

Do you know HOW?

9. Does the equation $6y = 18x$ represent a direct variation? If it does, what is its constant of variation?

10. Suppose y varies directly with x, and $y = 30$ when $x = 3$. What direct variation equation relates x and y?

11. A recipe for 12 corn muffins calls for 1 cup of flour. The number of muffins you can make varies directly with the amount of flour you use. You have $2\frac{1}{2}$ cups of flour. How many muffins can you make?

12. Does y vary directly with x? If it does, what is an equation for the direct variation?

x	y
−2	1
2	−1
4	−2

Do you UNDERSTAND?

MATHEMATICAL PRACTICES

Vocabulary In Exercises 13–15, determine whether each statement is *always*, *sometimes*, or *never* true.

13. The ordered pair (0, 0) is a solution of the direct variation equation $y = kx$.

14. You can write a direct variation in the form $y = k + x$, where $k \neq 0$.

15. The constant of variation for a direct variation represented by $y = kx$ is $\frac{y}{x}$.

16. Reasoning Suppose q varies directly with p. Does this imply that p varies directly with q? Explain.

More Practice and Problem-Solving Exercises

MATHEMATICAL PRACTICES

B Apply

Suppose y varies directly with x. Write a direct variation equation that relates x and y. Then graph the equation.

17. $y = \frac{1}{2}$ when $x = 3$

18. $y = -5$ when $x = \frac{1}{4}$

19. $y = \frac{6}{5}$ when $x = -\frac{5}{6}$

20. $y = 7.2$ when $x = 1.2$.

21. Think About a Plan The amount of blood in a person's body varies directly with body weight. A person who weighs 160 lb has about 4.6 qt of blood. About how many quarts of blood are in the body of a 175-lb person?

- How can you find the constant of variation?
- Can you write an equation that relates quarts of blood to weight?
- How can you use the equation to determine the solution?

STEM **22. Electricity** Ohm's Law $V = I \times R$ relates the voltage, current, and resistance of a circuit. V is the voltage measured in volts. I is the current measured in amperes. R is the resistance measured in ohms.

a. Find the voltage of a circuit with a current of 24 amperes and a resistance of 2 ohms.

b. Find the resistance of a circuit with a current of 24 amperes and a voltage of 18 volts.

Reasoning **Tell whether the two quantities vary directly. Explain your reasoning.**

23. the number of ounces of cereal and the number of Calories the cereal contains

24. the time it takes to travel a certain distance and the rate at which you travel

25. the perimeter of a square and the side length of the square

26. the amount of money you have left and the number of items you purchase

27. a. Graph the following direct variation equations in the same coordinate plane: $y = x$, $y = 2x$, $y = 3x$, and $y = 4x$.

b. Look for a Pattern Describe how the graphs of the lines change as the constant of variation increases.

c. Predict how the graph of $y = \frac{1}{2}x$ would appear.

28. Error Analysis Use the table at the right. A student says that y varies directly with x because as x increases by 1, y also increases by 1. Explain the student's error.

x	y
0	3
1	4
2	5

29. Writing Suppose y varies directly with x. Explain how the value of y changes in each situation.

a. The value of x is doubled.

b. The value of x is halved.

STEM **30. Physics** The force you need to apply to a lever varies directly with the weight you want to lift. Suppose you can lift a 50-lb weight by applying 20 lb of force to a certain lever.

a. What is the ratio of force to weight for the lever?

b. Write an equation relating force and weight. What is the force you need to lift a friend who weighs 130 lb?

Challenge

The ordered pairs in each exercise are for the same direct variation. Find each missing value.

31. $(3, 4)$ and $(9, y)$ **32.** $(1, y)$ and $\left(\frac{3}{2}, -9\right)$ **33.** $(-5, 3)$ and $(x, -4.8)$

34. Gas Mileage A car gets 32 mi per gallon. The number of gallons g of gas used varies directly with the number of miles m traveled.

a. Suppose the price of gas is \$3.85 per gallon. Write a function giving the cost c for g gallons of gas. Is this a direct variation? Explain your reasoning.

b. Write a direct variation equation relating the cost of gas to the miles traveled.

c. How much will it cost to buy gas for a 240-mi trip?

TECHNOLOGY LAB

Use With Lesson 3-3

Investigating $y = mx + b$

F.IF.7.a Graph . . . functions and show intercepts, maxima, and minima.
Also F.IF.7, F.BF.3

MATHEMATICAL PRACTICES

You can use a graphing calculator to explore the graph of an equation in the form $y = mx + b$. For this activity, choose a standard screen by pressing zoom 6.

1. Graph these equations on the same screen. Then complete each statement.

$y = x + 3$ $\qquad$ $y = 2x + 3$ $\qquad$ $y = \frac{1}{2}x + 3$

a. The graph of ________________ is steepest.

b. The graph of ________________ is the least steep.

2. Match each equation with the best choice for its graph.

A. $y = \frac{1}{4}x - 2$ $\qquad$ **B.** $y = 4x - 2$ $\qquad$ **C.** $y = x - 2$

I.

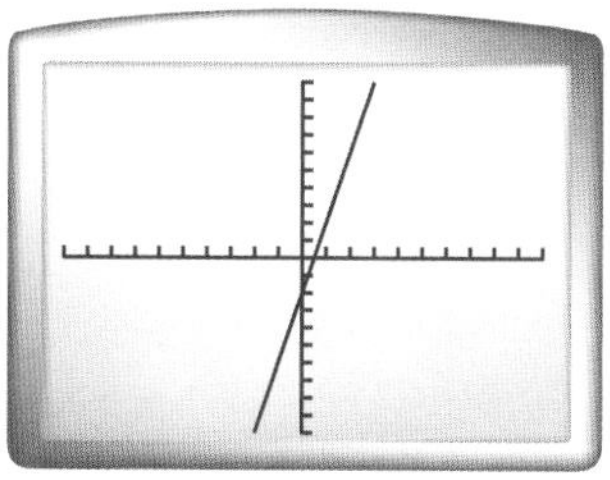

II.

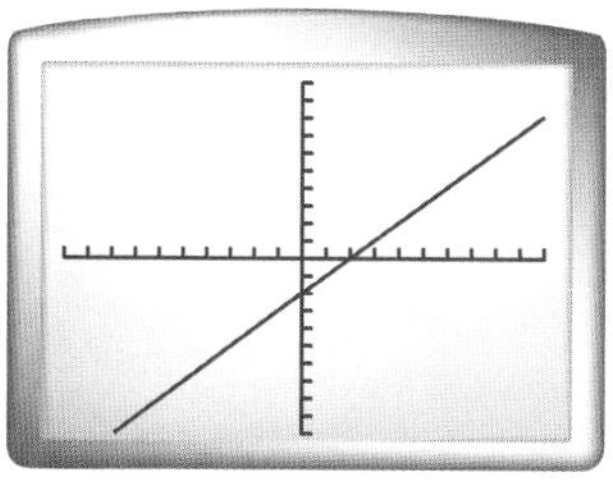

III.

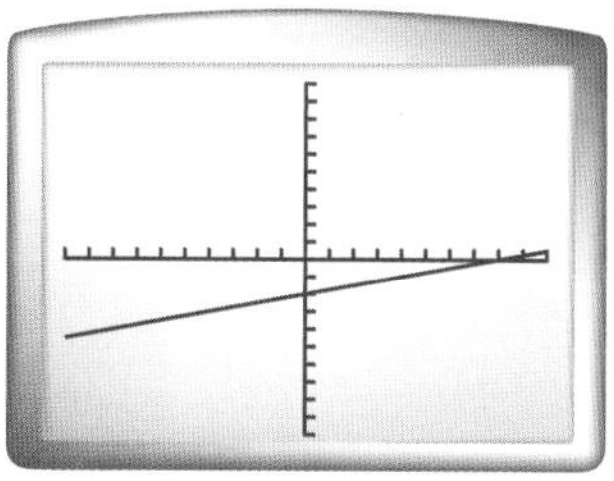

3. Graph these equations on the same screen.

$y = 2x + 3$ $\qquad$ $y = -2x + 3$

How does the sign of m affect the graph of the equation?

4. **Reasoning** How does changing the value of m affect the graph of an equation in the form $y = mx + b$?

5. Graph these equations on the same screen.

$y = 2x + 3$ $\quad\quad$ $y = 2x - 3$ $\quad\quad$ $y = 2x + 2$

Where does the graph of each equation cross the y-axis? (*Hint:* Use the **ZOOM** feature to better see the points of intersection.)

6. Match each equation with the best choice for its graph.

A. $y = \frac{1}{3}x - 3$ $\quad\quad$ **B.** $y = \frac{1}{3}x + 1$ $\quad\quad$ **C.** $y = \frac{1}{3}x$

I.

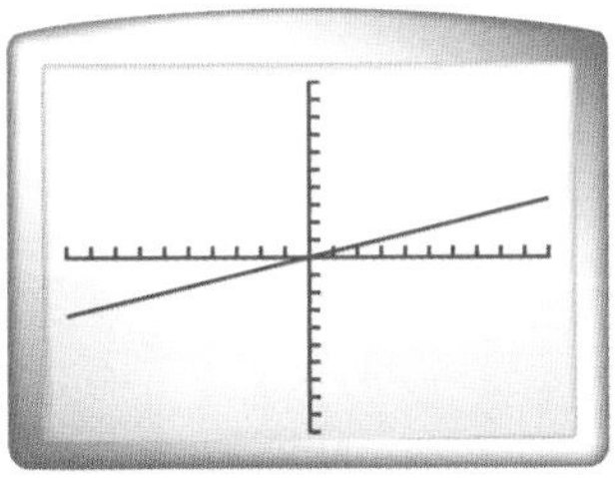

II.

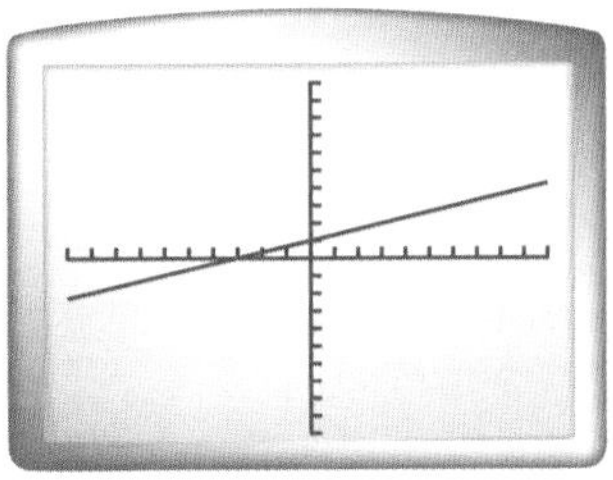

III.

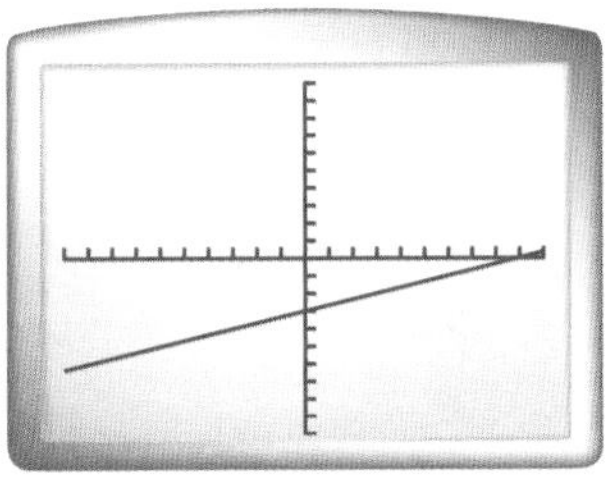

7. **Reasoning** How does changing the value of b affect the graph of an equation in the form $y = mx + b$?

3-3 Slope-Intercept Form

F.IF.7.a Graph . . . functions and show intercepts, maxima, and minima. Also F.IF.4, F.LE.2, F.LE.5

Objectives To write linear equations using slope-intercept form
To graph linear equations in slope-intercept form

Solve It! Write your solution to the Solve It in the space below.

The function in the Solve It is a linear function, but it is not a direct variation. Direct variations are only part of the family of linear functions.

A family of functions is a group of functions with common characteristics. A **parent function** is the simplest function with these characteristics. The **linear parent function** is $y = x$ or $f(x) = x$. The graphs of three linear functions are shown at the right.

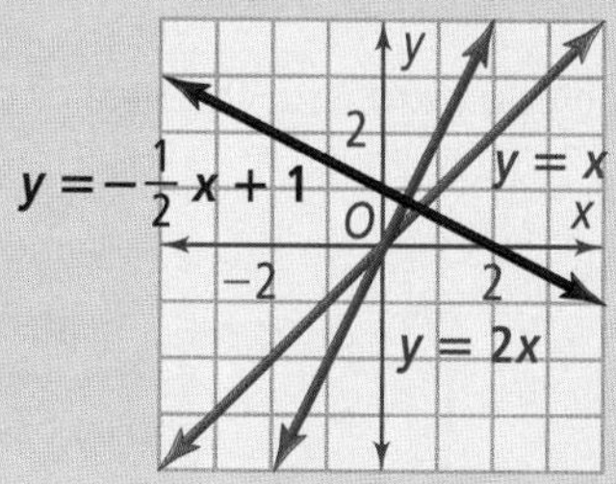

A **linear equation** is an equation that models a linear function. In a linear equation, the variables cannot be raised to a power other than 1. So $y = 2x$ is a linear equation, but $y = x^2$ and $y = 2^x$ are not. The graph of a linear equation contains all the ordered pairs that are solutions of the equation.

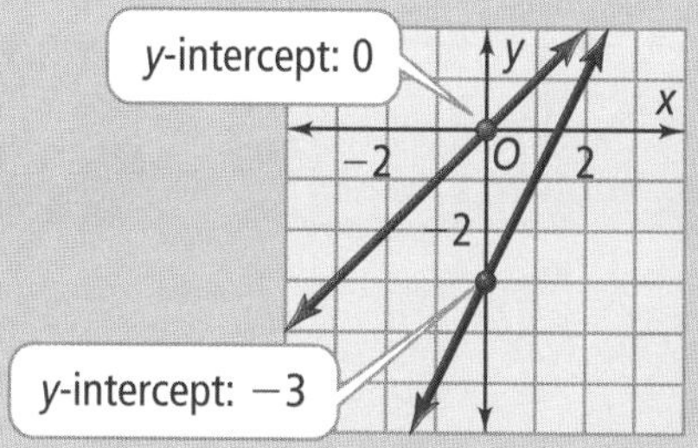

Graphs of linear functions may cross the y-axis at any point. A ***y*-intercept** of a graph is the y-coordinate of a point where the graph crosses the y-axis.

Essential Understanding You can use the slope and y-intercept of a line to write and graph an equation of the line.

take note

Key Concept Slope-Intercept Form of a Linear Equation

The **slope-intercept form** of a linear equation of a nonvertical line is $y = mx + b$.

m ↑ **slope** b ↑ ***y*-intercept**

Problem 1 Identifying Slope and y-Intercept

Got It? **a.** What are the slope and y-intercept of the graph of $y = -\frac{1}{2}x + \frac{2}{3}$?

b. Reasoning How do the graph of the line and the equation in part (a) change if the y-intercept is moved down 3 units?

Practice **Find the slope and y-intercept of the graph of each equation.**

1. $y = -x + 4$

2. $y = \frac{1}{4}x - \frac{1}{3}$

Problem 2 Writing an Equation in Slope-Intercept Form

Got It? What is an equation of the line with slope $\frac{3}{2}$ and y-intercept -1?

A Practice **Write an equation in slope-intercept form of the line with the given slope m and y-intercept b.**

3. $m = -0.5, b = 1.5$

4. $m = -2, b = \frac{8}{5}$

Problem 3 Writing an Equation From a Graph

Got It? **a.** What do you expect the slope of the line to be from looking at the graph? Explain.

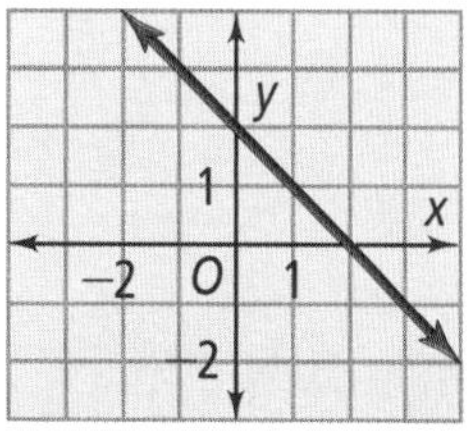

Think
What does the graph tell you about the slope?

b. What is an equation of the line shown above?

c. Reasoning Does the equation of the line depend on the points you use to find the slope? Explain.

Practice Write an equation in slope-intercept form of each line.

5.

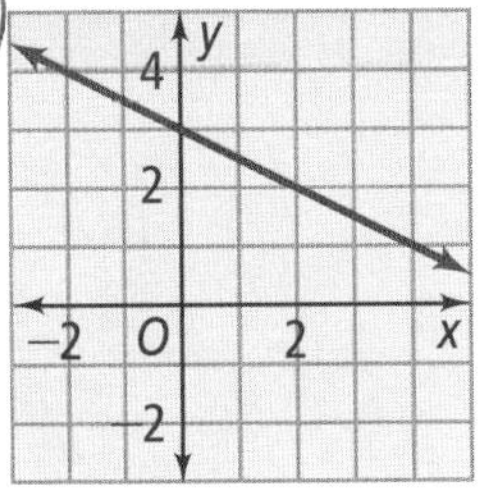

6.

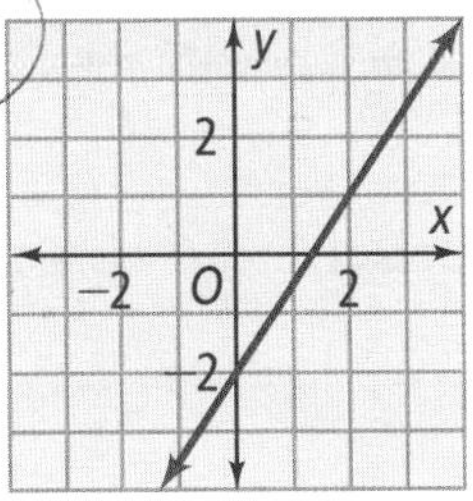

Problem 4 Writing an Equation From Two Points

Got It? What equation in slope-intercept form represents the line that passes through the points (3, −2) and (1, −3)?

1. slope
2. intercept
3. Plug in

3 −2

1 −3

$\frac{-3 - (+2)}{1 - 3}$ $\frac{-1}{-2}$ $= \frac{1}{2}$

$\frac{1}{2}(3)$

-3

$y = \frac{1}{2}(1) + b$ $2\frac{1}{2}$

$-3 = \frac{1}{2} + b$

$y = \frac{1}{2}x + \frac{5}{2}$

Practice **Write an equation in slope-intercept form of the line that passes through the given points.**

7. (−2, 4) and (3, −1)

8. (−3, 3) and (1, 2)

You can use the slope and y-intercept from an equation to graph a line.

Problem 5 Graphing a Linear Equation

Think

What information can you get from each equation?

Got It? What is the graph of each linear equation?

a. $y = -3x + 4$

b. $y = 4x - 8$

Practice Graph each equation.

9. $y = 3x + 4$

10. $y = -2x + 1$

Slope-intercept form is useful for modeling real-life situations where you are given a starting value (the y-intercept) and a rate of change (the slope).

Problem 6 Modeling a Function

Got It? A plumber charges a \$65 fee for a repair plus \$35 per hour. Write an equation to model the total cost y of a repair that takes x hours. What graph models the total cost?

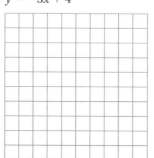

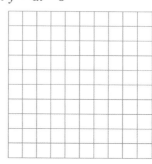

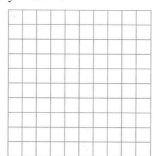

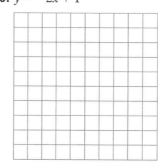

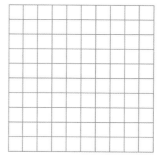

A Practice **11. Retail Sales** Suppose you have a \$5-off coupon at a fabric store. You buy fabric that costs \$7.50 per yard. Write an equation that models the total amount of money y you pay if you buy x yards of fabric. What is the graph of the equation?

12. Temperature The temperature at sunrise is 65°F. Each hour during the day, the temperature rises 5°F. Write an equation that models the temperature y, in degrees Fahrenheit, after x hours during the day. What is the graph of the equation?

Lesson Check

Do you know HOW?

13. What is an equation of the line with slope 6 and y-intercept -4?

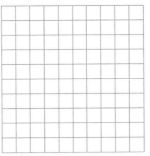

14. What equation in slope-intercept form represents the line that passes through the points (−3, 4) and (2, −1)?

$2x + 3y = 6$

$4x - 5y = 20$

15. What is the graph of $y = 5x + 2$?

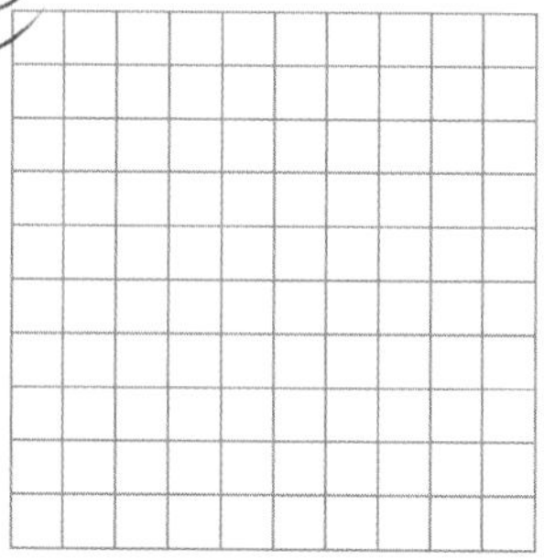

Do you UNDERSTAND?

MATHEMATICAL PRACTICES

16. **Vocabulary** Is $y = 5$ a linear equation? Explain.

17. **Reasoning** Is it *always, sometimes,* or *never* true that an equation in slope-intercept form represents a direct variation? Support your answer with examples.

18. Writing Describe two different methods you can use to graph the equation $y = 2x + 4$. Which method do you prefer? Explain.

More Practice and Problem-Solving Exercises

MATHEMATICAL PRACTICES

B Apply

19. Using the tables at the right, predict whether the two graphs will intersect. Plot the points and sketch the lines. Do the two lines appear to intersect? Explain.

x	y
−2	9
−1	7
0	5
1	3
2	1

x	y
−2	−18
−1	−14
0	−10
1	−6
2	−2

Find the slope and y-intercept of the graph of each equation.

20. $y - 2 = -3x$

21. $y + \frac{1}{2}x = 0$

22. $y - 9x = \frac{1}{2}$

23. $2y - 6 = 3x$

24. $-2y = 6(5 - 3x)$

25. $y - d = cx$

26. $y = (2 - a)x + a$

27. $2y + 4n = -6x$

28. Think About a Plan Polar bears are listed as a threatened species. In 2005, there were about 25,000 polar bears in the world. If the number of polar bears declines by 1000 each year, in what year will polar bears become extinct?

- What equation models the number of polar bears?
- How can graphing the equation help you solve the problem?

29. Error Analysis A student drew the graph at the right for the equation $y = -2x + 1$. What error did the student make? Draw the correct graph.

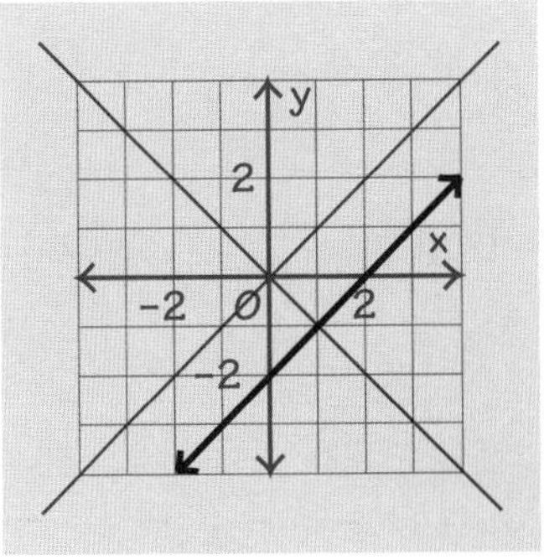

30. Computers A computer repair service charges \$50 for diagnosis and \$35 per hour for repairs. Let x be the number of hours it takes to repair a computer. Let y be the total cost of the repair.

a. Write an equation in slope-intercept form that relates x and y.

b. Graph the equation.

c. Reasoning Explain why you should draw the line only in Quadrant I.

Use the slope and y-intercept to graph each equation.

31. $y = 7 - 3x$

32. $2y + 4x = 0$

33. $3y + 6 = -2x$

34. $y + 2 = 5x - 4$

35. $4x + 3y = 2x - 1$

36. $-2(3x + 4) + y = 0$

Write a recursive formula and an explicit formula in slope-intercept form that model each arithmetic sequence. How does the recursive formula relate to the slope-intercept form?

37. 3, 5, 7, 9, . . .

38. −1, 3, 7, 11, . . .

39. 0.7, 0.3, −0.1, −0.5, . . .

40. Writing Describe two ways you can determine whether an equation is linear.

41. Hobbies Suppose you are doing a 5000-piece puzzle. You have already placed 175 pieces. Every minute you place 10 more pieces.

a. Write an equation in slope-intercept form to model the number of pieces placed. Graph the equation.

b. After 50 more minutes, how many pieces will you have placed?

Challenge

Find the value of a such that the graph of the equation has the given slope m.

42. $y = 2ax + 4,\ m = -1$

43. $y = -\frac{1}{2}ax - 5,\ m = \frac{5}{2}$

44. $y = \frac{3}{4}ax + 3,\ m = \frac{9}{16}$

45. Sailing A sailboat begins a voyage with 145 lb of food. The crew plans to eat a total of 15 lb of food per day.

a. Write an equation in slope-intercept form relating the remaining food supply y to the number of days x.

b. Graph your equation.

c. The crew plans to have 25 lb of food remaining when they end their voyage. How many days does the crew expect their voyage to last?

3-4 Point-Slope Form

F.LE.2 Construct linear and exponential functions, including arithmetic and geometric sequences, given a graph, a description of a relationship, or two input-output pairs . . . Also **A.CED.2, F.IF.7, F.BF.1**

Objective To write and graph linear equations using point-slope form

Solve It! Write your solution to the Solve It in the space below.

You have learned how to write an equation of a line by using its y-intercept. In this lesson, you will learn how to write an equation *without* using the y-intercept.

Essential Understanding You can use the slope of a line and any point on the line to write and graph an equation of the line. Any two equations for the same line are equivalent.

take note

Key Concept Point-Slope Form of a Linear Equation

Definition

The **point-slope form** of an equation of a nonvertical line with slope m and through point (x_1, y_1) is $y - y_1 = m(x - x_1)$.

Symbols

$$y - y_1 = m(x - x_1)$$

↑ y-coordinate ↑ slope ↑ x-coordinate

Graph

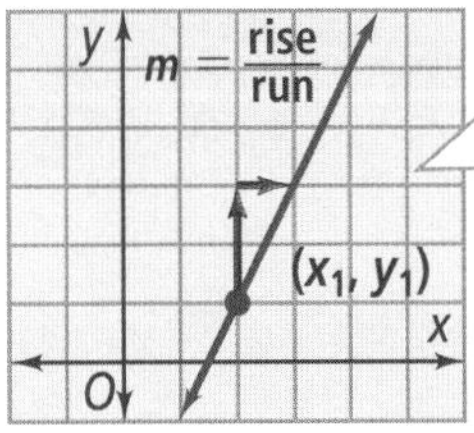

When you use $y - y_1 = m(x - x_1)$, (x_1, y_1) represents a *specific* point and (x, y) represents *any* point.

Here's Why It Works Given a point (x_1, y_1) on a line and the line's slope m, you can use the definition of slope to derive point-slope form.

$\frac{y_2 - y_1}{x_2 - x_1} = m$	Use the definition of slope.
$\frac{y - y_1}{x - x_1} = m$	Let (x, y) be any point on the line. Substitute (x, y) for (x_2, y_2).
$\frac{y - y_1}{x - x_1} \cdot (x - x_1) = m(x - x_1)$	Multiply each side by $(x - x_1)$.
$y - y_1 = m(x - x_1)$	Simplify the left side of the equation.

Problem 1 Writing an Equation in Point-Slope Form

Got It? A line passes through $(8, -4)$ and has slope $\frac{2}{3}$. What is an equation in point-slope form of the line?

Practice **Write an equation in point-slope form of the line that passes through the given point and with the given slope *m*.**

1. $(4, 2)$; $m = -\frac{5}{3}$

2. $(-2, -7)$; $m = \frac{4}{5}$

Problem 2 Graphing Using Point-Slope Form

Got It? What is the graph of the equation $y + 7 = -\frac{4}{5}(x - 4)$?

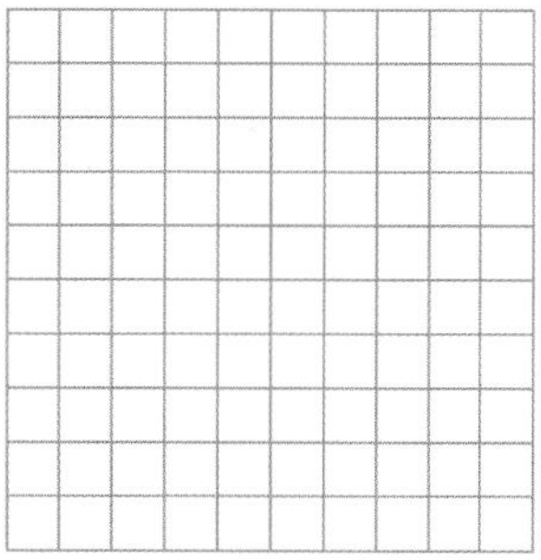

Plan

How does the equation help you make a graph?

A Practice Graph each equation.

3. $y + 5 = -(x + 2)$

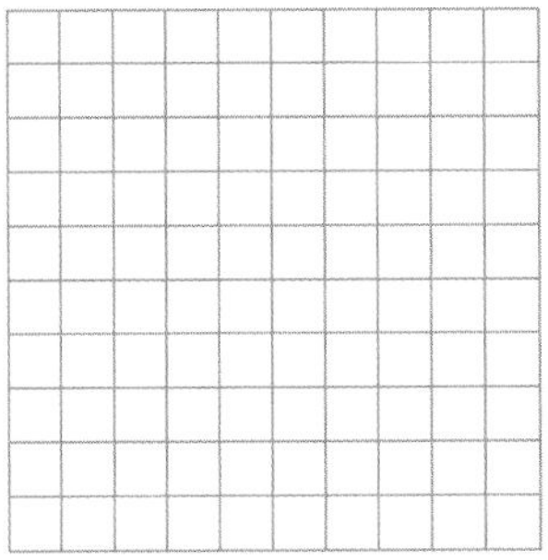

4. $y - 2 = \frac{4}{9}(x - 3)$

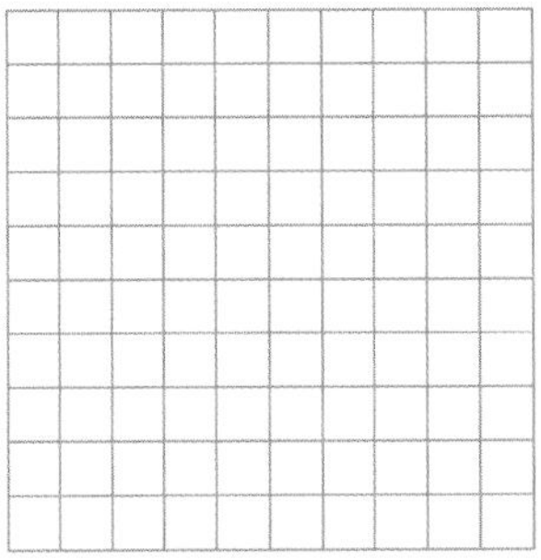

You can write the equation of a line given any two points on the line. First use the two given points to find the slope. Then use the slope and one of the points to write the equation.

Problem 3 Using Two Points to Write an Equation

Think

What variables do you substitute for?

Got It? **a.** In the last step of Problem 3, use the point $(-2, -3)$ instead of $(1, 4)$ to write an equation of the line.

b. Reasoning Rewrite the equations in Problem 3 and part (a) in slope-intercept form. Compare the two rewritten equations. What can you conclude?

Practice Write an equation in point-slope form for each line.

5.

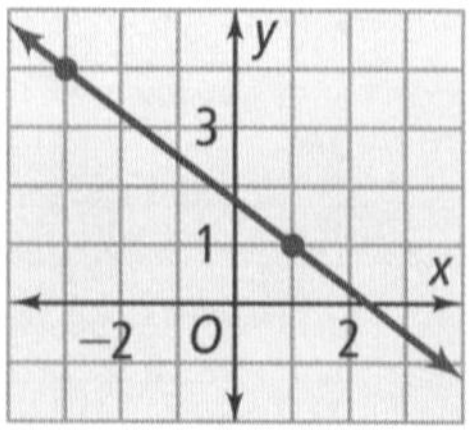

6.

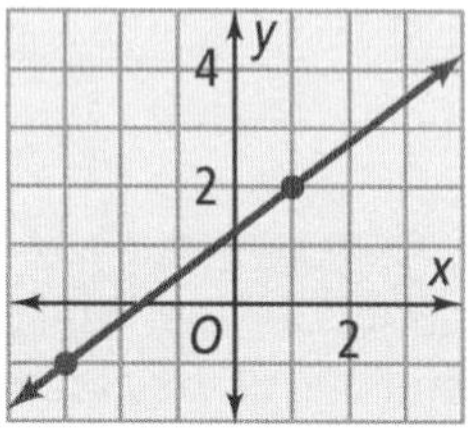

Problem 4 Using a Table to Write an Equation

Got It? a. The table shows the number of gallons of water y in a tank after x hours. The relationship is linear. What is an equation in point-slope form that models the data? What does the slope represent?

Volume of Water in Tank

Time, x (h)	Water, y (gal)
2	3320
3	4570
5	7070
8	10,820

b. **Reasoning** Write the equation from part (a) in slope-intercept form. What does the y-intercept represent?

Practice Model the data in each table with a linear equation in slope-intercept form. Then tell what the slope and y-intercept represent.

7.

Time Painting, x (days)	Volume of Paint, y (gal)
2	56
3	44
5	20

8.

Time Worked, x (h)	Wages Earned, y ($)
1	8.50
3	25.50
6	51.00

Lesson Check

Do you know HOW?

9. What are the slope and one point on the graph of $y - 12 = \frac{4}{9}(x + 7)$?

10. What is an equation of the line that passes through the point (3, −8) and has slope −2?

11. What is the graph of the equation $y - 4 = 3(x + 2)$?

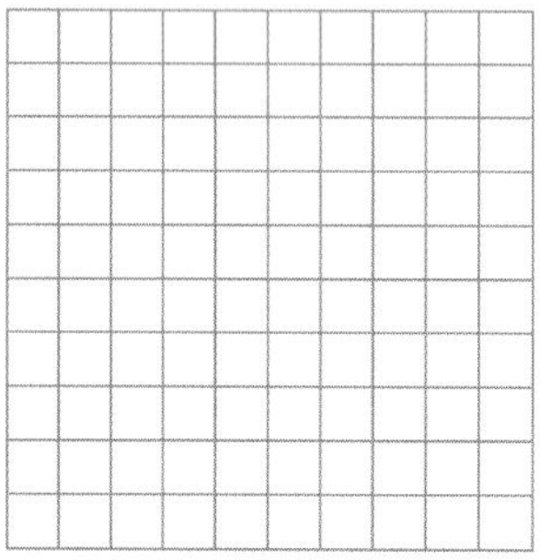

12. What is an equation of the line that passes through the points (−1, −2) and (2, 4)?

Do you UNDERSTAND?

MATHEMATICAL PRACTICES

13. Vocabulary What features of the graph of the equation $y - y_1 = m(x - x_1)$ can you identify?

14. Reasoning Is $y - 4 = 3(x + 1)$ an equation of a line through $(-2, 1)$? Explain.

15. Reasoning Can any equation in point-slope form also be written in slope-intercept form? Give an example to explain.

More Practice and Problem-Solving Exercises

MATHEMATICAL PRACTICES

B Apply

Graph the line that passes through the given point and has the given slope *m*.

16. $(-3, -2)$; $m = 2$

17. $(6, -1)$; $m = -\frac{5}{3}$

18. $(-3, 1)$; $m = \frac{1}{3}$

19. Think About a Plan The relationship of degrees Fahrenheit (°F) and degrees Celsius (°C) is linear. When the temperature is 50°F, it is 10°C. When the temperature is 77°F, it is 25°C. Write an equation giving the Celsius temperature *C* in terms of the Fahrenheit temperature *F*. What is the Celsius temperature when it is 59°F?
- How can point-slope form help you write the equation?
- What are two points you can use to find the slope?

20. a. Geometry Figure *ABCD* is a rectangle. Write equations in point-slope form of the lines containing the sides of *ABCD*.

b. Reasoning Make a conjecture about the slopes of parallel lines.

c. Use your conjecture to write an equation of the line that passes through $(0, -4)$ and is parallel to $y - 9 = -7(x + 3)$.

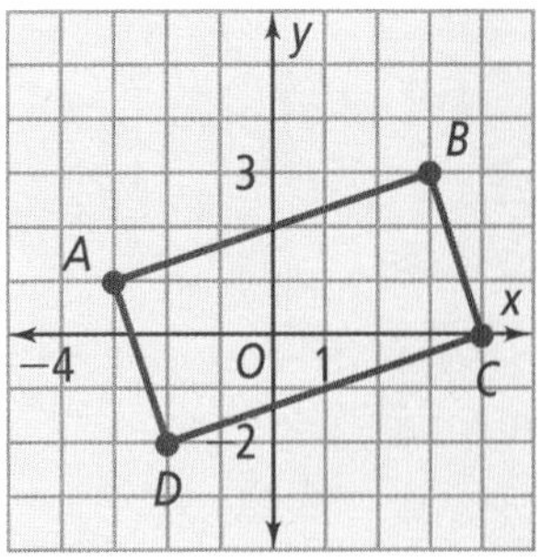

STEM **21. Boiling Point** The relationship between altitude and the boiling point of water is linear. At an altitude of 8000 ft, water boils at 197.6°F. At an altitude of 4500 ft, water boils at 203.9°F. Write an equation giving the boiling point *b* of water, in degrees Fahrenheit, in terms of the altitude *a*, in feet. What is the boiling point of water at 2500 ft?

22. Using a graphing calculator, graph $f(x) = 3x + 2$.

a. If $f(x) = 3x + 2$ and $g(x) = 4f(x)$, write the equation for $g(x)$. Graph $g(x)$ and compare it to the graph of $f(x)$.

b. If $f(x) = 3x + 2$ and $h(x) = f(4x)$, write the equation for $h(x)$. Graph $h(x)$ and compare it to the graph of $f(x)$.

c. Compare how multiplying a function by a number and multiplying the x-value of a function by a number change the graphs of the functions.

23. Using a graphing calculator, graph $f(x) = 2x - 5$.

a. If $f(x) = 2x - 5$ and $j(x) = f(x) + 3$, write the equation for $j(x)$. Graph $j(x)$ and compare it to the graph of $f(x)$.

b. If $f(x) = 2x - 5$ and $k(x) = f(x + 3)$, write the equation for $k(x)$. Graph $k(x)$ and compare it to the graph of $f(x)$.

c. Compare how adding a number to a function and adding a number to the x-value of a function change the graphs of the functions.

Challenge

24. Forestry A forester plants a tree and measures its circumference yearly over the next four years. The table shows the forester's measurements.

Tree Growth

Time (yr)	1	2	3	4
Circumference (in.)	2	4	6	8

a. Show that the data are linear, and write an equation that models the data.

b. Predict the circumference of the tree after 10 yr.

c. The circumference of the tree after 10 yr was actually 43 in. After four more years, the circumference was 49 in. Based on this new information, does the relationship between time and circumference continue to be linear? Explain.

3-5 Standard Form

A.CED.2 Create equations in two or more variables . . .; graph equations on coordinate axes with labels and scales. Also F.IF.4, F.IF.7.a, F.IF.9

Objectives To graph linear equations using intercepts
To write linear equations in standard form

Solve It! Write your solution to the Solve It in the space below.

In this lesson, you will learn to use intercepts to graph a line. Recall that a y-intercept is the y-coordinate of a point where a graph crosses the y-axis. The **x-intercept** is the x-coordinate of a point where a graph crosses the x-axis.

Essential Understanding One form of a linear equation, called *standard form,* allows you to find intercepts quickly. You can use the intercepts to draw the graph.

take note

Key Concept **Standard Form of a Linear Equation**

The **standard form of a linear equation** is $Ax + By = C$, where A, B, and C are real numbers, and A and B are not both zero.

Problem 1 Finding x- and y-Intercepts

Got It? What are the x- and y-intercepts of the graph of each equation?

a. $5x - 6y = 60$

b. $3x + 8y = 12$

Think
What do you substitute for y when you are finding the x-intercept?

Practice Find the x- and y-intercepts of the graph of each equation.

1. $7x - y = 21$

2. $-5x + 3y = -7.5$

Problem 2 Graphing a Line Using Intercepts

Think

How can you use the intercepts to help you graph a line?

Got It? What is the graph of $2x + 5y = 20$?

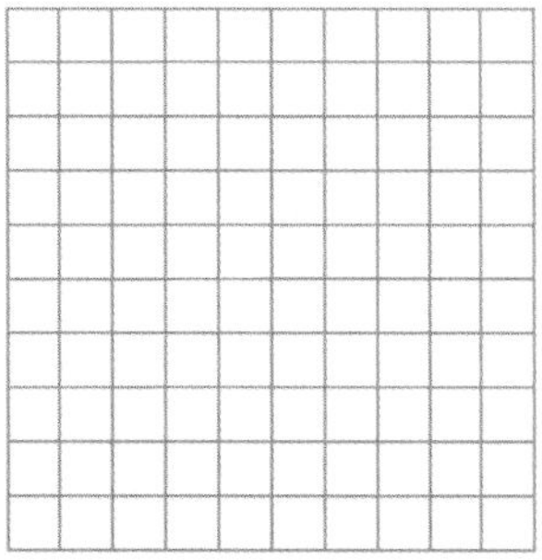

Practice Graph each equation using x- and y-intercepts.

3. $x - y = -8$

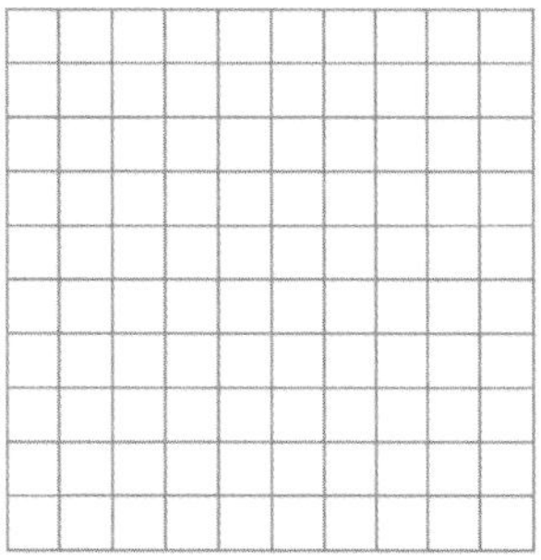

4. $6x - 2y = 18$

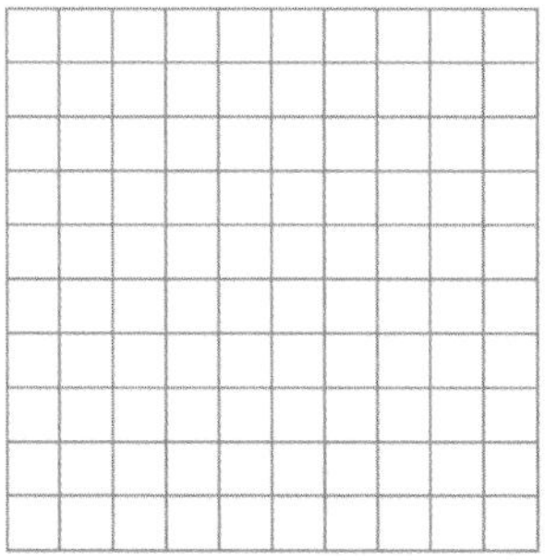

If $A = 0$ in the standard form $Ax + By = C$, then you can write the equation in the form $y = b$, where b is a constant. If $B = 0$, you can write the equation in the form $x = a$, where a is a constant. The graph of $y = b$ is a horizontal line, and the graph of $x = a$ is a vertical line.

Problem 3 Graphing Horizontal and Vertical Lines

Got It? What is the graph of each equation?

a. $x = 4$

b. $x = -1$

c. $y = 0$

d. $y = 1$

Practice Graph each equation.

5. $y = -2$

6. $x = 7$

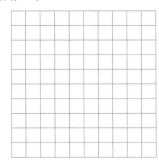

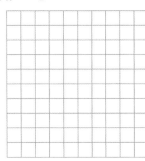

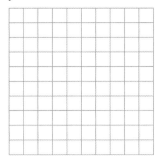

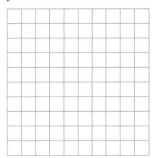

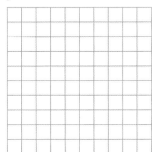

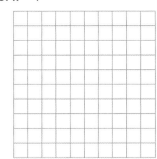

Given an equation in slope-intercept form or point-slope form, you can rewrite the equation in standard form using only integers.

Problem 4 Transforming to Standard Form

Got It? Write $y - 2 = -\frac{1}{3}(x + 6)$ in standard form using integers.

Practice Write each equation in standard form using integers.

7. $y = \frac{1}{4}x - 2$

8. $y = -\frac{2}{3}x - 1$

Problem 5 Using Standard Form as a Model

Got It? **a.** In Problem 5, suppose the store charged \$15 for each movie. What equation describes the numbers of songs and movies you can purchase for \$60?

b. Reasoning What domain and range are reasonable for the equation in part (a)? Explain.

Practice **9. Video Games** In a video game, you earn 5 points for each jewel you find. You earn 2 points for each star you find. Write and graph an equation that represents the numbers of jewels and stars you must find to earn 250 points. What are three combinations of jewels and stars you can find that will earn you 250 points?

10. Clothing A store sells T-shirts for \$12 each and sweatshirts for \$15 each. You plan to spend \$120 on T-shirts and sweatshirts. Write and graph an equation that represents this situation. What are three combinations of T-shirts and sweatshirts you can buy for \$120?

take note

Concept Summary Linear Equations

You can describe any line using one or more of these forms of a linear equation. Any two equations for the same line are equivalent.

Graph

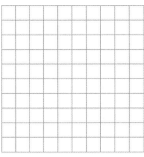

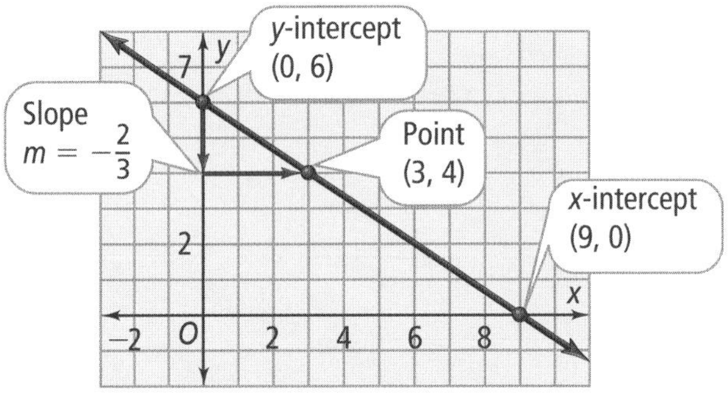

Forms

Slope-Intercept Form

$y = mx + b$

$y = -\frac{2}{3}x + 6$

Point-Slope Form

$y - y_1 = m(x - x_1)$

$y - 4 = -\frac{2}{3}(x - 3)$

Standard Form

$Ax + By = C$

$2x + 3y = 18$

Lesson Check

Do you know HOW?

11. What are the x- and y-intercepts of the graph of $3x - 4y = 9$?

12. What is the graph of $5x + 4y = 20$?

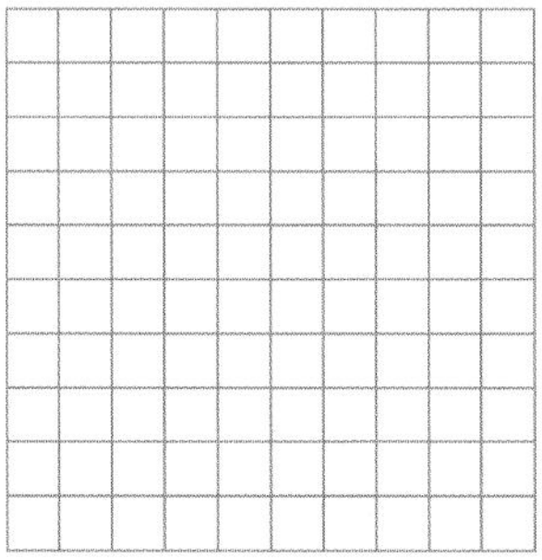

13. Is the graph of $y = -0.5$ a *horizontal line,* a *vertical line,* or *neither*?

14. What is $y = \frac{1}{2}x + 3$ written in standard form using integers?

15. A store sells gift cards in preset amounts. You can purchase gift cards for $10 or $25. You have spent $285 on gift cards. Write an equation in standard form to represent this situation. What are three combinations of gift cards you could have purchased?

Do you UNDERSTAND?

MATHEMATICAL PRACTICES

16. Vocabulary Tell whether each linear equation is in *slope-intercept form*, *point-slope form*, or *standard form*.

a. $y + 5 = -(x - 2)$

b. $y = -2x + 5$

c. $y - 10 = -2(x - 1)$

d. $2x + 4y = 12$

17. Reasoning Which form would you use to write an equation of the line at the right: *slope-intercept form*, *point-slope form*, or *standard form*? Explain.

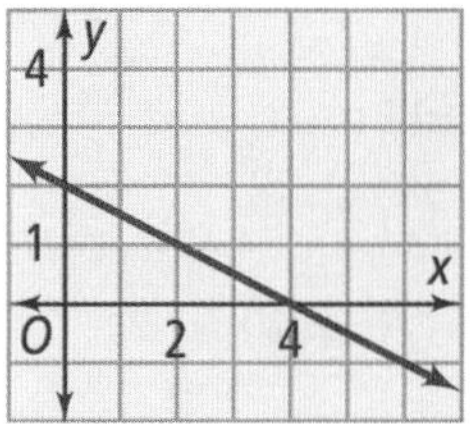

More Practice and Problem-Solving Exercises

MATHEMATICAL PRACTICES

B Apply

18. Writing The three forms of linear equations you have studied are slope-intercept form, point-slope form, and standard form. Explain when each form is most useful.

19. Think About a Plan You are preparing a fruit salad. You want the total carbohydrates from pineapple and watermelon to equal 24 g. Pineapple has 3 g of carbohydrates per ounce and watermelon has 2 g of carbohydrates per ounce. What is a graph that shows all possible combinations of ounces of pineapple and ounces of watermelon?
- Can you write an equation to model the situation?
- What domain and range are reasonable for the graph?

20. Compare and Contrast Graph $3x + y = 6$, $3x - y = 6$, and $-3x + y = 6$. How are the graphs similar? How are they different?

21. Reasoning What are the slope and y-intercept of the graph of $Ax + By = C$?

22. Error Analysis A student says the equation $y = 4x + 1$ can be written in standard form as $4x - y = 1$. Describe and correct the student's error.

23. Reasoning The coefficients of x and y in the standard form of a linear equation cannot both be zero. Explain why.

Graphing Calculator Use a graphing calculator to graph each equation. Make a sketch of the graph. Include the x- and y-intercepts.

24. $2x - 8y = -16$ **25.** $-3x - 4y = 0$ **26.** $x + 3.5y = 7$

27. $-x + 2y = -8$ **28.** $3x + 3y = -15$ **29.** $4x - 6y = 9$

30. Compare and Contrast The graph below represents one function, and the table represents a different function. How are the functions similar? How are they different?

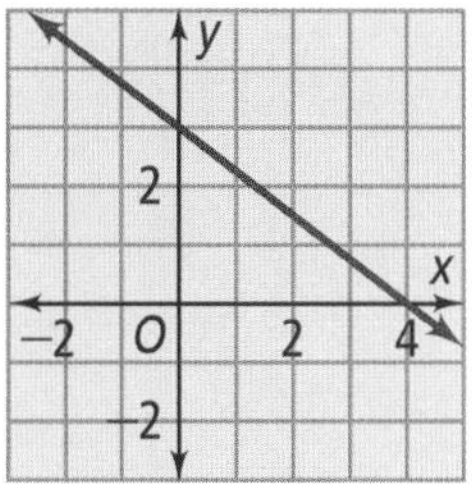

x	−4	−2	0	2	4
y	5	4	3	2	1

Find the x- and y-intercepts of the line that passes through the given points.

31. $(-6, 4), (3, -5)$ **32.** $(-5, -5), (4, -2)$ **33.** $(-7, 6), (-4, 11)$

34. $(-2, 8), (4, 2)$ **35.** $(3, -8), (-4, 13)$ **36.** $(5, 0.4), (-1, -2)$

37. Sports The scoreboard for a football game is shown at the right. All of the points the home team scored came from field goals worth 3 points and touchdowns with successful extra-point attempts worth 7 points. Write and graph a linear equation that represents this situation. List every possible combination of field goals and touchdowns the team could have scored.

Challenge

38. Geometry Graph $x + 4y = 8$, $4x - y = -1$, $x + 4y = -12$, and $4x - y = 20$ in the same coordinate plane. What figure do the four lines appear to form?

Write an equation of each line in standard form.

39. The line contains the point $(-4, -7)$ and has the same slope as the graph of $y + 3 = 5(x + 4)$.

40. The line has the same slope as $4x - y = 5$ and the same y-intercept as the graph of $3y - 13x = 6$.

41. a. Graph $2x + 3y = 6$, $2x + 3y = 12$, and $2x + 3y = 18$ in the same coordinate plane.

b. How are the lines from part (a) related?

c. As C increases, what happens to the graph of $2x + 3y = C$?

42. a. Fundraising Suppose your school is having a talent show to raise money for new band supplies. You think that 200 students and 150 adults will attend. It will cost \$200 to put on the talent show. What is an equation that describes the ticket prices you can set for students and adults to raise \$1000?

b. Open-Ended Graph your equation. What are three possible prices you could set for student and adult tickets?

3-6 Slopes of Parallel and Perpendicular Lines

G.GPE.5 Prove the slope criteria for parallel and perpendicular lines and use them . . . to solve problems . . .
Also **A.CED.2, F.IF.7.a, F.LE.2**

Objectives To determine whether lines are parallel, perpendicular, or neither
To write equations of parallel lines and perpendicular lines

Solve It! Write your solution to the Solve It in the space below.

Two distinct lines in a coordinate plane either intersect or are *parallel*. **Parallel lines** are lines in the same plane that never intersect.

Essential Understanding You can determine the relationship between two lines by comparing their slopes and y-intercepts.

take note

Key Concept Slopes of Parallel Lines

Words

Nonvertical lines are parallel if they have the same slope and different y-intercepts. Vertical lines are parallel if they have different x-intercepts.

Example

The graphs of $y = \frac{1}{2}x + 1$ and $y = \frac{1}{2}x - 2$ are lines that have the same slope, $\frac{1}{2}$, and different y-intercepts. The lines are parallel.

Graph

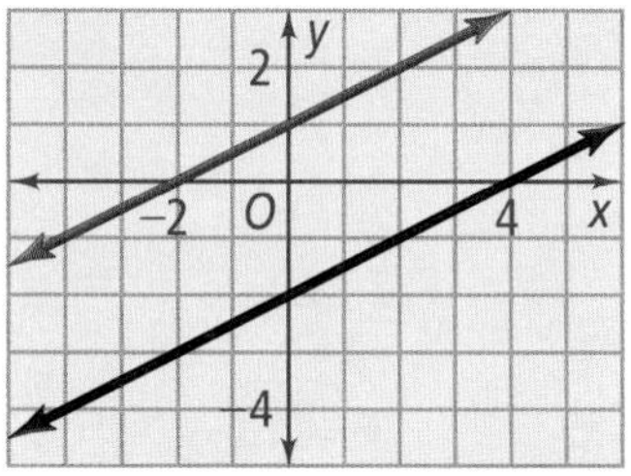

You can use the fact that the slopes of parallel lines are the same to write an equation of a line parallel to a given line.

Problem 1 Writing an Equation of a Parallel Line

Got It? A line passes through $(-3, -1)$ and is parallel to the graph of $y = 2x + 3$. What equation represents the line in slope-intercept form?

Practice **Write an equation in slope-intercept form of the line that passes through the given point and is parallel to the graph of the given equation.**

1. $(2, -1)$; $y = -\frac{3}{2}x + 6$

2. $(0, 0)$; $y = \frac{2}{3}x + 1$

You can also use slope to determine whether two lines are *perpendicular*. **Perpendicular lines** are lines that intersect to form right angles.

take note

Key Concept Slopes of Perpendicular Lines

Words

Two nonvertical lines are perpendicular if the product of their slopes is -1. A vertical line and a horizontal line are also perpendicular.

Example

The graph of $y = \frac{1}{2}x - 1$ has a slope of $\frac{1}{2}$. The graph of $y = -2x + 1$ has a slope of -2. Since $\frac{1}{2}(-2) = -1$, the lines are perpendicular.

Graph

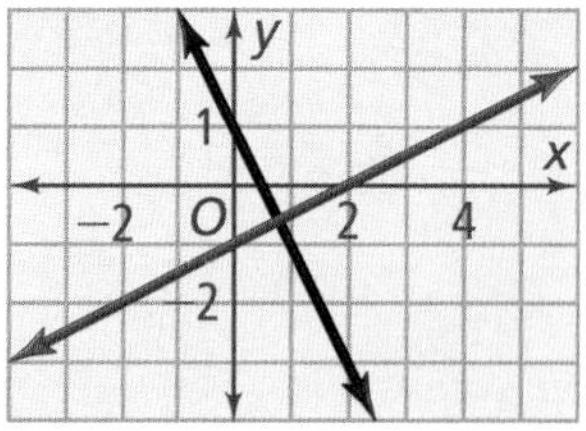

Two numbers whose product is -1 are **opposite reciprocals**. So, the slopes of perpendicular lines are opposite reciprocals. To find the opposite reciprocal of $-\frac{3}{4}$, for example, first find the reciprocal, $-\frac{4}{3}$. Then write its opposite, $\frac{4}{3}$. Since $-\frac{3}{4} \cdot \frac{4}{3} = -1$, $\frac{4}{3}$ is the opposite reciprocal of $-\frac{3}{4}$.

Problem 2 Classifying Lines

Got It? Are the graphs of the equations *parallel, perpendicular,* or *neither*? Explain.

a. $y = \frac{3}{4}x + 7$ and $4x - 3y = 9$

b. $6y = -x + 6$ and $y = -\frac{1}{6}x + 6$

Practice **Determine whether the graphs of the given equations are *parallel, perpendicular,* or *neither*. Explain.**

3. $y = -7$
$x = 2$

4. $y = 4x - 2$
$-x + 4y = 0$

Problem 3 Writing an Equation of a Perpendicular Line

Got It? A line passes through (1, 8) and is perpendicular to the graph of $y = 2x + 1$. What equation represents the line in slope-intercept form?

A Practice **Write an equation in slope-intercept form of the line that passes through the given point and is perpendicular to the graph of the given equation.**

5. (5, 0); $y + 1 = 2(x - 3)$

6. (1, −6); $x - 2y = 4$

Problem 4 Solving a Real-World Problem

Got It? What equation could the architect in Problem 4 enter to represent a second beam whose graph will pass through the corner at (0, 10) and be parallel to the existing beam? Give your answer in slope-intercept form.

Practice 7. **Urban Planning** A path for a new city park will connect the park entrance to Main Street. The path should be perpendicular to Main Street. What is an equation that represents the path?

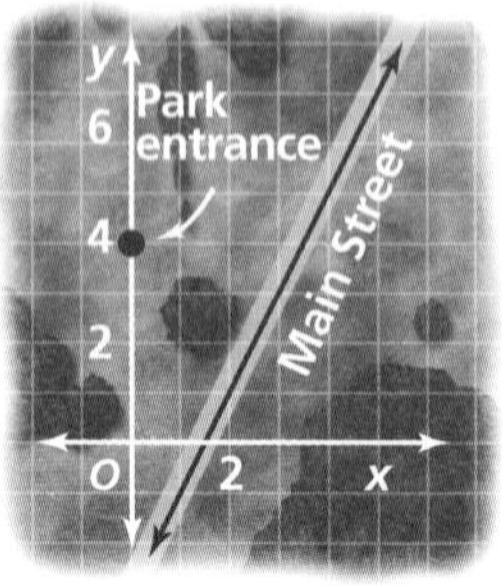

8. **Bike Path** A bike path is being planned for the park in Exercise 7. The bike path will be parallel to Main Street and will pass through the park entrance. What is an equation of the line that represents the bike path?

Lesson Check

Do you know HOW?

9. Which equations below have graphs that are parallel to one another? Which have graphs that are perpendicular to one another?

$y = -\frac{1}{6}x$
$y = 6x$
$y = 6x - 2$

10. What is an equation of the line that passes through $(3, -1)$ and is parallel to $y = -4x + 1$? Give your answer in slope-intercept form.

11. What is an equation of the line that passes through $(2, -3)$ and is perpendicular to $y = x - 5$? Give your answer in slope-intercept form.

Do you UNDERSTAND?

MATHEMATICAL PRACTICES

12. Vocabulary Tell whether the two numbers in each pair are opposite reciprocals.

a. $-2, \frac{1}{2}$ **b.** $\frac{1}{4}, 4$ **c.** $5, -5$

13. Open-Ended Write equations of two parallel lines.

14. Compare and Contrast How is determining if two nonvertical lines are parallel similar to determining if they are perpendicular? How are the processes different?

More Practice and Problem-Solving Exercises

MATHEMATICAL PRACTICES

B Apply

15. Identify each pair of parallel lines. Then identify each pair of perpendicular lines.

line a: $y = 3x + 3$ line b: $x = -1$ line c: $y - 5 = \frac{1}{2}(x - 2)$

line d: $y = 3$ line e: $y + 4 = -2(x + 6)$ line f: $9x - 3y = 5$

Determine whether each statement is *always, sometimes,* or *never* true. Explain.

16. A horizontal line is parallel to the x-axis.

17. Two lines with positive slopes are parallel.

18. Two lines with the same slope and different y-intercepts are perpendicular.

19. Reasoning For an arithmetic sequence, the first term is $A(1) = 3$. Each successive term adds 2 to the previous term. Another arithmetic sequence has the rule $B(n) = 5 + (n - 1)d$, where n is the term number and d is the common difference. If the graphs of the two sequences are parallel, what is the value of d? Explain.

x	−1	0	1	2
y	−1	3	7	11

20. Reasoning Will the graph of the line represented by the table intersect the graph of $y = 4x + 5$? Explain.

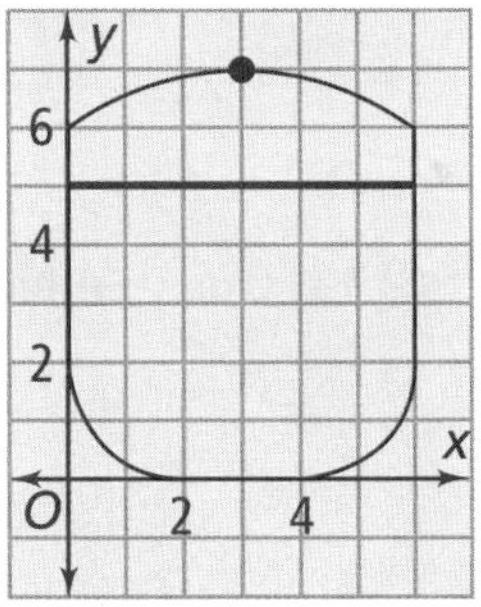

21. Think About a Plan A designer is creating a new logo, as shown at the right. The designer wants to add a line to the logo that will be perpendicular to the blue line and pass through the red point. What equation represents the new line?

- What is the slope of the blue line?
- What is the slope of the new line?

22. Reasoning For what value of k are the graphs of $12y = -3x + 8$ and $6y = kx - 5$ parallel? For what value of k are they perpendicular?

23. Agriculture Two farmers use combines to harvest corn from their fields. One farmer has 600 acres of corn, and the other has 1000 acres of corn. Each farmer's combine can harvest 100 acres per day. Write two equations for the number of acres y of corn *not* harvested after x days. Are the graphs of the equations *parallel, perpendicular,* or *neither*? How do you know?

C Challenge

24. Geometry In a rectangle, opposite sides are parallel and adjacent sides are perpendicular. Figure $ABCD$ has vertices $A(-3, 3)$, $B(-1, -2)$, $C(4, 0)$, and $D(2, 5)$. Show that $ABCD$ is a rectangle.

25. Geometry A right triangle has two sides that are perpendicular to each other. Triangle PQR has vertices $P(4, 3)$, $Q(2, -1)$, and $R(0, 1)$. Determine whether PQR is a right triangle. Explain your reasoning.

3 Chapter Review

MathXL® for School
Go to pearsonsuccessnet.com

3-1 Rate of Change and Slope

Quick Review

Rate of change shows the relationship between two changing quantities. The **slope** of a line is the ratio of the vertical change (the rise) to the horizontal change (the run).

$$\text{slope} = \frac{\text{rise}}{\text{run}} = \frac{y_2 - y_1}{x_2 - x_1}$$

The slope of a horizontal line is 0, and the slope of a vertical line is undefined.

Example

What is the slope of the line that passes through the points (1, 12) and (6, 22)?

$$\text{slope} = \frac{y_2 - y_1}{x_2 - x_1} = \frac{22 - 12}{6 - 1} = \frac{10}{5} = 2$$

Exercises

Find the slope of the line that passes through each pair of points.

1. (2, 2), (3, 1)

2. (4, 2), (0, 2)

3. (−1, 2), (0, 5)

4. (−3, −2), (−3, 2)

Find the slope of each line.

5.

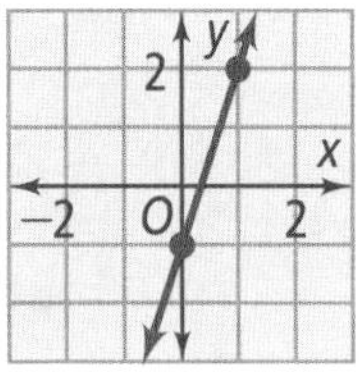

6.

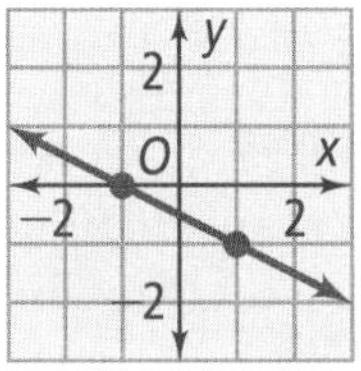

3-2 Direct Variation

Quick Review

A function represents a **direct variation** if it has the form $y = kx$, where $k \neq 0$. The coefficient k is the **constant of variation.**

Example

Suppose y varies directly with x, and $y = 15$ when $x = 5$. Write a direct variation equation that relates x and y. What is the value of y when $x = 9$?

$y = kx$	Start with the general form of a direct variation.
$15 = k(5)$	Substitute 5 for x and 15 for y.
$3 = k$	Divide each side by 5 to solve for k.
$y = 3x$	Write an equation. Substitute 3 for k in $y = kx$.

The equation $y = 3x$ relates x and y. When $x = 9$, $y = 3(9)$, or 27.

Exercises

Suppose y varies directly with x. Write a direct variation equation that relates x and y. Then find the value of y when $x = 7$.

7. $y = 8$ when $x = -4$.

8. $y = 15$ when $x = 6$.

9. $y = 3$ when $x = 9$.

10. $y = -4$ when $x = 4$.

For the data in each table, tell whether y varies directly with x. If it does, write an equation for the direct variation.

11.

x	y
−1	−6
2	3
5	12
9	24

12.

x	y
−3	7.5
−1	2.5
2	−5
5	−12.5

3-3, 3-4, and 3-5 Forms of Linear Equations

Quick Review

The graph of a linear equation is a line. You can write a linear equation in different forms.

The **slope-intercept form** of a linear equation is $y = mx + b$, where m is the slope and b is the **y-intercept**.

The **point-slope form** of a linear equation is $y - y_1 = m(x - x_1)$, where m is the slope and (x_1, y_1) is a point on the line.

The **standard form** of a linear equation is $Ax + By = C$, where A, B, and C are real numbers, and A and B are not both zero.

Example

What is an equation of the line that has slope −4 and passes through the point (−1, 7)?

$y - y_1 = m(x - x_1)$	Use point-slope form.
$y - 7 = -4(x - (-1))$	Substitute (−1, 7) for (x_1, y_1) and −4 for m.
$y - 7 = -4(x + 1)$	Simplify inside grouping symbols.

An equation of the line is $y - 7 = -4(x + 1)$.

Exercises

Write an equation in slope-intercept form of the line that passes through the given points.

13. (−3, 4), (1, 4) **14.** (3, −2), (6, 1)

Write an equation of each line.

15.

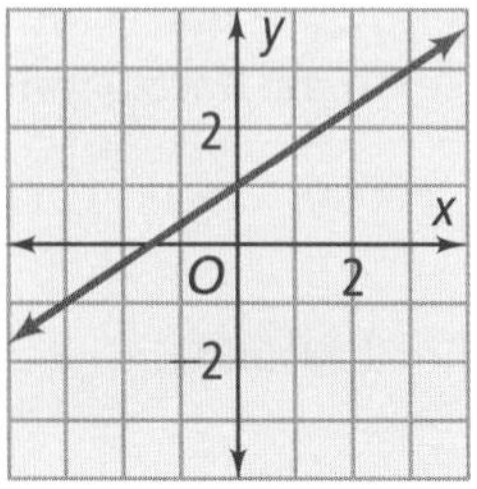

16.

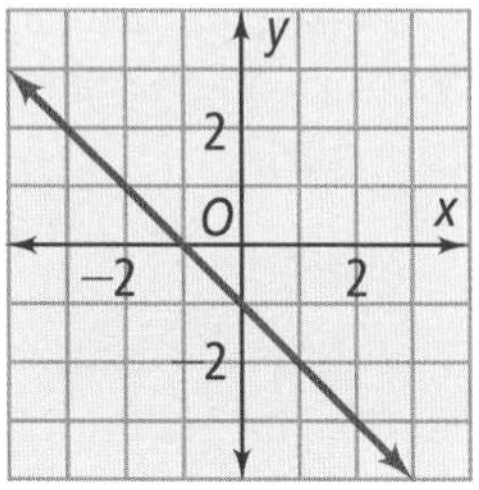

Graph each equation.

17. $y = 4x - 3$ **18.** $y = 2$

19. $y + 3 = 2(x - 1)$ **20.** $x + 4y = 10$

3-6 Slopes of Parallel and Perpendicular Lines

Quick Review

Parallel lines are lines in the same plane that never intersect. Two lines are **perpendicular** if they intersect to form right angles.

Example

Are the graphs of $y = \frac{4}{3}x + 5$ and $y = -\frac{3}{4}x + 2$ *parallel, perpendicular,* or *neither*? Explain.

The slope of the graph of $y = \frac{4}{3}x + 5$ is $\frac{4}{3}$.

The slope of the graph of $y = -\frac{3}{4}x + 2$ is $-\frac{3}{4}$.

$$\frac{4}{3}\left(-\frac{3}{4}\right) = -1$$

The slopes are opposite reciprocals, so the graphs are perpendicular.

Exercises

Write an equation of the line that passes through the given point and is parallel to the graph of the given equation.

21. (2, −1); $y = 5x - 2$ **22.** (0, −5); $y = 9x$

Determine whether the graphs of the two equations are *parallel, perpendicular,* or *neither*. Explain.

23. $y = 6x + 2$
$18x - 3y = 15$

24. $2x - 5y = 0$
$y + 3 = \frac{5}{2}x$

Write an equation of the line that passes through the given point and is perpendicular to the graph of the given equation.

25. (3, 5); $y = -3x + 7$ **26.** (4, 10); $y = 8x - 1$

3 Pull It All Together

PERFORMANCE TASK

ASSESSMENT

Analyzing Advertising Revenue

A local weekly newspaper offers advertising in its print edition and on its Web site. The table shows the amount of revenue the newspaper received from print advertising for various years.

Print Advertising

Year	Revenue
2000	$95,000
2006	$77,000
2009	$68,000
2010	$65,000
2012	$59,000

In 2010, the newspaper's revenue from online advertising was $31,000. The revenue from online advertising has been increasing steadily at a rate of $2500 per year.

Task Description

Determine the first year in which revenue from online advertising will exceed revenue from print advertising, and find the total advertising revenue in that year.

a. Is the rate of change in revenue from print advertising with respect to time constant? If so, what does the rate of change represent?

b. Let $x =$ the number of years since 2000.
Let $y =$ the revenue from print advertising in thousands of dollars.

Write an equation in slope-intercept form that models the revenue from print advertising, in thousands of dollars, x years after 2000.

c. Explain how you can use point-slope form to write an equation that models the revenue from online advertising, in thousands of dollars, x years after 2000. Describe what the point you use represents and what the slope represents. Then write the equation.

d. What is the first year in which revenue from online advertising will exceed revenue from print advertising? What is the total advertising revenue for that year? Justify your answer with tables and/or graphs.

CHAPTER 4

Get Ready!

Solving Equations

Solve each equation. If the equation is an identity, write *identity*. If it has no solution, write *no solution*.

1. $3(2 - 2x) = -6(x - 1)$ **2.** $3p + 1 = -p + 5$ **3.** $4x - 1 = 3(x + 1) + x$

4. $\frac{1}{2}(6c - 4) = 4 + c$ **5.** $5x = 2 - (x - 7)$ **6.** $v + 5 = v - 5$

Solving Inequalities

Solve each inequality.

7. $5x + 3 < 18$ **8.** $-\frac{r}{5} + 1 \geq -6$ **9.** $-3t - 5 < 34$

10. $-(7f + 18) - 2f \leq 0$ **11.** $8s + 7 > -3(5s - 4)$ **12.** $\frac{1}{2}(x + 6) + 1 \geq -5$

Writing Functions

13. The height of a triangle is 1 cm less than twice the length of the base. Let $x =$ the length of the base.

a. Write an expression for the height of the triangle.

b. Write a function rule for the area of the triangle.

c. What is the area of such a triangle if the length of its base is 16 cm?

Graphing Linear Equations

Graph each equation.

14. $2x + 4y = -8$ **15.** $y = -\frac{2}{3}x + 3$ **16.** $y + 5 = -2(x - 2)$

VOCABULARY

Looking Ahead Vocabulary

17. Two answers to a question are said to be *inconsistent* if they could not both be true. Two answers to a question are said to be *consistent* if they could both be true. If there is no solution that makes both equations in a system of two linear equations true, do you think the system is *inconsistent* or *consistent*?

18. After a team loses a game, they're *eliminated* from a tournament. The *elimination method* is a way to solve a system of equations. Do you think using the elimination method adds or deletes a variable from a system of equations?

CHAPTER
4

Systems of Equations and Inequalities

Big Ideas

1 Solving Equations and Inequalities
Essential Question: How can you solve a system of equations or inequalities?

2 Modeling
Essential Question: Can systems of equations model real-world situations?

Domains

- Creating Equations
- Reasoning with Equations and Inequalities

Chapter Preview

Interactive Digital Path

Log in to **pearsonsuccessnet.com** and click on Interactive Digital Path to access the Solve Its and animated Problems.

Vocabulary

English/Spanish Vocabulary Audio Online:

English	Spanish
consistent, *p. 226*	consistente
dependent, *p. 226*	dependiente
elimination method, *p. 240*	eliminación
inconsistent, *p. 226*	inconsistente
independent, *p. 226*	independiente
linear inequality, *p. 256*	desigualdad lineal
solution of an inequality, *p. 256*	solución de una desigualdad
solution of a system of linear equations, *p. 224*	solución de un sistema de ecuaciones lineales
solution of a system of linear inequalities, *p. 264*	solución de un sistema de desigualdades lineales
substitution method, *p. 233*	método de sustitución

4-1 Solving Systems by Graphing

A.REI.6 Solve systems of linear equations . . . focusing on pairs of linear equations in two variables. Also **A.CED.3**

Objectives To solve systems of equations by graphing
To analyze special systems

Solve It! Write your solution to the Solve It in the space below.

Two or more linear equations form a **system of linear equations**. Any ordered pair that makes *all* of the equations in a system true is a **solution of a system of linear equations**.

Essential Understanding You can use systems of linear equations to model problems. Systems of equations can be solved in more than one way. One method is to graph each equation and find the intersection point, if one exists.

Problem 1 Solving a System of Equations by Graphing

Think
How does graphing each equation help you find the solution?

Got It? What is the solution of the system? Check your answer.

$y = 2x + 4$
$y = x + 2$

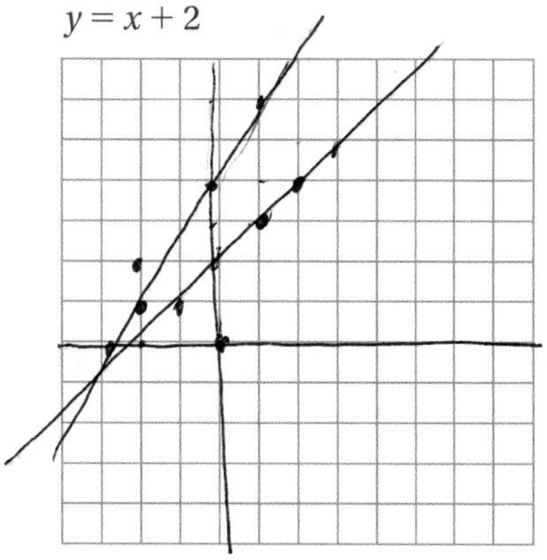

A Practice Solve each system by graphing. Check your solution.

1. $y = 2x$

   $y = -2x + 8$

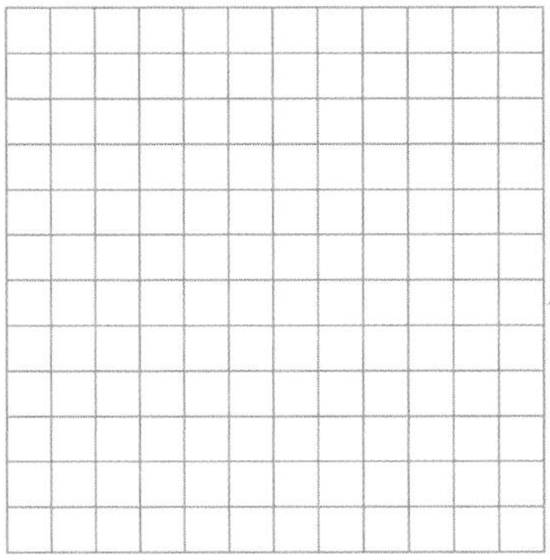

2. $y = \frac{1}{2}x + 7$

   $y = \frac{3}{2}x + 3$

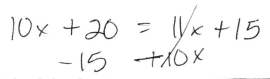

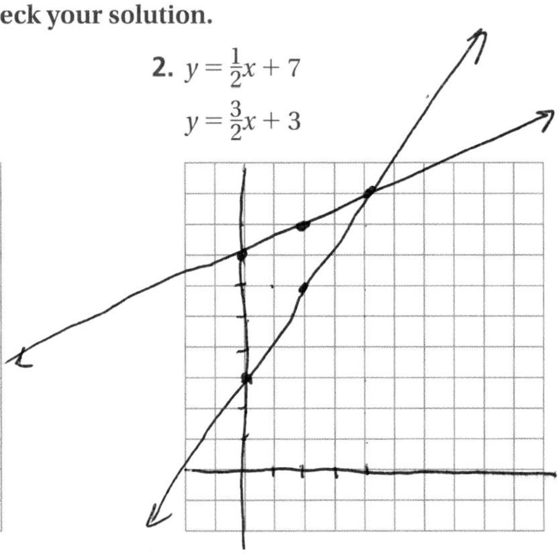

(4, 9)

Problem 2 Writing a System of Equations

Got It? One satellite radio service charges \$10 per month plus an activation fee of \$20. A second service charges \$11 per month plus an activation fee of \$15. In what month was the cost of both services the same?

Think What are the initial cost and the rate of change for each service?

$y = 10x + 20$

$y = 11x + 15$

$10x + 20 = 11x + 15$

$-15 \quad +10x$

$-1x + 15$

A Practice 3. **Student Statistics** The number of right-handed students in a mathematics class is nine times the number of left-handed students. The total number of students in the class is 30. How many right-handed students are in the class? How many left-handed students are in the class?

$y = -1x + 5$

4. **Plants** A plant nursery is growing a tree that is 3 ft tall and grows at an average rate of 1 ft per year. Another tree at the nursery is 4 ft tall and grows at an average rate of 0.5 ft per year. After how many years will the trees be the same height?

$1ft + 3 = 4 + .5ft$

$-.5 \quad -3$

$.5f = 1$ $f = .5$

A system of equations that has at least one solution is **consistent**. A consistent system can be either *independent* or *dependent*.

A consistent system that is **independent** has exactly one solution. For example, the systems in Problems 1 and 2 are consistent and independent. A consistent system that is **dependent** has infinitely many solutions.

A system of equations that has no solution is **inconsistent**.

Problem 3 Systems with Infinitely Many Solutions or No Solution

Got It? What is the solution of each system in parts (a) and (b)? Describe the number of solutions.

a. $y = -x - 3$
$y = -x + 5$

b. $y = 3x - 3$
$3y = 9x - 9$

c. Reasoning Before graphing the equations, how can you determine whether a system of equations has exactly one solution, infinitely many solutions, or no solution?

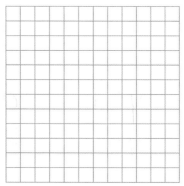

Practice Solve each system by graphing. Tell whether the system has *one solution*, *infinitely many solutions*, or *no solution*.

5. $2x + 2y = 4$
$12 - 3x = 3y$

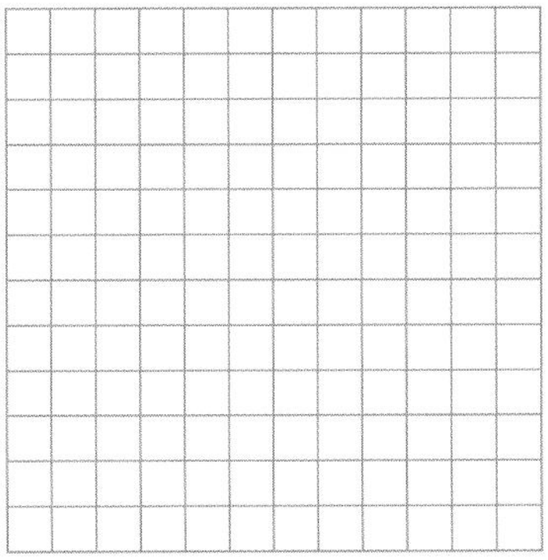

6. $2y = x - 2$
$3y = \frac{3}{2}x - 3$

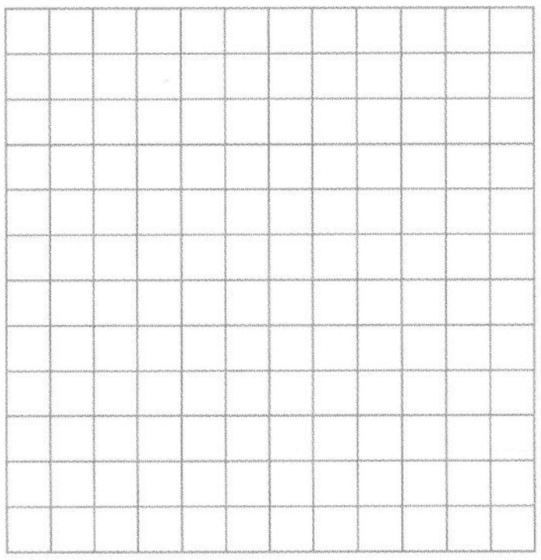

take note — Concept Summary: Systems of Linear Equations

One solution

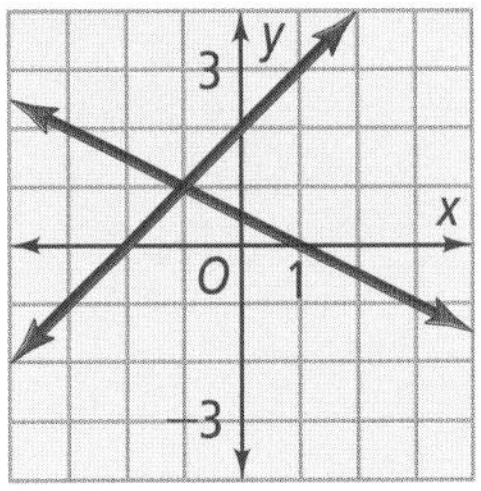

The lines intersect at one point. The lines have different slopes. The equations are consistent and independent.

Infinitely many solutions

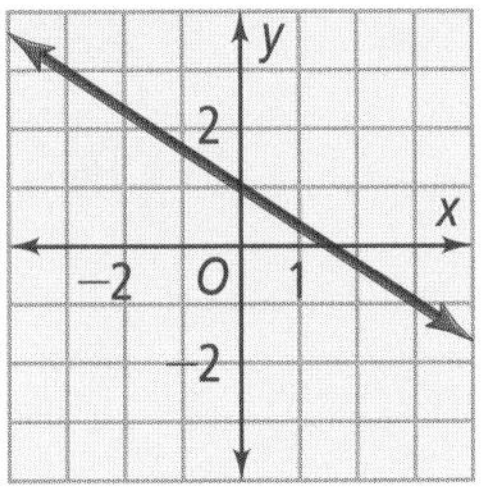

The lines are the same. The lines have the same slope and *y*-intercept. The equations are consistent and dependent.

No solution

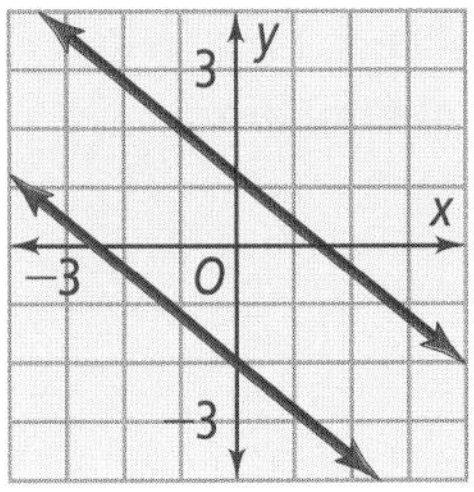

The lines are parallel. The lines have the same slope and different *y*-intercepts. The equations are inconsistent.

Lesson Check

Do you know HOW?

Solve each system by graphing.

7. $y = x + 7$
$y = 2x + 1$

(6,13)

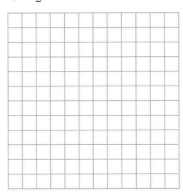

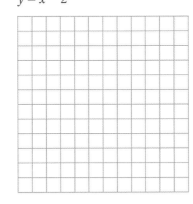

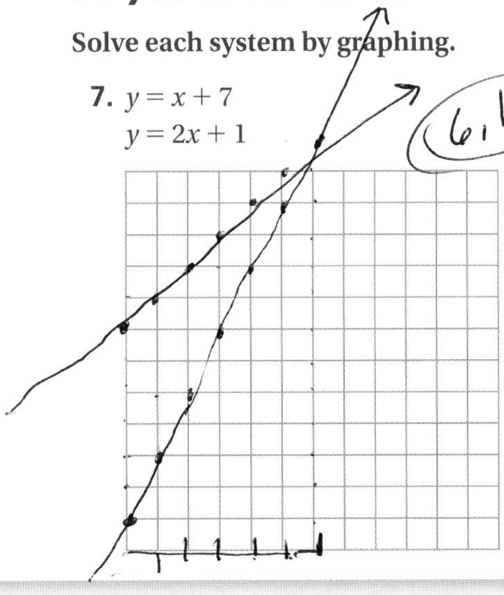

8. $y = \frac{1}{2}x + 6$
$y = x - 2$

9. $y = -3x - 3$
$y = 2x + 2$

10. $y = -x - 4$
$4x - y = -1$

11. Concert Tickets Tickets for a concert cost $10 each if you order them online, but you must pay a service charge of $8 per order. The tickets are $12 each if you buy them at the door on the night of the concert.

a. Write a system of equations to model the situation. Let c be the total cost. Let t be the number of tickets.

b. Graph the equations and find the intersection point. What does this point represent?

Do you UNDERSTAND?

MATHEMATICAL PRACTICES

12. Vocabulary Match each type of system with the number of solutions the system has.

A. inconsistent
B. consistent and dependent
C. consistent and independent

I. exactly one
II. infinitely many
III. no solution

13. Writing Suppose you graph a system of linear equations. If a point is on only one of the lines, is it a solution of the system? Explain.

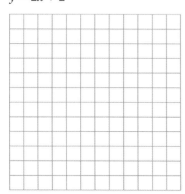

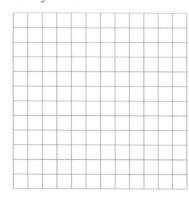

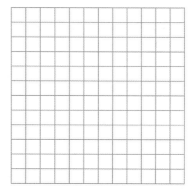

14. **Reasoning** Can a system of two linear equations have exactly two solutions? Explain.

15. **Reasoning** Suppose you find that two linear equations are true when $x = -2$ and $y = 3$. What can you conclude about the graphs of the equations? Explain.

More Practice and Problem-Solving Exercises

MATHEMATICAL PRACTICES

B Apply

16. **Think About a Plan** You are looking for an after-school job. One job pays \$9 per hour. Another pays \$12 per hour, but you must buy a uniform that costs \$39. After how many hours of work would your net earnings from either job be the same?
    - What equations can you write to model the situation?
    - How will graphing the equations help you solve the problem?

17. **Error Analysis** A student graphs the system $y = -x + 3$ and $y = -2x - 1$ as shown at the right. The student concludes there is no solution. Describe and correct the student's error.

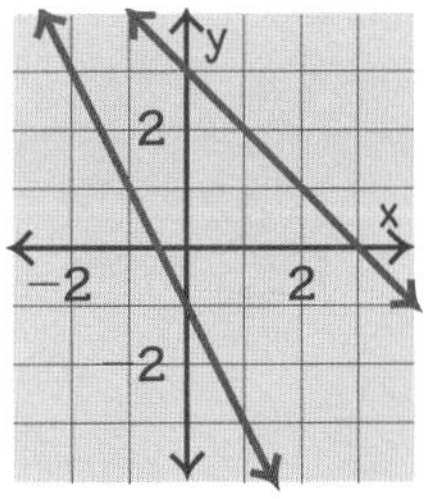

18. **Reasoning** Suppose you graph a system of linear equations and the intersection point appears to be (3, 7). Can you be sure that the ordered pair (3, 7) is the solution? What must you do to be sure?

19. **Cell Phone Plans** A cell phone provider offers a plan that costs \$40 per month plus \$.20 per text message sent or received. A comparable plan costs \$60 per month but offers unlimited text messaging.
    a. How many text messages would you have to send or receive in order for the plans to cost the same each month?
    b. If you send or receive an average of 50 text messages each month, which plan would you choose? Why?

Without graphing, decide whether each system has *one solution, infinitely many solutions*, or *no solution*. Justify your answer.

20. $y = x - 4$
    $y = x - 3$

21. $x - y = -\frac{1}{2}$
    $2x - 2y = -1$

22. $y = 5x - 1$
    $10x = 2y + 2$

23. $3x + 2y = 1$
    $4y = 6x + 2$

24. Banking The graph at the right shows the balances in two bank accounts over time. Use the graph to write a system of equations giving the amount in each account over time. Let t = the time in weeks and let b = the balance in dollars. If the accounts continue to grow as shown, when will they have the same balance?

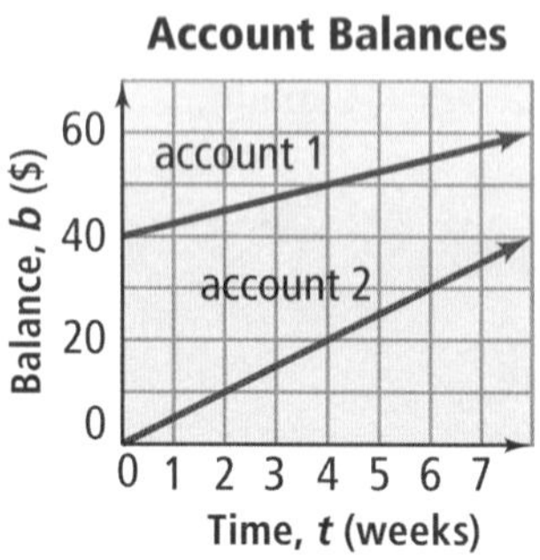

25. Open-Ended One equation in a system is $y = \frac{1}{2}x - 2$.

a. Write a second equation so that the system has one solution.

b. Write a second equation so that the system has no solution.

c. Write a second equation so that the system has infinitely many solutions.

Challenge

26. Reasoning Consider the system at the right.

$$y = gx + 3$$
$$y = hx + 7$$

a. If $g \geq h$, will the system *always, sometimes,* or *never* have exactly one solution? Explain your reasoning.

b. If $g \leq h$, will the system *always, sometimes,* or *never* have infinitely many solutions? Explain your reasoning.

27. Hiking Two hikers are walking along a marked trail. The first hiker starts at a point 6 mi from the beginning of the trail and walks at a speed of 4 mi/h. At the same time, the second hiker starts 1 mi from the beginning and walks at a speed of 3 mi/h.

a. What is a system of equations that models the situation?

b. Graph the two equations and find the intersection point.

c. Is the intersection point meaningful in this situation? Explain.

TECHNOLOGY LAB

Use With Lesson 4-1

Solving Systems Using Tables and Graphs

A.REI.11 Explain why the x-coordinates of the points where the graphs of the equations $y = f(x)$ and $y = g(x)$ intersect are the solutions of the equation $f(x) = g(x)$; find the solutions approximately . . . Also **A.REI.6**

Activity 1

MATHEMATICAL PRACTICES

Solve the system using a table. $y = 3x - 7$
$y = -0.5x + 7$

Step 1
Enter the equations in the y= screen.

Step 2
Use the tblset function. Set TblStart to 0 and Δ Tbl to 1.

Step 3
Press table to show the table on the screen.

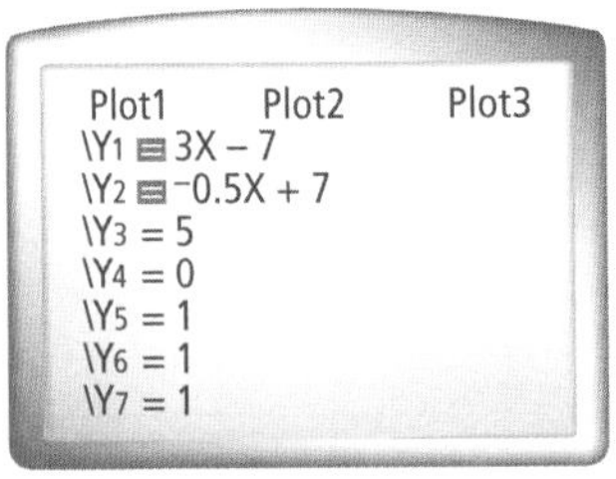

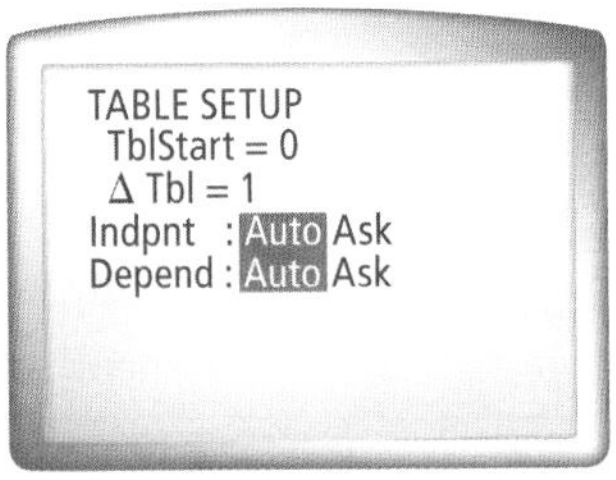

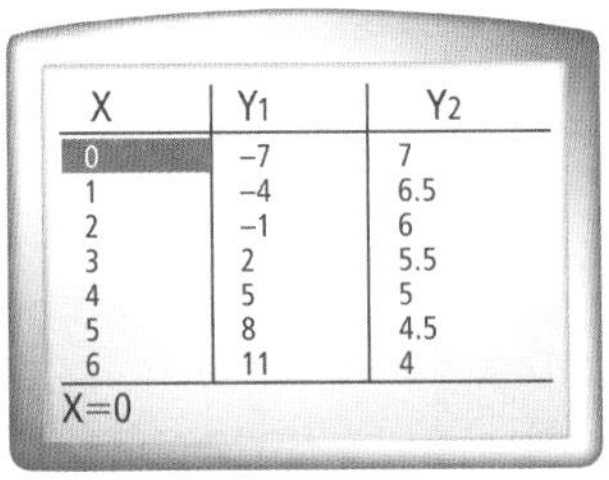

X Y1 Y2
0 −7 7
1 −4 6.5
2 −1 6
3 2 5.5
4 5 5
5 8 4.5
6 11 4
X=0

1. Which x-value gives the same value for $\mathbf{Y_1}$ and $\mathbf{Y_2}$?

2. What ordered pair is the solution of the system?

Activity 2

Solve the system using a graph. $y = -5x + 6$
$y = -x - 2$

Step 1 Enter the equations in the y= screen.

Step 2 Graph the equations. Use a standard graphing window.

Step 3 Use the calc feature. Choose **INTERSECT** to find the point where the lines intersect.

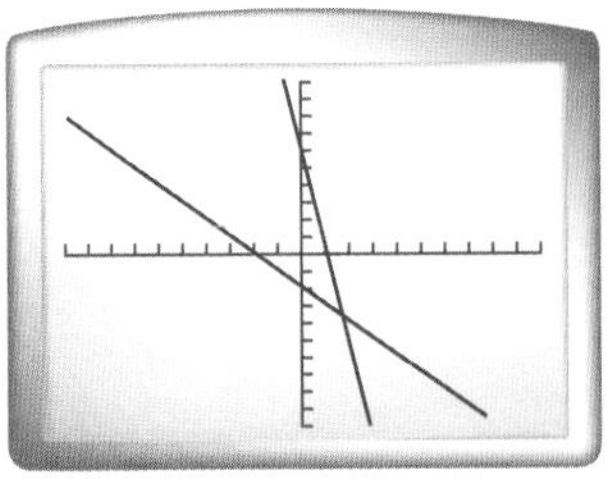

3. Complete: The lines intersect at (______, ______), so this point is the solution of the system.

4. How can you use the graph to find the solution of the equation $-5x + 6 = -x - 2$?

Exercises

Use the table and graph to solve each system. Sketch your graph.

5. $y = 5x - 3$
$y = 3x + 1$

6. $y = 2x - 13$
$y = x - 9$

7. $2x - y = 1.5$
$y = -\frac{1}{2}x - 1.5$

8. How can you use the graph of a system to find the solution of the equation $5x - 3 = 3x + 1$?

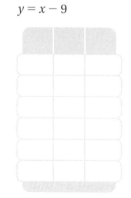

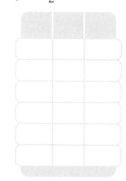

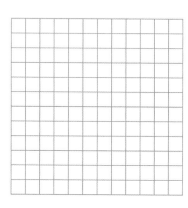

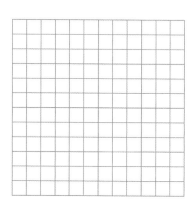

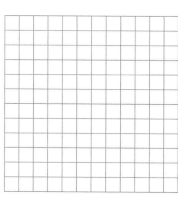

4-2 Solving Systems Using Substitution

A.REI.6 Solve systems of linear equations . . . focusing on pairs of linear equations in two variables. Also **A.CED.3**

Objective To solve systems of equations using substitution

Solve It! Write your solution to the Solve It in the space below.

You can solve linear systems by solving one of the equations for one of the variables. Then substitute the expression for the variable into the other equation. This is called the **substitution method**.

Essential Understanding Systems of equations can be solved in more than one way. When a system has at least one equation that can be solved quickly for a variable, the system can be solved efficiently using substitution.

Problem 1 Using Substitution

Got It? What is the solution of the system? Use substitution. Check your answer.

$y = 2x + 7$
$y = x - 1$

Think
Which variable should you substitute for?

Practice Solve each system using substitution. Check your answer.

1. $x + y = 8$
   $y = 3x$

2. $2x + 2y = 38$
   $y = x + 3$

To use substitution to solve a system of equations, one of the equations must be solved for a variable.

Problem 2 Solving for a Variable and Using Substitution

Got It? **a.** What is the solution of the system? Use substitution. $6y + 5x = 8$
$x + 3y = -7$

b. Reasoning In your first step in part (a), which variable did you solve for? Which equation did you use to solve for the variable?

Practice Solve each system using substitution. Check your answer.

3. $4x = 3y - 2$
   $18 = 3x + y$

4. $2 = 2y - x$
   $23 = 5y - 4x$

Problem 3 Using Systems of Equations

Got It? You pay $22 to rent 6 video games. The store charges $4 for new games and $2 for older games. How many new games did you rent?

Practice

5. **Transportation** A school is planning a field trip for 142 people. The trip will use six drivers and two types of vehicles: buses and vans. A bus can seat 51 passengers. A van can seat 10 passengers. Write and solve a system of equations to find how many buses and how many vans will be needed.

6. **Geometry** The measure of one acute angle in a right triangle is four times the measure of the other acute angle. Write and solve a system of equations to find the measures of the acute angles.

If you get an identity, like $2 = 2$, when you solve a system of equations, then the system has infinitely many solutions. If you get a false statement, like $8 = 2$, then the system has no solution.

Problem 4 Systems With Infinitely Many Solutions or No Solution

Got It? How many solutions does the system have? Explain.

$$6y + 5x = 8$$
$$2.5x + 3y = 4$$

Think

How many solutions can a system of linear equations have?

Practice Tell whether the system has *one solution, infinitely many solutions,* or *no solution.*

7. $5 = \frac{1}{2}x + 3y$
$10 - x = 6y$

8. $17 = 11y + 12x$
$12x + 11y = 14$

Lesson Check

Do you know HOW?

Solve each system using substitution. Check your solution.

9. $4y = x$
$3x - y = 70$

10. $-2x + 5y = 19$
$3x - 4 = y$

Tell whether the system has *one solution, infinitely many solutions,* or *no solution.*

11. $y = 2x + 1$
$4x - 2y = 6$

12. $-x + \frac{1}{2}y = 13$
$x + 15 = \frac{1}{2}y$

13. Talent Show In a talent show of singing and comedy acts, singing acts are 5 min long and comedy acts are 3 min long. The show has 12 acts and lasts 50 min. How many singing acts and how many comedy acts are in the show?

Do you UNDERSTAND?

MATHEMATICAL PRACTICES

14. Vocabulary When is the substitution method a better method than graphing for solving a system of linear equations?

For each system, tell which equation you would first use to solve for a variable in the first step of the substitution method. Explain your choice.

15. $-2x + y = -1$
$4x + 2y = 12$

16. $2.5x - 7y = 7.5$
$6x - y = 1$

Tell whether each statement is *true* or *false*. Explain.

17. When solving a system using substitution, if you obtain an identity, then the system has no solution.

18. You cannot use substitution to solve a system that does not have a variable with a coefficient of 1 or −1.

More Practice and Problem-Solving Exercises

B Apply

19. Geometry The rectangle shown has a perimeter of 34 cm and the given area. Its length is 5 more than twice its width. Write and solve a system of equations to find the dimensions of the rectangle.

ℓ

w | $A = 52$ cm²

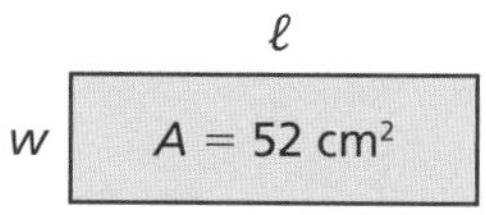

20. Writing What would your first step be in solving the system below? Explain.
$$1.2x + y = 2$$
$$1.4y = 2.8x + 1$$

21. Coins You have $3.70 in dimes and quarters. You have 5 more quarters than dimes. How many of each type of coin do you have?

22. Error Analysis Describe and correct the error at the right in finding the solution of the following system:
$$7x + 5y = 14$$
$$x + 8y = 21$$

Step 1 $x + 8y = 21$
 $x = 21 - 8y$

Step 2 $x + 8y = 21$
 $(21 - 8y) + 8y = 21$
 $21 = 21$

The system has infinitely many solutions.

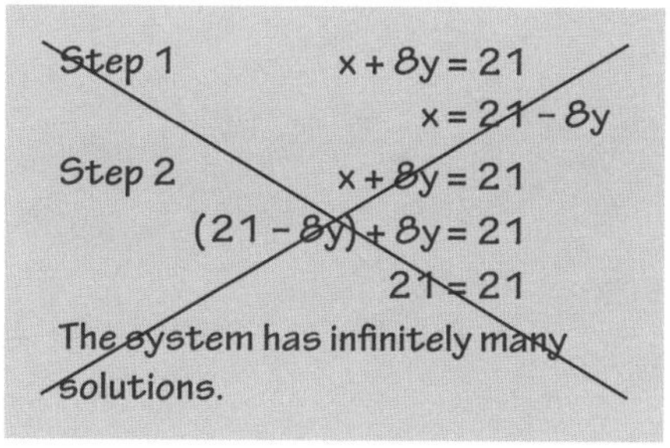

23. Art An artist is going to sell two sizes of prints at an art fair. The artist will charge \$20 for a small print and \$45 for a large print. The artist would like to sell twice as many small prints as large prints. The booth the artist is renting for the day costs \$510. How many of each size print must the artist sell in order to break even at the fair?

24. Think About a Plan At a certain high school, 350 students are taking an algebra course. The ratio of boys to girls taking algebra is 33 : 37. How many more girls are taking algebra than boys?
- How can you write a system of equations to model the situation?
- Which equation will you solve for a variable in the first step of solving the system? Why?
- How can you interpret the solution in the context of the problem?

25. **a.** **Compare and Contrast** Using a graph, how can you tell when a system of linear equations has no solution?
b. Using substitution, how can you tell when a system of linear equations has no solution?
c. How can you tell by looking at a table of values if two lines will intersect in one point, no points, or an infinite number of points?

26. Fireworks A pyrotechnician plans for two fireworks to explode together at the same height in the air. They travel at the speeds shown at the right. Firework B is launched 0.25 s before Firework A. How many seconds after Firework B launches will both fireworks explode?

27. Writing Let a be any real number. Will the system at the right *always*, *sometimes*, or *never* have a solution? Explain.

$$y = ax$$
$$y = ax + 4$$

28. Reasoning Explain how you can use substitution to show that the system at the right has no solution.

$$y + x = x$$
$$\frac{3x}{2y} = 4$$

Challenge

29. Agriculture A farmer grows corn, tomatoes, and sunflowers on a 320-acre farm. This year, the farmer wants to plant twice as many acres of tomatoes as acres of sunflowers. The farmer also wants to plant 40 more acres of corn than of tomatoes. How many acres of each crop should the farmer plant?

30. Track and Field Michelle and Pam are running a 200-m race. Michelle runs at an average of 7.5 m/s. Pam averages 7.8 m/s, but she starts 1 s after Michelle.
a. How long will it take Pam to catch up to Michelle?
b. Will Pam overtake Michelle before the finish line? Explain.

4-3 Solving Systems Using Elimination

A.REI.5 Prove that, given . . . two equations . . . replacing one equation by the sum of that equation and a multiple of the other produces a system with the same solutions. Also **A.CED.3, A.REI.6**

Objective To solve systems by adding or subtracting to eliminate a variable

Solve It! Write your solution to the Solve It in the space below.

By the Addition and Subtraction Properties of Equality, if $a = b$ and $c = d$, then $a + c = b + d$ and $a - c = b - d$. For example, $5 + 1 = 6$ and $3 + 4 = 7$, so $(5 + 1) + (3 + 4) = 6 + 7$. In the **elimination method**, you use these properties to add or subtract equations in order to eliminate a variable in a system.

Essential Understanding There is more than one way to solve a system of equations. Some systems are written in a way that makes eliminating a variable a good method to use.

Problem 1 Solving a System by Adding Equations

Got It? What is the solution of each system? Use elimination.

a. $5x - 6y = -32$
$3x + 6y = 48$

$8x + 0y = 16$

$x = 2$

$y = 7$

b. $-3x - 3y = 9$
$3x - 4y = 5$

Think
Which variable should you eliminate?

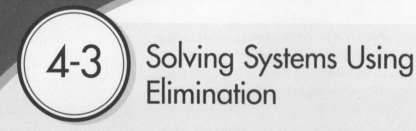

(A) Practice Solve each system using elimination. *eliminate one of them*

1. $3x + 3y = 27$
 $x - 3y = -11$

1) add

$4x + 0y = 16$

$\dfrac{4x}{4} = \dfrac{16}{4}$

$x = 4$

$(4, -5)$

2. $4x - 7y = 3$ $3 + (+15)$
 $x - 7y = -15$

$3x - 7y - (-7y)$

$3x = -18$

add or subtract

$4 - 3y = 11$
 $-4 \quad -4$

$-3y = 15$

$y = -5$

Problem 2 Solving a System by Subtracting Equations

Got It? Washing 2 cars and 3 trucks takes 130 min. Washing 2 cars and 5 trucks takes 190 min. How long does it take to wash each type of vehicle?

Think
What system of equations can model this situation?

(A) Practice **3. Talent Show** Your school's talent show will feature 12 solo acts and 2 ensemble acts. The show will last 90 min. The 6 solo performers judged best will give a repeat performance at a second 60-min show, which will also feature the 2 ensemble acts. Each solo act lasts *x* minutes, and each ensemble act lasts *y* minutes.

 a. Write a system of equations to model the situation.

 b. Solve the system from part (a). How long is each solo act? How long is each ensemble act?

4. Furniture A carpenter is designing a drop-leaf table with two drop leaves of equal size. The lengths of the table when one leaf is folded up and when both leaves are folded up are shown. How long is the table when no leaves are folded up?

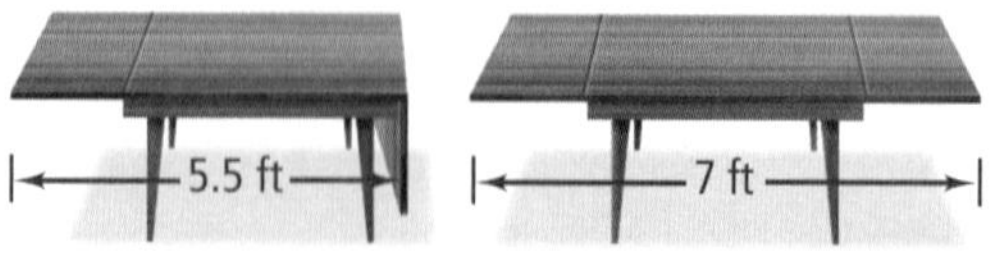

In Problems 1 and 2, a variable is eliminated because the sum or difference of its coefficients is zero. From the Multiplication Property of Equality, you know that you can multiply each side of an equation to get a new equation that is equivalent to the original. That is, $a + b = c$ is equivalent to $d(a + b) = dc$, or $da + db = dc$.

Since this is true, you can eliminate a variable by adding or subtracting, if you first multiply an equation by an appropriate number. You can prove that the results are the same simply by substituting the values for the variables in the original equations to show that the equations are true.

Problem 3 Solving a System by Multiplying One Equation

Got It? **a.** How can you use the Multiplication Property of Equality to change an equation in the system at the right in order to solve it using elimination?

$$-5x - 2y = 6$$
$$3x + 6y = 6$$

b. Write and solve a revised system.

c. Show that the solution of the revised system is a solution of the original system.

Practice **Solve each system using elimination.**

5. $3x + y = 5$
$2x - 2y = -2$

6. $6x + 4y = 42$
$-3x + 3y = -6$

Problem 4 Solving a System by Multiplying Both Equations

Got It? **a.** How can you use the Multiplication Property of Equality to change the equations in the system at the right in order to solve it using elimination?

$4x + 3y = -19$
$3x - 2y = -10$

b. Write and solve a revised system.

c. Show that the solution of the revised system is a solution of the original system.

Practice **Solve each system using elimination.**

7. $6x - 3y = 15$
$7x + 4y = 10$

8. $5x - 9y = -43$
$3x + 8y = 68$

Recall that if you get a false statement as you solve a system, then the system has no solution. If you get an identity, then the system has infinitely many solutions.

Problem 5 Finding the Number of Solutions

Got It? How many solutions does the system at the right have?

$$-2x + 5y = 7$$
$$-2x + 5y = 12$$

Practice **Tell whether the system has *one solution, infinitely many solutions,* or *no solution.***

9. $5x - 3y = 10$
$10x + 6y = 20$

10. $4x - 7y = 15$
$-8x + 14y = -30$

The flowchart below can help you decide which steps to take when solving a system of equations using elimination.

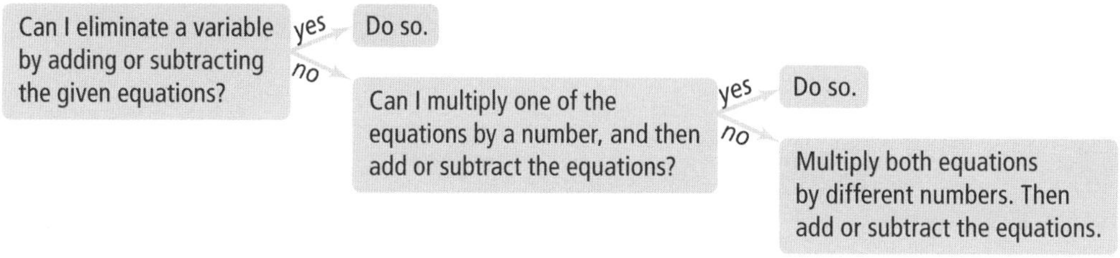

Can I eliminate a variable by adding or subtracting the given equations?
yes
Do so.
no
Can I multiply one of the equations by a number, and then add or subtract the equations?
yes
Do so.
no
Multiply both equations by different numbers. Then add or subtract the equations.

Lesson Check

Do you know HOW?

Solve each system using elimination.

11. $3x - 2y = 0$
$4x + 2y = 14$

12. $3p + q = 7$
$2p - 2q = -6$

13. $3x - 2y = 1$
$8x + 3y = 2$

Do you UNDERSTAND?

MATHEMATICAL PRACTICES

14. Vocabulary If you add two equations in two variables and the sum is an equation in one variable, what method are you using to solve the system? Explain.

15. Reasoning Explain how the Addition Property of Equality allows you to add equations.

16. Writing Explain how you would solve a system of equations using elimination.

More Practice and Problem-Solving Exercises

MATHEMATICAL PRACTICES

B Apply

17. Think About a Plan A photo studio offers portraits in 8×10 and wallet-sized formats. One customer bought two 8×10 portraits and four wallet-sized portraits and paid \$52. Another customer bought three 8×10 portraits and two wallet-sized portraits and paid \$50. What is the cost of an 8×10 portrait? What is the cost of a wallet-sized portrait?

- Can you eliminate a variable simply by adding or subtracting?
- If not, how many of the equations do you need to multiply by a constant?

18. Reasoning A toy store worker packed two boxes of identical dolls and plush toys for shipping in boxes that weigh 1 oz when empty. One box held 3 dolls and 4 plush toys. The worker marked the weight as 12 oz. The other box held 2 dolls and 3 plush toys. The worker marked the weight as 10 oz. Explain why the worker must have made a mistake.

19. Error Analysis A student solved a system of equations by elimination. Describe and correct the error made in the part of the solution shown.

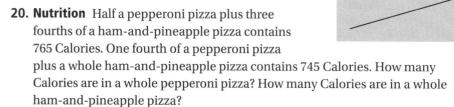

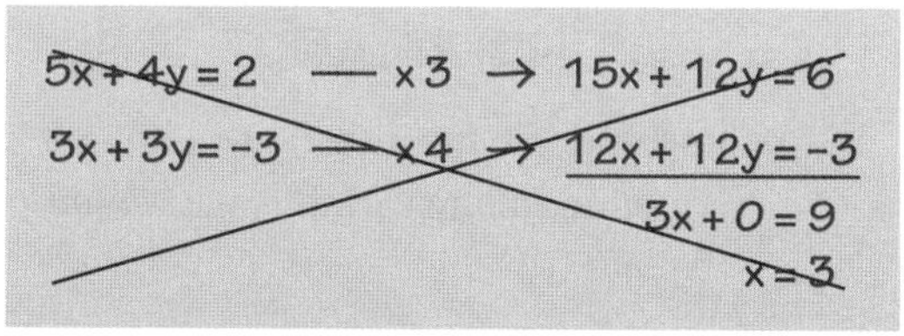

20. Nutrition Half a pepperoni pizza plus three fourths of a ham-and-pineapple pizza contains 765 Calories. One fourth of a pepperoni pizza plus a whole ham-and-pineapple pizza contains 745 Calories. How many Calories are in a whole pepperoni pizza? How many Calories are in a whole ham-and-pineapple pizza?

21. Open-Ended Write a system of equations that can be solved efficiently by elimination. Explain what you would do to eliminate one of the variables. Then solve the system.

Solve each system using any method. Explain why you chose the method you used.

22. $y = 2.5x$
$2y + 3x = 32$

23. $2x + y = 4$
$6x + 7y = 12$

24. $3x + 2y = 5$
$4x + 5y = 16$

25. $y = \frac{2}{3}x + 1$
$2x + 3y = 27$

26. $x + y = 1.5$
$2x + y = 1$

27. $\frac{1}{3}x + \frac{1}{2}y = 0$
$\frac{1}{2}x + \frac{1}{5}y = \frac{11}{5}$

28. Compare and Contrast What do the substitution method and the elimination method have in common? Explain. Give an example of a system that you would prefer to solve using one method instead of the other. Justify your choice.

29. Vacations A hotel offers two activity packages. One costs \$192 and includes 3 h of horseback riding and 2 h of parasailing. The second costs \$213 and includes 2 h of horseback riding and 3 h of parasailing. What is the cost for 1 h of each activity?

30. **Geometry** Each of the squares in the figures shown at the right has the same area, and each of the triangles has the same area. The total area of Figure A is 141 cm^2. The total area of Figure B is 192 cm^2. What is the area of each square and each triangle?

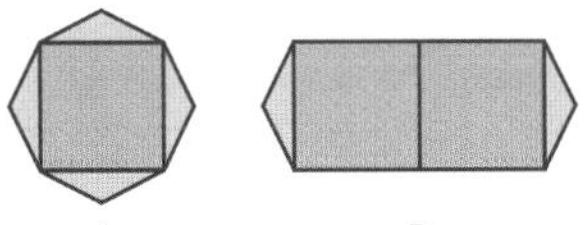

31. In parts (a)–(c), show that given a system of two equations in two variables, replacing one equation by the sum of that equation and a multiple of the other produces a system with the same solutions.
   a. What is the solution to the following system of equations with the variables x and y, where a, b, c, d, e, and f are real numbers?
   $ax + by = c$
   $dx + ey = f$
   b. What is the sum of the second equation and k times the first equation?
   c. Solve the system that results when you replace the second equation with your answer from part (b).

Challenge

Solve each system using elimination.

32. $\frac{2}{x} - \frac{3}{y} = -5$
$\frac{4}{x} + \frac{6}{y} = 14$

33. $2x = 5(2 - y)$
$y = 3(-x + 5)$

34. $2x - 3y + z = 0$
$2x + y + z = 12$
$y - z = 4$

35. **Reasoning** The dartboard at the right shows the number of points you score for hitting each region. Can you score exactly 100 points with seven darts that all land on the board? Explain.

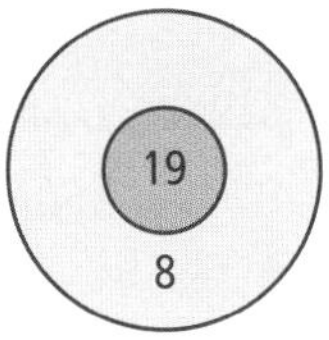

4-4 Applications of Linear Systems

A.CED.3 Represent constraints by equations or inequalities, and by systems of equations and inequalities, and interpret solutions as viable or non-viable . . . Also **N.Q.2, N.Q.3, A.REI.6**

Objective To choose the best method for solving a system of linear equations

Solve It! Write your solution to the Solve It in the space below.

Essential Understanding You can solve systems of linear equations using a graph, the substitution method, or the elimination method. The best method to use depends on the forms of the given equations and how precise the solution should be.

take note

Concept Summary Choosing a Method for Solving Linear Systems

Method	When to Use
Graphing	When you want a visual display of the equations, or when you want to estimate a solution
Substitution	When one equation is already solved for one of the variables, or when it is easy to solve for one of the variables
Elimination	When the coefficients of one variable are the same or opposites, or when it is not convenient to use graphing or substitution

Systems of equations are useful for modeling problems involving mixtures, rates, and break-even points.

The break-even point for a business is the point at which income equals expenses. The graph shows the break-even point for one business.

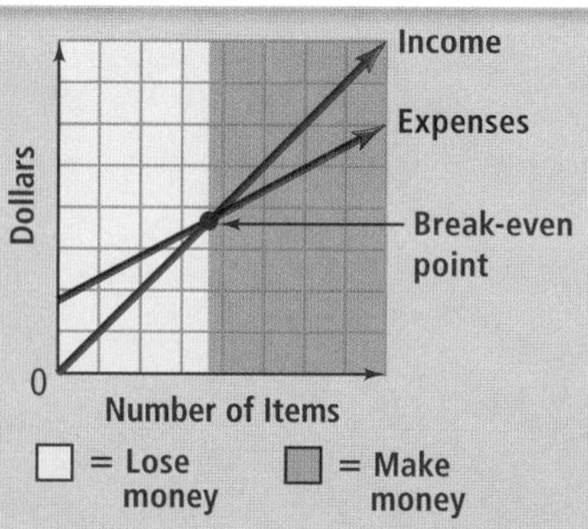

Notice that the values of y on the red line represent dollars spent on expenses. The values of y on the blue line represent dollars received as income. So y is used to represent both expenses and income.

Problem 1 Finding a Break-Even Point

Think

What equations should you write?

Got It? A puzzle expert wrote a new sudoku puzzle book. His initial costs are \$864. Binding and packaging each book costs \$.80. The price of the book is \$2. How many copies must be sold to break even?

Practice

1. **Business** A bicycle store costs \$2400 per month to operate. The store pays an average of \$60 per bike. The average selling price of each bicycle is \$120. How many bicycles must the store sell each month to break even?

2. **Theater** Producing a musical costs \$88,000 plus \$5900 per performance. One sold-out performance earns \$7500 in revenue. If every performance sells out, how many performances are needed to break even?

In real-world situations, you need to consider the constraints described in the problem in order to write equations. Once you solve an equation, you need to consider the viability of the solution. For example, a solution that has a negative number of hours is not a viable solution.

Problem 2 Identifying Constraints and Viable Solutions

Got It? The zoo has two water tanks that are leaking. One tank contains 10 gal of water and is leaking at a constant rate of 2 gal/h. The second tank contains 6 gal of water and is leaking at a constant rate of 4 gal/h. When will the tanks have the same amount of water? Explain.

A Practice

3. **Investment** You split $1500 between two savings accounts. Account A pays 5% annual interest and Account B pays 4% annual interest. After one year, you have earned a total of $69.50 in interest. How much money did you invest in each account? Explain.

STEM 4. **Biology** A group of scientists studied the effect of a chemical on various strains of bacteria. Strain A started with 6000 cells and decreased at a constant rate of 2000 cells per hour after the chemical was applied. Strain B started with 2000 cells and decreased at a constant rate of 1000 cells per hour after the chemical was applied. When will the strains have the same number of cells? Explain.

When a plane travels from west to east across the United States, the steady west-to-east winds act as tailwinds. This increases the plane's speed relative to the ground. When a plane travels from east to west, the winds act as headwinds. This decreases the plane's speed relative to the ground.

From West to East

air speed + wind speed = ground speed

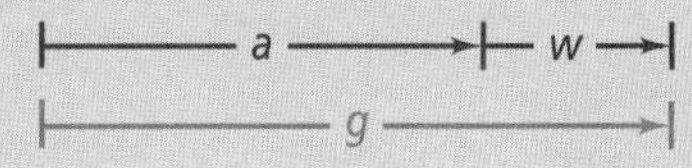

From East to West

air speed − wind speed = ground speed

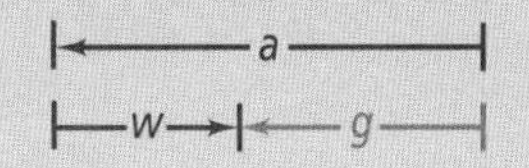

Problem 3 Solving a Wind or Current Problem

Think

How are the speeds related?

Got It? **a.** You row upstream at a speed of 2 mi/h. You travel the same distance downstream at a speed of 5 mi/h. What would be your rowing speed in still water? What is the speed of the current?

b. Reasoning Suppose your rowing speed in still water is 3 mi/h and the speed of the current is 4 mi/h. What happens when you try to row upstream?

Practice

5. **Airports** A traveler is walking on a moving walkway in an airport. The traveler must walk back on the walkway to get a bag he forgot. The traveler's ground speed is 2 ft/s against the walkway and 6 ft/s with the walkway. What is the traveler's speed off the walkway? What is the speed of the moving walkway?

6. **Kayaking** A kayaker paddles upstream from camp to photograph a waterfall and returns. The kayaker's speed while traveling upstream is 4 miles per hour and downstream is 7 miles per hour. What is the kayaker's speed in still water? What is the speed of the current?

c + s = 4 mph

c + s = 7 mph   c = 5.5 mph

2 = 11 mph / 2   5.5 + 6 = 7 mph / 5.5

c = 1.5 mph.

Lesson Check

Do you know HOW?

7. **Newsletters** Printing a newsletter costs \$1.50 per copy plus \$450 in printer's fees. The copies are sold for \$3 each. How many copies of the newsletter must be sold to break even?

8. Jewelry A metal alloy is a metal made by blending 2 or more types of metal. A jeweler has supplies of two metal alloys. One alloy is 30% gold and the other is 10% gold. How much of each alloy should the jeweler combine to create 4 kg of an alloy containing 15% gold?

9. Flying With a tailwind, a bird flew at a ground speed of 3 mi/h. Flying the same path against the same wind, the bird travels at a ground speed of 1.5 mi/h. What is the bird's air speed? What is the wind speed?

Do you UNDERSTAND?

MATHEMATICAL PRACTICES

10. Vocabulary What is the relationship between income and expenses before a break-even point is reached? What is the relationship between income and expenses after a break-even point is reached?

11. Reasoning Which method would you use to solve the following system? Explain.

$$3x + 2y = 9$$
$$-2x + 3y = 5$$

12. Reasoning One brand of cranberry-apple drink is 15% cranberry juice. Another brand is 40% cranberry juice. You would like to combine the brands to make a drink that is 25% cranberry juice. Without calculating, which brand of juice will you need more of to make your drink? Explain.

More Practice and Problem-Solving Exercises

MATHEMATICAL PRACTICES

B Apply

13. Money You have a jar of pennies and quarters. You want to choose 15 coins that are worth exactly \$4.35.

a. Write and solve a system of equations that models the situation.

b. Is your solution reasonable in terms of the original problem? Explain.

Solve each system. Explain why you chose the method you used.

14. $4x + 5y = 3$
$3x - 2y = 8$

15. $2x + 7y = -20$
$y = 3x + 7$

16. $5x + 2y = 17$
$x - 2y = 8$

17. Reasoning Find A and B so that the system below has the solution (2, 3).

$$Ax - 2By = 6$$
$$3Ax - By = -12$$

18. Think About a Plan A tugboat can pull a boat 24 mi downstream in 2 h. Going upstream, the tugboat can pull the same boat 16 mi in 2 h. What is the speed of the tugboat in still water? What is the speed of the current?

- How can you use the formula $d = rt$ to help you solve the problem?
- How are the tugboat's speeds when traveling upstream and downstream related to its speed in still water and the speed of the current?

Open-Ended Without solving, decide which method you would use to solve each system: graphing, substitution, or elimination. Explain.

19. $y = 3x - 1$
$y = 4x$

20. $3m - 4n = 1$
$3m - 2n = -1$

21. $4s - 3t = 8$
$t = -2s - 1$

22. Business A perfume maker has stocks of two perfumes on hand. Perfume A sells for \$15 per ounce. Perfume B sells for \$35 per ounce. How much of each should be combined to make a 3-oz bottle of perfume that can be sold for \$63?

STEM **23. Chemistry** In a chemistry lab, you have two vinegars. One is 5% acetic acid, and one is 6.5% acetic acid. You want to make 200 mL of a vinegar with 6% acetic acid. How many milliliters of each vinegar do you need to mix together?

24. Boating A boat is traveling in a river with a current that has a speed of 1.5 km/h. In one hour, the boat can travel twice the distance downstream that it can travel upstream. What is the boat's speed in still water?

25. **Reasoning** A student claims that the best way to solve the system below is by substitution. Do you agree? Explain.

$$y - 3x = 4$$
$$y - 6x = 12$$

26. **Entertainment** A contestant on a quiz show gets 150 points for every correct answer and loses 250 points for each incorrect answer. After answering 20 questions, the contestant has 200 points. How many questions has the contestant answered correctly? Incorrectly?

Challenge

27. **Number Theory** You can represent the value of any two-digit number with the expression $10a + b$, where a is the tens' place digit and b is the ones' place digit. For example, if a is 5 and b is 7, then the value of the number is $10(5) + 7$, or 57. What two-digit number is described below?
    - The ones' place digit is one more than twice the tens' place digit.
    - The value of the number is two more than five times the ones' place digit.

28. **Mixed Nuts** You want to sell 1-lb jars of mixed peanuts and cashews for \$5. You pay \$3 per pound for peanuts and \$6 per pound for cashews. You plan to combine 4 parts peanuts and 1 part cashews to make your mix. You have spent \$70 on materials to get started. How many jars must you sell to break even?

4-5 Linear Inequalities

A.REI.12 Graph the solutions to a linear inequality in two variables as a half-plane . . . and graph the solution . . . to a system of linear inequalities in two variables as the intersection of the corresponding half-planes. Also **A.CED.3**

Objectives To graph linear inequalities in two variables
To use linear inequalities when modeling real-world situations

Solve It! Write your solution to the Solve It in the space below.

A **linear inequality** in two variables, such as $y > x - 3$, can be formed by replacing the equal sign in a linear equation with an inequality symbol. A **solution of an inequality** in two variables is an ordered pair that makes the inequality true.

Essential Understanding A linear inequality in two variables has an infinite number of solutions. These solutions can be represented in the coordinate plane as the set of all points on one side of a boundary line.

Problem 1 Identifying Solutions of a Linear Inequality

Got It? **a.** Is (3, 6) a solution of $y \leq \frac{2}{3}x + 4$? Explain.

$6 \leq \frac{2}{3}(3) + 4$

$6 \leq 2 + 4$

$6 \leq 6$

b. Reasoning Suppose an ordered pair is not a solution of $y > x + 10$. Must it be a solution of $y < x + 10$? Explain.

A Practice **Determine whether the ordered pair is a solution of the linear inequality.**

1. $y \leq -2x + 1$; (2, 2)

$2 \leq -2(2) + 1$

$-4 + 1$

$2 \leq -3$ (NO)

2. $3y > 5x - 12$; (−6, 1)

$3(1) > 5(-6) - 12$

$3 > -30 - 12$

$3 > -42$ (yes)

The graph of a linear inequality in two variables consists of all points in the coordinate plane that represent solutions. The graph is a region called a *half-plane* that is bounded by a line. All points on one side of the boundary line are solutions, while all points on the other side are not solutions.

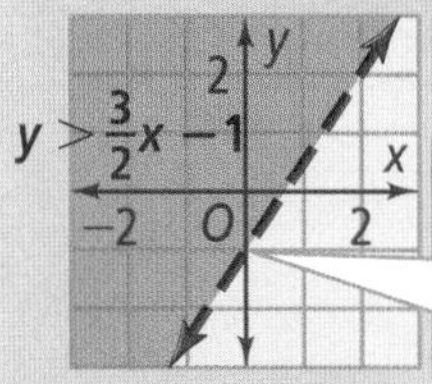

Each point on a *dashed* line is not a solution. A dashed line is used for inequalities with > or <.

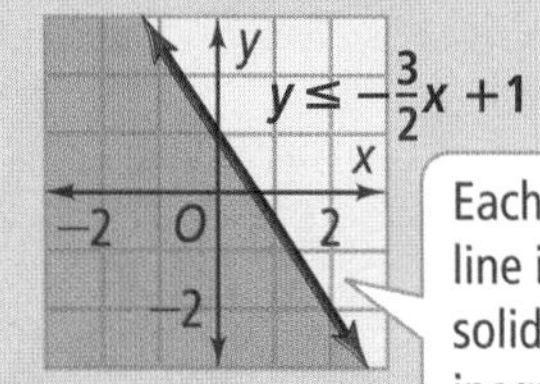

Each point on a *solid* line is a solution. A solid line is used for inequalities with ≥ or ≤.

Problem 2 Graphing an Inequality in Two Variables

Think

What is the boundary line for the graph?

Got It? What is the graph of $y \leq \frac{1}{2}x + 1$?

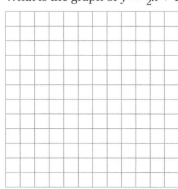

1 ≥ 3(1) − 2
0 ≥ 3(0) − 2
2 ≥ 3(2) − 2
2 ≥ 6 − 2
2 ≥ 4

Practice Graph each linear inequality.

3. $y \geq 3x - 2$ 0 > −2 T

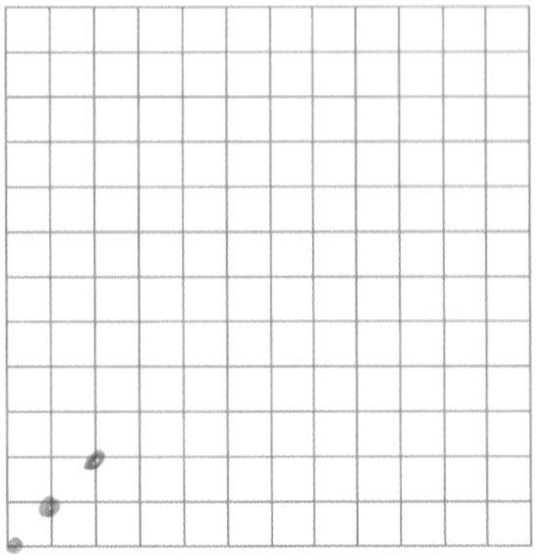

4. $y < -4x - 1$

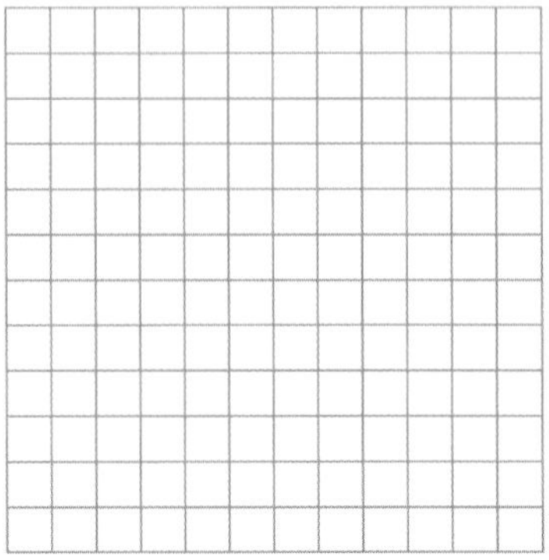

An inequality in one variable can be graphed on a number line or in the coordinate plane. When graphed in a coordinate plane, the boundary line will be a horizontal or vertical line.

Problem 3 Graphing a Linear Inequality in One Variable

Got It? What is the graph of each inequality?

a. $x < -5$

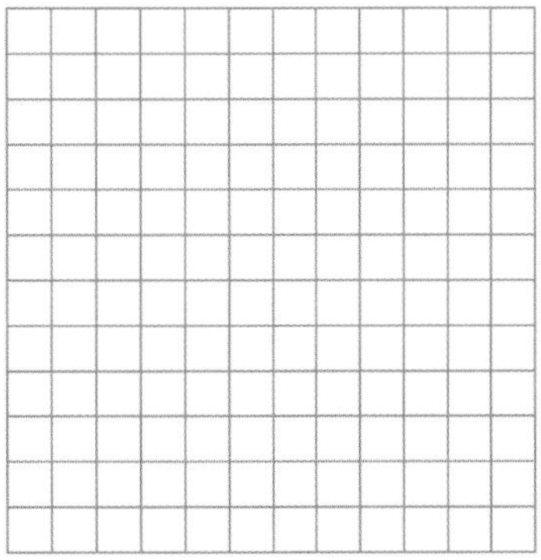

b. $y \leq 2$

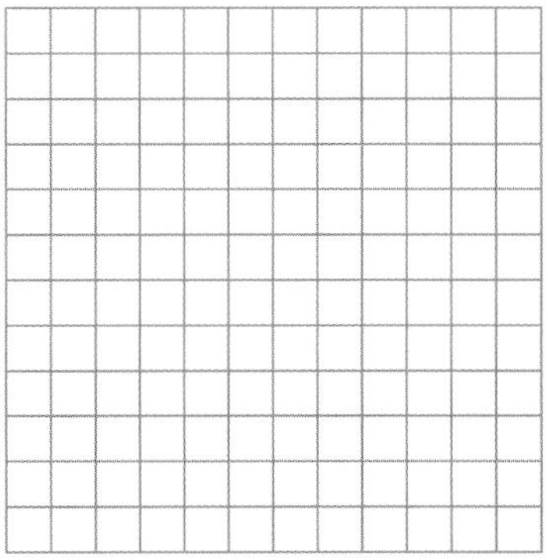

Practice Graph each inequality in the coordinate plane.

5. $x \leq 4$

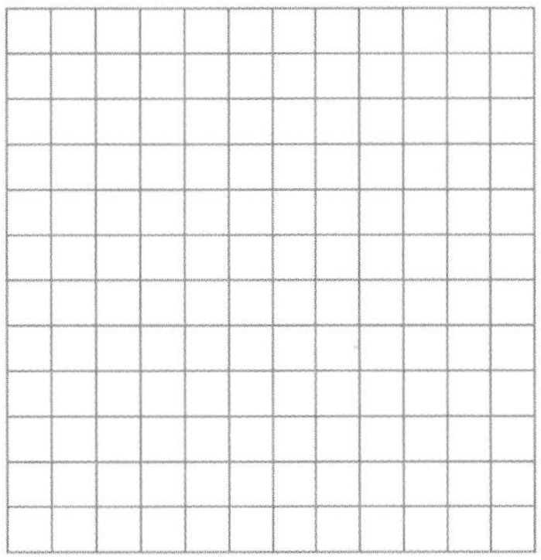

6. $x > -2$

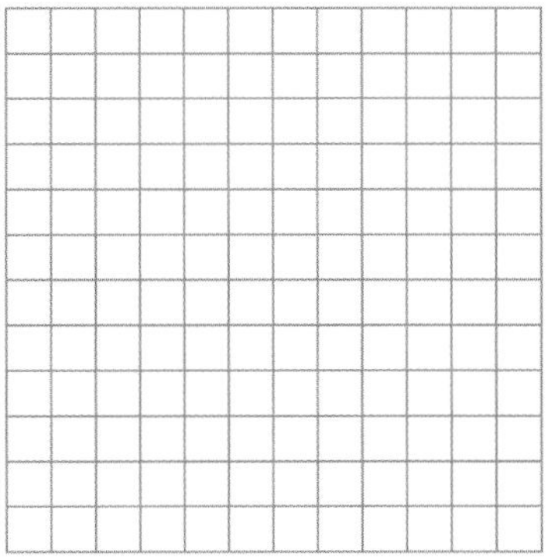

When a linear inequality is solved for y, the direction of the inequality symbol determines which side of the boundary line to shade. If the symbol is $<$ or $\leq$, shade below the boundary line. If the symbol is $>$ or $\geq$, shade above it.

Sometimes you must first solve an inequality for y before using the method described above to determine where to shade.

Problem 4 Rewriting to Graph an Inequality

Got It? For a party, you can spend no more than \$12 on nuts. Peanuts cost \$2/lb. Cashews cost \$4/lb. What are three possible combinations of peanuts and cashews you can buy?

Think

What inequality can you write to help solve the problem?

Practice

7. **Carpentry** You budget \$200 for wooden planks for outdoor furniture. Cedar costs \$2.50 per foot and pine costs \$1.75 per foot. Let $x =$ the number of feet of cedar and let $y =$ the number of feet of pine. What is an inequality that shows how much of each type of wood you can buy? Graph the inequality. What are three possible amounts of each type of wood that can be bought within your budget?

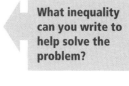

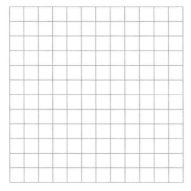

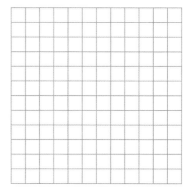

8. Business A fish market charges \$9 per pound for cod and \$12 per pound for flounder. Let x = the number of pounds of cod. Let y = the number of pounds of flounder. What is an inequality that shows how much of each type of fish the store must sell today to reach a daily quota of at least \$120? Graph the inequality. What are three possible amounts of each fish that would satisfy the quota?

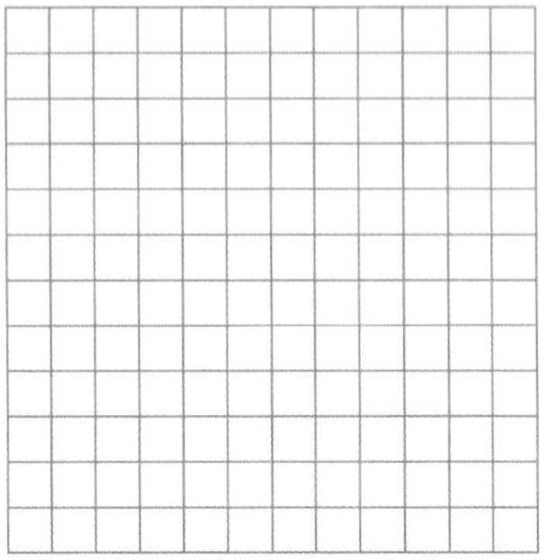

Problem 5 Writing an Inequality From a Graph

Got It? You are writing an inequality from a graph. The boundary line is dashed and has slope $\frac{1}{3}$ and y-intercept -2. The area above the line is shaded. What inequality should you write?

A Practice **Write a linear inequality that represents each graph.**

9.

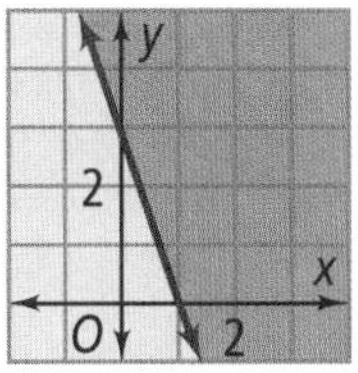

10.

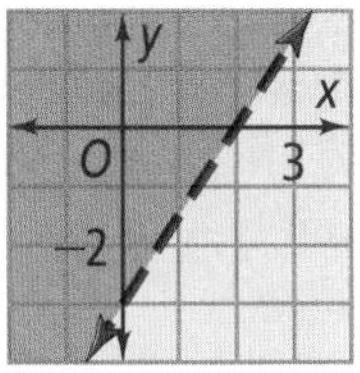

11.

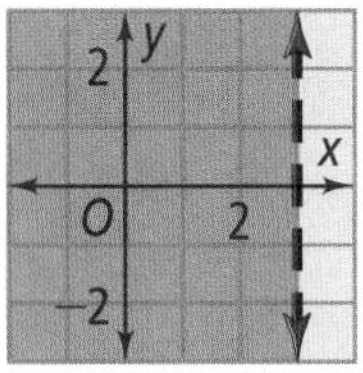

Lesson Check

Do you know HOW?

12. Is $(-1, 4)$ a solution of the inequality $y < 2x + 5$? Explain.

Graph each linear inequality.

13. $y \leq -2x + 3$

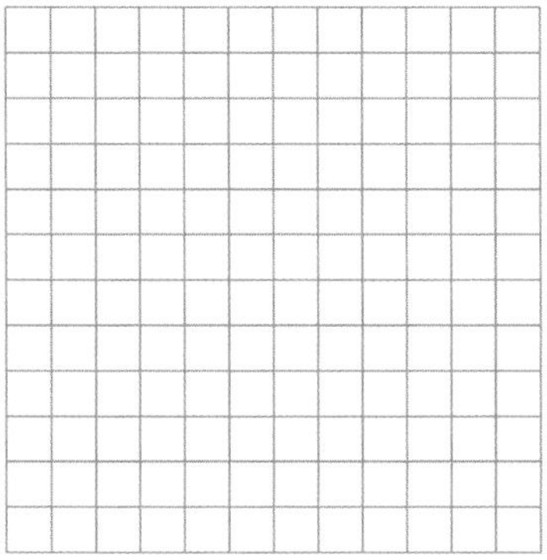

14. $x < -1$

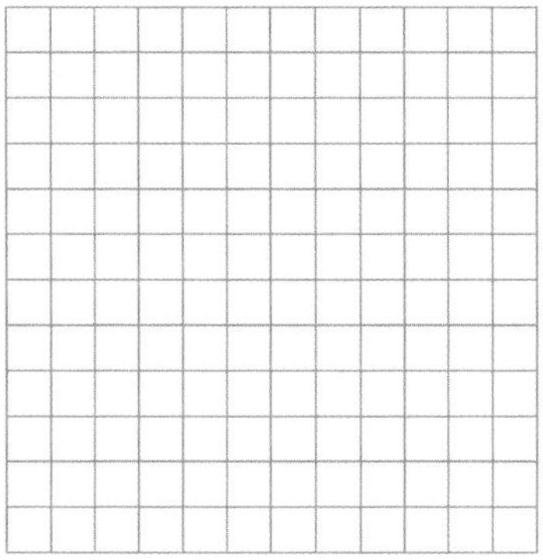

15. What is an inequality that represents the graph at the right?

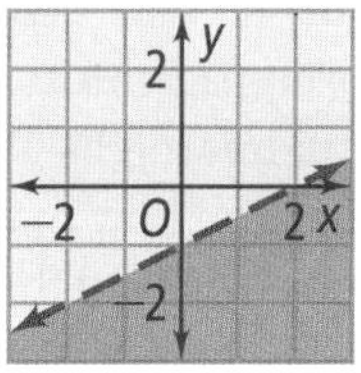

Do you UNDERSTAND?

MATHEMATICAL PRACTICES

16. Vocabulary How is a linear inequality in two variables like a linear equation in two variables? How are they different?

17. Writing To graph the inequality $y < \frac{3}{2}x + 3$ inequality, do you shade above or below the boundary line? Explain.

18. Reasoning Write an inequality that describes the region of the coordinate plane *not* included in the graph of $y < 5x + 1$.

More Practice and Problem-Solving Exercises

MATHEMATICAL PRACTICES

B Apply

19. Think About a Plan A truck that can carry no more than 6400 lb is being used to transport refrigerators and upright pianos. Each refrigerator weighs 250 lb and each piano weighs 475 lb. Write and graph an inequality to show how many refrigerators and how many pianos the truck could carry. Will 12 refrigerators and 8 pianos overload the truck? Explain.

- Which inequality symbol should you use?
- Which side of the boundary line should you shade?

20. Employment A student with two summer jobs earns \$10 per hour at a cafe and \$8 per hour at a market. The student would like to earn at least \$800 per month.

a. Write and graph an inequality to represent the situation.

b. The student works at the market for 60 h per month and can work at most 90 h per month. Can the student earn at least \$800 each month? Explain how you can use your graph to determine this.

21. Error Analysis A student graphed $y \geq 2x + 3$ as shown at the right. Describe and correct the student's error.

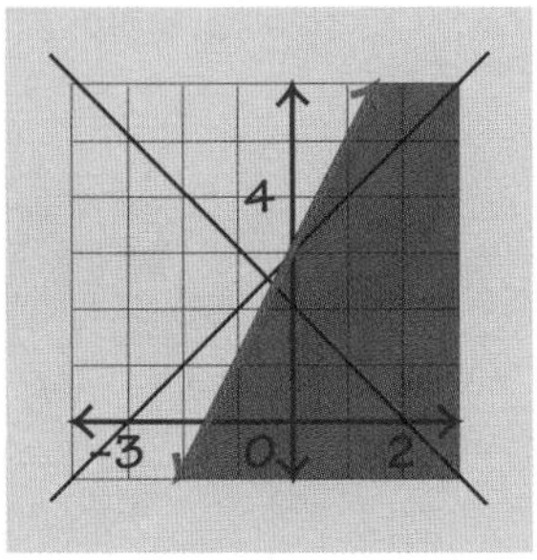

22. Writing When graphing an inequality, can you always use (0, 0) as a test point to determine where to shade? If not, how would you choose a test point?

Challenge

23. **Music Store** A music store sells used CDs for \$5 each and buys used CDs for \$1.50 each. You go to the store with \$20 and some CDs to sell. You want to have at least \$10 left when you leave the store. Write and graph an inequality to show how many CDs you could buy and sell.

24. **Groceries** At your grocery store, milk normally costs \$3.60 per gallon. Ground beef costs \$3 per pound. Today there are specials: Milk is discounted \$.50 per gallon, and ground beef is 20% off. You want to spend no more than \$20. Write and graph a linear inequality to show how many gallons of milk and how many pounds of ground beef you can buy today.

25. **Reasoning** You are graphing a linear inequality of the form $y > mx + b$. The point (1, 2) is not a solution, but (3, 2) is. Is the slope of the boundary line *positive, negative, zero,* or *undefined*? Explain.

4-6 Systems of Linear Inequalities

A.REI.12 Graph the solutions to a linear inequality in two variables as a half-plane . . . and graph the solution . . . to a system of linear inequalities in two variables as the intersection of the corresponding half-planes. Also **A.CED.3**

Objectives To solve systems of linear inequalities by graphing
To model real-world situations using systems of linear inequalities

Solve It! Write your solution to the Solve It in the space below.

A **system of linear inequalities** is made up of two or more linear inequalities. A **solution of a system of linear inequalities** is an ordered pair that makes all the inequalities in the system true. The graph of a system of linear inequalities is the set of points that represent all of the solutions of the system.

Essential Understanding You can graph the solutions of a system of linear inequalities in the coordinate plane. The graph of the system is the region where the graphs of the individual inequalities overlap.

Problem 1 Graphing a System of Inequalities

Think
What boundary lines should you graph first?

Got It? What is the graph of the system at the right?

$$y \geq -x + 5$$
$$-3x + y \leq -4$$

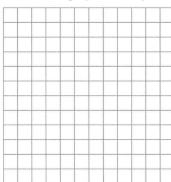

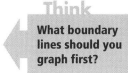

Practice **Solve each system of inequalities by graphing.**

1. $y < 2x + 4$
$-3x - 2y \geq 6$

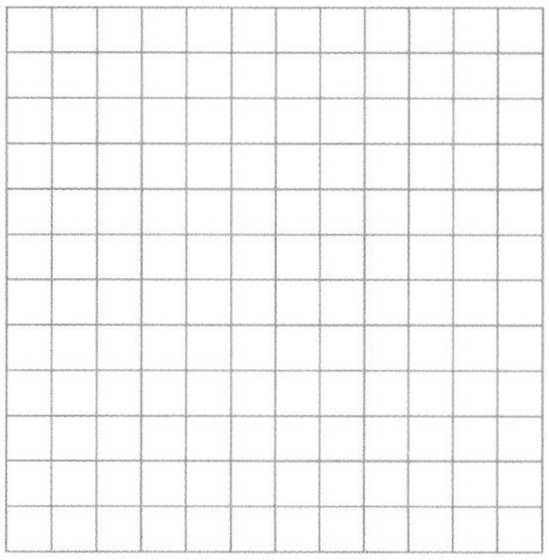

2. $y \leq 0.75x - 2$
$y > 0.75x - 3$

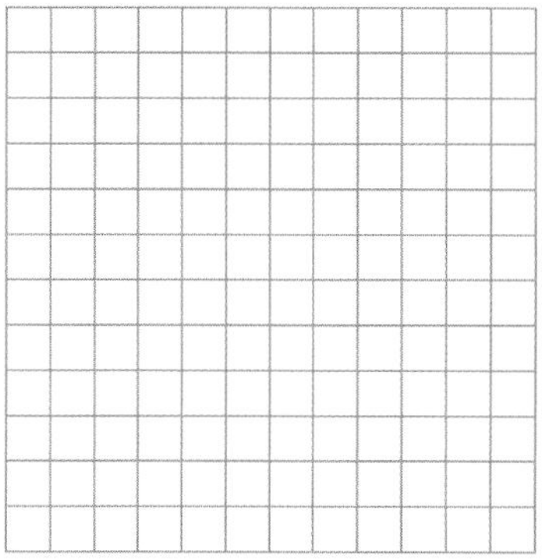

Determine whether the ordered pair is a solution of the given system.

3. (2, 12);
$y > 2x + 4$
$y < 3x + 7$

4. (8, 2);
$3x - 2y \leq 17$
$0.3x + 4y > 9$

You can combine your knowledge of linear equations with your knowledge of inequalities to describe a graph using a system of inequalities.

Problem 2 Writing a System of Inequalities From a Graph

Think

How can you break this down into two simpler problems?

Got It? **a.** What system of inequalities is represented by the graph?

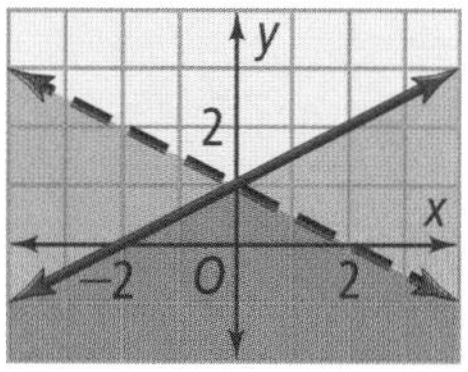

b. Reasoning In part (a), is the point where the boundary lines intersect a solution of the system? Explain.

Practice Write a system of inequalities for each graph.

5.
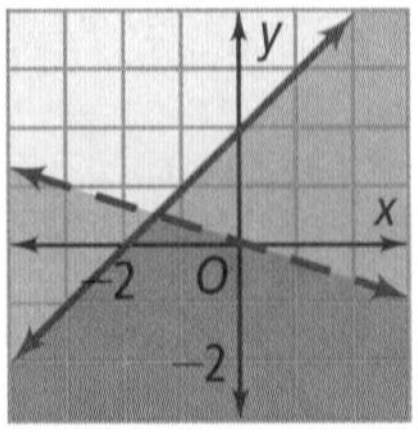

6.
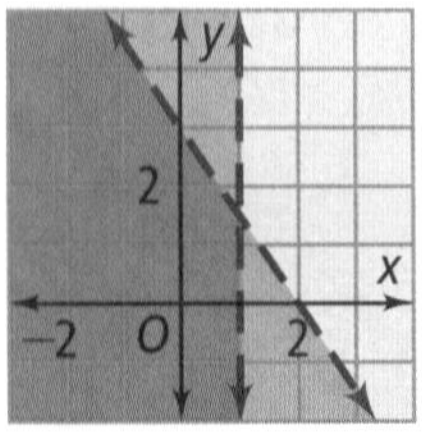

7.
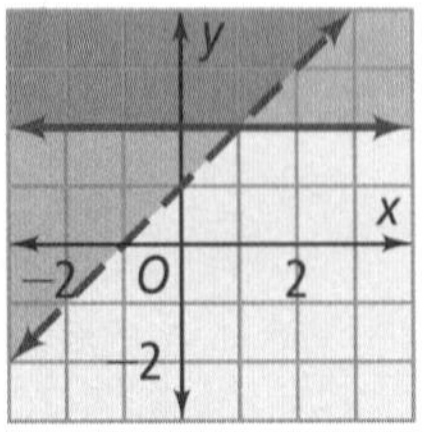

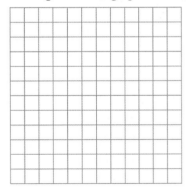

You can model many real-world situations by writing and graphing systems of linear inequalities. Some real-world situations involve three or more restrictions, so you must write a system of at least three inequalities.

Problem 3 Using a System of Inequalities

Got It? You want to build a fence for a rectangular dog run. You want the run to be at least 10 ft wide. The run can be at most 50 ft long. You have 126 ft of fencing. What is a graph showing the possible dimensions of the dog run?

Practice **8. Earnings** Suppose you have a job mowing lawns that pays \$12 per hour. You also have a job at a clothing store that pays \$10 per hour. You need to earn at least \$350 per week, but you can work no more than 35 h per week. You must work a minimum of 10 h per week at the clothing store. What is a graph showing how many hours per week you can work at each job?

9. Driving Two friends agree to split the driving on a road trip from Philadelphia, Pennsylvania, to Denver, Colorado. One friend drives at an average speed of 60 mi/h. The other friend drives at an average speed of 55 mi/h. They want to drive at least 500 mi per day. They plan to spend no more than 10 h driving each day. The friend who drives slower wants to drive fewer hours. What is a graph showing how they can split the driving each day?

Lesson Check

Do you know HOW?

10. What is the graph of the system at the right?

$y > 3x - 2$

$2y - x \leq 6$

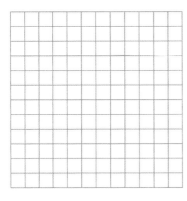

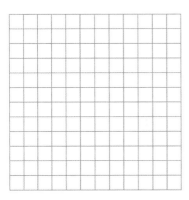

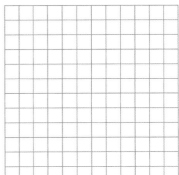

11. What system of inequalities is represented by the graph at the right?

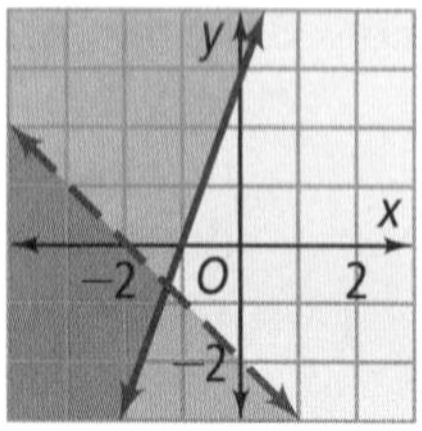

12. Cherries cost $4/lb. Grapes cost $2.50/lb. You can spend no more than $15 on fruit, and you need at least 4 lb in all. What is a graph showing the amount of each fruit you can buy?

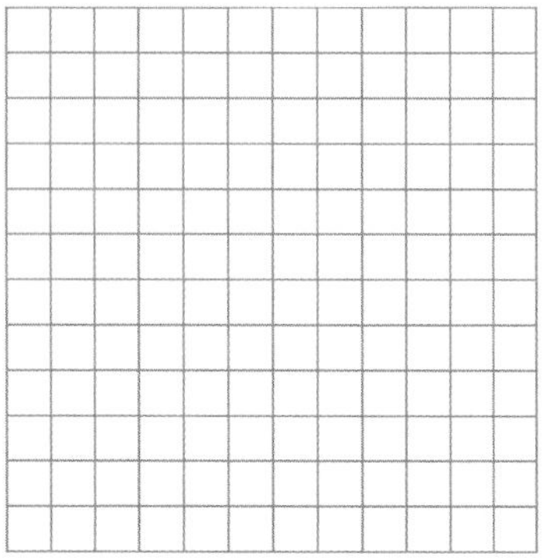

Do you UNDERSTAND?

MATHEMATICAL PRACTICES

13. Vocabulary How can you determine whether an ordered pair is a solution of a system of linear inequalities?

14. Reasoning Suppose you are graphing a system of two linear inequalities, and the boundary lines for the inequalities are parallel. Does that mean that the system has no solution? Explain.

15. Writing How is finding the solution of a system of inequalities different from finding the solution of a system of equations? How is it the same? Explain.

More Practice and Problem-Solving Exercises

MATHEMATICAL PRACTICES

B Apply

16. Think About a Plan You are fencing in a rectangular area for a garden. You have only 150 ft of fence. You want the length of the garden to be at least 40 ft. You want the width of the garden to be at least 5 ft. What is a graph showing the possible dimensions your garden could have?

- What variables will you use? What will they represent?
- How many inequalities do you need to write?

17. **a.** Graph the system $y > 3x + 3$ and $y \leq 3x - 5$.

b. **Writing** Will the boundary lines $y = 3x + 3$ and $y = 3x - 5$ ever intersect? How do you know?

c. Do the shaded regions in the graph from part (a) overlap?

d. Does the system of inequalities have any solutions? Explain.

18. Error Analysis A student graphs the system as shown at the right. Describe and correct the student's error.

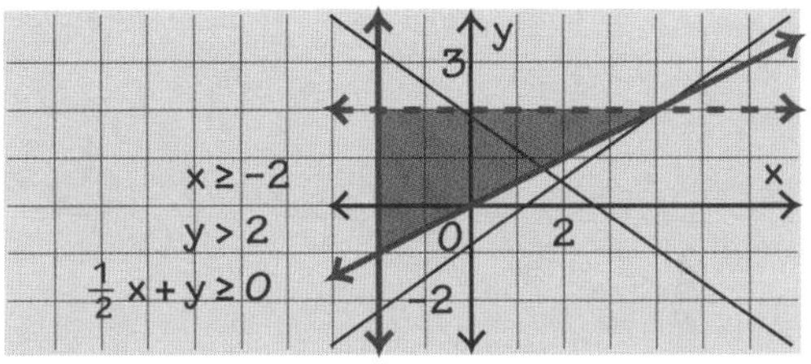

19. Gift Certificates You received a \$100 gift certificate to a clothing store. The store sells T-shirts for \$15 and dress shirts for \$22. You want to spend no more than the amount of the gift certificate. You want to leave at most \$10 of the gift certificate unspent. You need at least one dress shirt. What are all of the possible combinations of T-shirts and dress shirts you could buy?

20. **a.** **Geometry** Graph the system of linear inequalities.

b. Describe the shape of the solution region.

c. Find the vertices of the solution region.

d. Find the area of the solution region.

$x \geq 2$
$y \geq -3$
$x + y \leq 4$

21. Which region represents the solution of the system? $y \leq -\frac{3}{2}x - 2$, $3y - 9x \geq 6$

A I
B II
C III
D IV

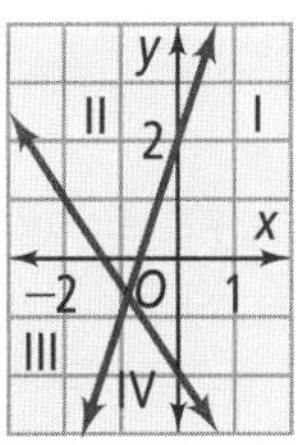

Open-Ended **Write a system of linear inequalities with the given characteristic.**

22. All solutions are in Quadrant III.

23. There are no solutions.

Challenge

24. Business A jeweler plans to produce a ring made of silver and gold. The price of gold is about \$25 per gram. The price of silver is approximately \$.40 per gram. She considers the following in deciding how much gold and silver to use in the ring.

- The total mass must be more than 10 g but less than 20 g.
- The ring must contain at least 2 g of gold.
- The total cost of the gold and silver must be less than \$90.

a. Write and graph the inequalities that describe this situation.

b. For one solution, find the mass of the ring and the cost of the gold and silver.

25. Student Art A teacher wants to post a row of student artwork on a wall that is 20 ft long. Some pieces are 8.5 in. wide. Other pieces are 11 in. wide. She is going to leave 3 in. of space to the left of each art piece. She wants to post at least 16 pieces of art. Write and graph a system of inequalities that describes how many pieces of each size she can post.

4 Chapter Review

MathXL® for School
Go to pearsonsuccessnet.com

4-1 Solving Systems by Graphing

Quick Review

One way to solve a system of linear equations is by graphing each equation and finding the intersection point of the graph, if one exists.

Example

What is the solution of the system? $y = -2x + 2$
$y = 0.5x - 3$

$y = -2x + 2$ Slope is -2; y-intercept is 2.

$y = 0.5x - 3$ Slope is 0.5; y-intercept is -3.

The lines appear to intersect at $(2, -2)$. Check if $(2, -2)$ makes both equations true.

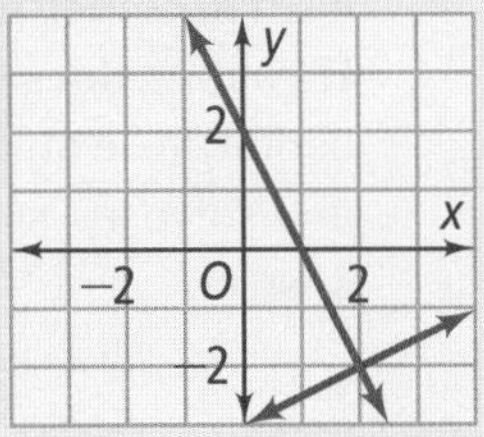

$-2 = -2(2) + 2$ ✓

$-2 = 0.5(2) - 3$ ✓

So, the solution is $(2, -2)$.

Exercises

Solve each system by graphing. Check your answer.

1. $y = 3x + 13$
$y = x - 3$

2. $y = -x + 4$
$y = 3x + 12$

3. $y = 2x + 3$
$y = \frac{1}{3}x - 2$

4. $y = 1.5x + 2$
$4.5x - 3y = -9$

5. $y = -2x - 21$
$y = x - 7$

6. $y = x + 1$
$2x - 2y = -2$

7. Songwriting Jay has written 24 songs to date. He writes an average of 6 songs per year. Jenna started writing songs this year and expects to write about 12 songs per year. How many years from now will Jenna have written as many songs as Jay? Write and graph a system of equations to find your answer.

8. Reasoning Describe the graph of a system of equations that has no solution.

4-2 Solving Systems Using Substitution

Quick Review

You can solve a system of equations by solving one equation for one variable and then substituting the expression for that variable into the other equation.

Example

What is the solution of the system? $y = -\frac{1}{3}x$
$3x + 3y = -18$

$3x + 3y = -18$	Write the second equation.
$3x + 3(-\frac{1}{3}x) = -18$	Substitute $-\frac{1}{3}x$ for y.
$2x = -18$	Simplify.
$x = -9$	Solve for x.
$y = -\frac{1}{3}(-9)$	Substitute -9 for x in the first equation.
$y = 3$	

The solution is $(-9, 3)$.

Exercises

Solve each system using substitution. Tell whether the system has *one solution, infinitely many solutions*, or *no solution*.

9. $y = 2x - 1$
$2x + 2y = 22$

10. $-x + y = -13$
$3x - y = 19$

11. $2x + y = -12$
$-4x - 2y = 30$

12. $\frac{1}{3}y = \frac{7}{3}x + \frac{5}{3}$
$x - 3y = 5$

13. $y = x - 7$
$3x - 3y = 21$

14. $3x + y = -13$
$-2x + 5y = -54$

15. Business The owner of a hair salon charges \$20 more per haircut than the assistant. Yesterday the assistant gave 12 haircuts. The owner gave 6 haircuts. The total earnings from haircuts were \$750. How much does the owner charge for a haircut? Solve by writing and solving a system of equations.

4-3 and 4-4
Solving Systems Using Elimination; Applications of Systems

Quick Review

You can add or subtract equations in a system to eliminate a variable. Before you add or subtract, you may have to multiply one or both equations by a constant to make eliminating a variable possible.

Example

What is the solution of the system? $3x + 2y = 41$
$5x - 3y = 24$

$3x + 2y = 41$ Multiply by 3. $9x + 6y = 123$
$5x - 3y = 24$ Multiply by 2. $\underline{10x - 6y = 48}$
$19x + 0 = 171$
$x = 9$

$3x + 2y = 41$ Write the first equation.

$3(9) + 2y = 41$ Substitute 9 for x.

$y = 7$ Solve for y.

The solution is (9, 7).

Exercises

Solve each system using elimination. Tell whether the system has *one solution, infinitely many solutions*, or *no solution*.

16. $x + 2y = 23$
$5x + 10y = 55$

17. $7x + y = 6$
$5x + 3y = 34$

18. $5x + 4y = -83$
$3x - 3y = -12$

19. $9x + \frac{1}{2}y = 51$
$7x + \frac{1}{3}y = 39$

20. $4x + y = 21$
$-2x + 6y = 9$

21. $y = 3x - 27$
$x - \frac{1}{3}y = 9$

22. Flower Arranging It takes a florist 3 h 15 min to make 3 small centerpieces and 3 large centerpieces. It takes 6 h 20 min to make 4 small centerpieces and 7 large centerpieces. How long does it take to make each small centerpiece and each large centerpiece? Write and solve a system of equations to find your answer.

4-5 and 4-6 Linear Inequalities and Systems of Inequalities

Quick Review

A *linear inequality* describes a region of the coordinate plane with a boundary line. Two or more inequalities form a *system of inequalities*. The system's solutions lie where the graphs of the inequalities overlap.

Example

What is the graph of the system? $y > 2x - 4$
$y \leq -x + 2$

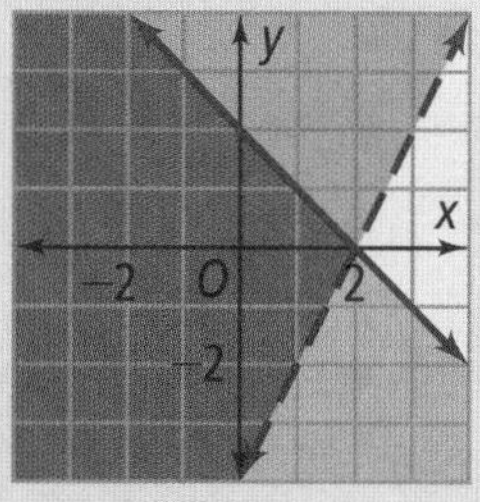

Graph the boundary lines $y = 2x - 4$ and $y = -x + 2$. For $y > 2x - 4$, use a dashed boundary line and shade above it. For $y \leq -x + 2$, use a solid boundary line and shade below. The region of overlap contains the system's solutions.

Exercises

Solve each system of inequalities by graphing.

23. $y \geq x + 4$
$y < 2x - 1$

24. $4y < -3x$
$y < -\frac{3}{4}x$

25. $2x - y > 0$
$3x + 2y \leq -14$

26. $x + 0.5y \geq 5.5$
$0.5x + y < 6.5$

27. $y < 10x$
$y > x - 5$

28. $4x + 4 > 2y$
$3x - 4y \geq 1$

29. Downloads You have 60 megabytes (MB) of space left on your portable media player. You can choose to download song files that use 3.5 MB or video files that use 8 MB. You want to download at least 12 files. What is a graph showing the numbers of song and video files you can download?

4

Pull It All Together

PERFORMANCE TASK

ASSESSMENT

Planning an Exercise Program

You use the rowing machine and the stair machine at the gym for your exercise program. You want an exercise program that meets these three conditions:

(1) You can spend at most 60 minutes at the gym.
(2) After 10 minutes of stretching you exercise for at least 30 minutes, dividing your time between the rowing machine and the stair machine.
(3) You want to spend at least twice as much time on the stair machine as on the rowing machine.

Task Description

Find the greatest length of time you can spend on the rowing machine and meet conditions (1)–(3) above.

a. The least amount of time you exercise after stretching is 30 minutes. What is the greatest amount of time you can exercise after stretching?

b. Let $x =$ the number of minutes spent on the rowing machine.
Let $y =$ the number of minutes spent on the stair machine.
Write a system of two inequalities that describes the total amount of time you spend on the two machines.

c. Write a third inequality that describes condition (3).

d. Graph your system of three inequalities from parts (b) and (c) to show the set of all possible combinations of times that meet your conditions. Explain why the graph should use only the first quadrant.

e. Which point of the solution region represents the greatest length of time you can spend on the rowing machine? Solve a system of equations to find the coordinates of this point. What is the greatest length of time you can spend on the rowing machine?

This page intentionally left blank.

Honors Appendix

TOPIC
A
Matrices

Interactive Digital Path

Log in to pearsonsuccessnet.com and click on Interactive Digital Path to access the Solve Its and animated Problems.

Download videos connecting math to your world. (VIDEO)

Math definitions in English and Spanish (VOCABULARY)

The online Solve It will get you in gear for each lesson. (SOLVE IT!)

Interactive! Vary numbers, graphs, and figures to explore math concepts. (DYNAMIC ACTIVITIES)

Online access to stepped-out problems aligned to Common Core (ONLINE PROBLEMS)

Get and view your assignments online. (ONLINE HOMEWORK)

Extra practice and review online (MathXL® FOR SCHOOL)

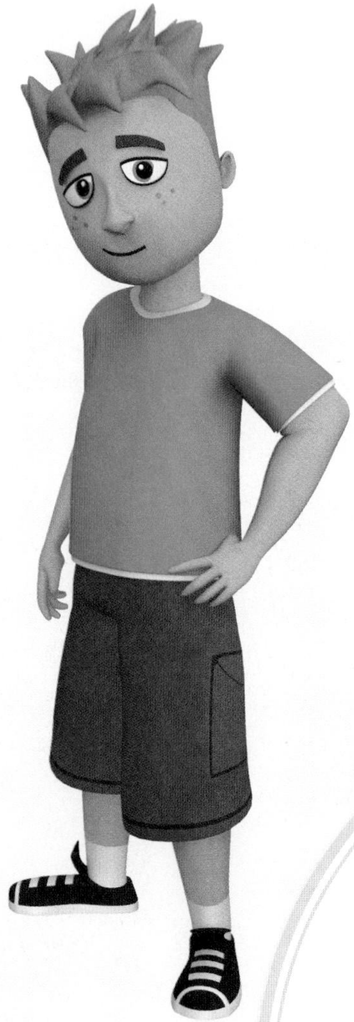

DOMAINS
- Vector and Matrix Quantities
- Congruence

Matrices are used to do encryption. The sculpture Kryptos pictured on the next page contains encrypted messages.

How can you add, subtract, and multiply arrays of numbers? How can you use a matrix to represent and solve systems of equations? And how can you use matrices to make transformations of geometric objects? You will learn how in this topic.

Vocabulary

English/Spanish Vocabulary Audio Online:

English	Spanish
determinant, *p. H24*	determinante
dilation, *p. H40*	dilatación
equal matrices, *p. H7*	matrices equivalentes
image, *p. H39*	imagen
matrix equation, *p. H5*	ecuación matricial
preimage, *p. H39*	preimagen
scalar multiplication, *p. H12*	multiplicación escalar
variable matrix, *p. H32*	matriz variable
zero matrix, *p. H6*	matriz cero

BIG ideas

1 **Data Representation**
Essential Question How can you use a matrix to organize data?

2 **Modeling**
Essential Question How can you use a matrix equation to model a real-world situation?

3 **Transformations**
Essential Question How can a matrix represent a transformation of a geometric figure in the plane?

Topic A Preview

A-1 **Adding and Subtracting Matrices**
A-2 **Matrix Multiplication**
A-3 **Determinants and Inverses**
A-4 **Inverse Matrices and Systems**
A-5 **Geometric Transformations**
A-6 **Vectors**

A-1 Adding and Subtracting Matrices

Content Standards

N.VM.8 Add, subtract, and multiply matrices of appropriate dimensions.

N.VM.10 Understand that the zero and identity matrices play a role in matrix addition and multiplication similar to the role of 0 and 1 . . .

Objective To add and subtract matrices and to solve matrix equations

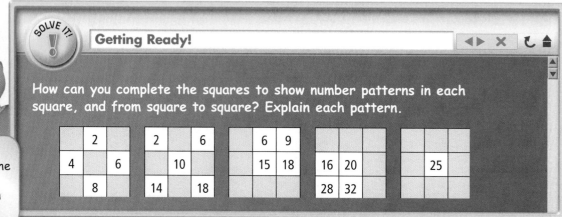

SOLVE IT! **Getting Ready!**

How can you complete the squares to show number patterns in each square, and from square to square? Explain each pattern.

	2	
4		6
	8	

2		6
	10	
14		18

	6	9
	15	18

16	20	
28	32	

	25	

If you get stuck, shift your perspective from the patterns in each square to the patterns between squares, or vice versa.

MATHEMATICAL PRACTICES

A matrix is a rectangular array of numbers. You usually display the array within brackets.

Lesson Vocabulary
- corresponding elements
- matrix equation
- zero matrix
- equal matrices

Essential Understanding You can extend the addition and subtraction of numbers to matrices.

The *dimensions* of a matrix are the numbers of rows and columns. A matrix with 2 rows and 3 columns is a 2×3 matrix. Each number in a matrix is a *matrix element.* In matrix A, a_{12} is the element in row 1 and column 2.

Sometimes you want to combine matrices to get new information. You can combine two matrices with equal dimensions by adding or subtracting the corresponding elements. **Corresponding elements** are elements in the same position in each matrix.

take note

Key Concept Matrix Addition and Subtraction

To add matrices A and B with the same dimensions, add corresponding elements. Similarly, to subtract matrices A and B with the same dimensions, subtract corresponding elements.

$$A = \begin{bmatrix} a_{11} & a_{12} \\ a_{21} & a_{22} \end{bmatrix} \qquad B = \begin{bmatrix} b_{11} & b_{12} \\ b_{21} & b_{22} \end{bmatrix}$$

$$A + B = \begin{bmatrix} a_{11} + b_{11} & a_{12} + b_{12} \\ a_{21} + b_{21} & a_{22} + b_{22} \end{bmatrix} \qquad A - B = \begin{bmatrix} a_{11} - b_{11} & a_{12} - b_{12} \\ a_{21} - b_{21} & a_{22} - b_{22} \end{bmatrix}$$

Problem 1 Adding and Subtracting Matrices

Think

To add matrices they need to have the same dimensions. What are the dimensions of C?

C has 2 rows and 3 columns, so it's a 2×3 matrix.

Given $C = \begin{bmatrix} 3 & 2 & 4 \\ -1 & 4 & 0 \end{bmatrix}$ and $D = \begin{bmatrix} 1 & 4 & 3 \\ -2 & 2 & 4 \end{bmatrix}$, what are the following?

A $C + D$

$$\begin{bmatrix} 3 & 2 & 4 \\ -1 & 4 & 0 \end{bmatrix} + \begin{bmatrix} 1 & 4 & 3 \\ -2 & 2 & 4 \end{bmatrix}$$

$$= \begin{bmatrix} 3+1 & 2+4 & 4+3 \\ -1+(-2) & 4+2 & 0+4 \end{bmatrix}$$

$$= \begin{bmatrix} 4 & 6 & 7 \\ -3 & 6 & 4 \end{bmatrix}$$

B $C - D$

$$\begin{bmatrix} 3 & 2 & 4 \\ -1 & 4 & 0 \end{bmatrix} - \begin{bmatrix} 1 & 4 & 3 \\ -2 & 2 & 4 \end{bmatrix}$$

$$= \begin{bmatrix} 3-1 & 2-4 & 4-3 \\ -1-(-2) & 4-2 & 0-4 \end{bmatrix}$$

$$= \begin{bmatrix} 2 & -2 & 1 \\ 1 & 2 & -4 \end{bmatrix}$$

Got It? **1.** Given $A = \begin{bmatrix} -12 & 24 \\ -3 & 5 \\ -1 & 10 \end{bmatrix}$ and $B = \begin{bmatrix} -3 & 1 \\ 2 & -4 \\ -1 & 5 \end{bmatrix}$, what are the following?

a. $A + B$

b. $A - B$

c. Reasoning Is matrix addition commutative? Explain.

A **matrix equation** is an equation in which the variable is a matrix. You can use the addition and subtraction properties of equality to solve a matrix equation. An example of a matrix equation is shown below.

$$\begin{bmatrix} 1 & 0 & 12 \\ 3 & 5 & 9 \\ 7 & 8 & -2 \end{bmatrix} + A = \begin{bmatrix} 8 & 11 & 9 \\ -5 & 5 & 2 \\ 10 & 7 & 8 \end{bmatrix}$$

Problem 2 Solving a Matrix Equation

Sports **The first table shows the teams with the four best records halfway through their season. The second table shows the full season records for the same four teams. Which team had the best record during the second half of the season?**

Records for the First Half of the Season

Team	Wins	Losses
Team 1	30	11
Team 2	29	12
Team 3	25	16
Team 4	24	17

Records for Season

Team	Wins	Losses
Team 1	53	29
Team 2	67	15
Team 3	58	24
Team 4	61	21

Know

- Records for the first half of the season
- Records for the full season

Need

Records for the second half of the season

Plan

- Use the equation: first half records + second half records = season records.
- Solve the matrix equation.

Step 1 Write 4 × 2 matrices to show the information from the two tables.

Let A = the first half records
B = the second half records
F = the final records

$$A = \begin{bmatrix} 30 & 11 \\ 29 & 12 \\ 25 & 16 \\ 24 & 17 \end{bmatrix} \quad F = \begin{bmatrix} 53 & 29 \\ 67 & 15 \\ 58 & 24 \\ 61 & 21 \end{bmatrix}$$

Think

What are the dimensions of matrix *B*?
B will have 4 rows and 2 columns. It is a 4 × 2 matrix.

Step 2 Solve $A + B = F$ for B.

$B = F - A$

$$B = \begin{bmatrix} 53 & 29 \\ 67 & 15 \\ 58 & 24 \\ 61 & 21 \end{bmatrix} - \begin{bmatrix} 30 & 11 \\ 29 & 12 \\ 25 & 16 \\ 24 & 17 \end{bmatrix} = \begin{bmatrix} 53-30 & 29-11 \\ 67-29 & 15-12 \\ 58-25 & 24-16 \\ 61-24 & 21-17 \end{bmatrix} = \begin{bmatrix} 23 & 18 \\ 38 & 3 \\ 33 & 8 \\ 37 & 4 \end{bmatrix}$$

Team 2 had the best record (38 wins and 3 losses) during the second half of the season.

Got It? **2.** If $B = \begin{bmatrix} 1 & 6 & -1 \\ 2 & 6 & 1 \\ -1 & -2 & 4 \end{bmatrix}$, $C = \begin{bmatrix} 2 & 0 & 0 \\ -1 & -3 & 6 \\ 2 & 3 & -1 \end{bmatrix}$, and $A - B = C$, what is A?

For $m \times n$ matrices, the additive identity matrix is the **zero matrix** O, or $O_{m \times n}$, with all elements zero. The *opposite*, or *additive inverse*, of an $m \times n$ matrix A is $-A$ where each element is the opposite of the corresponding element of A.

Problem 3 Using Identity and Opposite Matrices

What are the following sums?

Think

How is this like adding real numbers?
Adding zero leaves the matrix unchanged. Adding opposites give you zero.

A $\begin{bmatrix} 1 & 2 \\ 5 & -7 \end{bmatrix} + \begin{bmatrix} 0 & 0 \\ 0 & 0 \end{bmatrix}$

$= \begin{bmatrix} 1+0 & 2+0 \\ 5+0 & -7+0 \end{bmatrix} = \begin{bmatrix} 1 & 2 \\ 5 & -7 \end{bmatrix}$

B $\begin{bmatrix} 2 & 8 \\ -3 & 0 \end{bmatrix} + \begin{bmatrix} -2 & -8 \\ 3 & 0 \end{bmatrix}$

$= \begin{bmatrix} 2+(-2) & 8+(-8) \\ -3+3 & 0+0 \end{bmatrix} = \begin{bmatrix} 0 & 0 \\ 0 & 0 \end{bmatrix}$

Got It? **3.** What are the following sums?

a. $\begin{bmatrix} 14 & 5 \\ 0 & -2 \end{bmatrix} + \begin{bmatrix} -14 & -5 \\ 0 & 2 \end{bmatrix}$

b. $\begin{bmatrix} 0 & 0 & 0 \\ 0 & 0 & 0 \end{bmatrix} + \begin{bmatrix} -1 & 10 & -5 \\ 0 & 2 & -3 \end{bmatrix}$

take note

Properties Properties of Matrix Addition

If A, B, and C are $m \times n$ matrices, then

Example	Property
$A + B$ is an $m \times n$ matrix	**Closure Property of Addition**
$A + B = B + A$	**Commutative Property of Addition**
$(A + B) + C = A + (B + C)$	**Associative Property of Addition**
There is a unique $m \times n$ matrix O such that $O + A = A + O = A$	**Additive Identity Property**
For each A, there is a unique opposite, $-A$, such that $A + (-A) = O$	**Additive Inverse Property**

Equal matrices have the same dimensions and equal corresponding elements. For example, $\begin{bmatrix} 0.25 & 1.5 \\ -3 & \frac{4}{5} \end{bmatrix}$ and $\begin{bmatrix} \frac{1}{4} & 1\frac{1}{2} \\ -3 & 0.8 \end{bmatrix}$ are equal matrices. You can use the definition of equal matrices to find unknown values in matrix elements.

Problem 4 Finding Unknown Matrix Values

Multiple Choice What values of x and y make the equation true?

$$\begin{bmatrix} 9 & 3x + 1 \\ 2y - 1 & 10 \end{bmatrix} = \begin{bmatrix} 9 & 16 \\ -5 & 10 \end{bmatrix}$$

(A) $x = 3, y = 5$

(B) $x = \frac{17}{3}, y = 5$

(C) $x = 5, y = -2$

(D) $x = 5, y = -3$

Think

How can you solve the equation?
For the two matrices to be equal, the corresponding elements must be equal.

$3x + 1 = 16$	Set corresponding elements equal.	$2y - 1 = -5$
$3x = 16 - 1$	Isolate the variable term.	$2y = -5 + 1$
$3x = 15$	Simplify.	$2y = -4$
$x = 5$	Solve for x and y.	$y = -2$

The correct answer is C.

Got It? 4. What values of x, y, and z make the following equations true?

a. $\begin{bmatrix} x + 3 & -2 \\ y - 1 & x + 1 \end{bmatrix} = \begin{bmatrix} 9 & -2 \\ 2y + 5 & 7 \end{bmatrix}$

b. $\begin{bmatrix} z & -3 \\ 3x & 0 \end{bmatrix} - \begin{bmatrix} 10 & -4 \\ x & 2y + 6 \end{bmatrix} = \begin{bmatrix} 2 & 1 \\ 8 & 4y + 12 \end{bmatrix}$

Lesson Check

Do you know HOW?

Find each sum or difference.

1. $\begin{bmatrix} 1 & -1 \\ 2 & 3 \end{bmatrix} + \begin{bmatrix} 0 & 2 \\ -4 & 5 \end{bmatrix}$

2. $\begin{bmatrix} 5 & -3 & 7 \\ -1 & 0 & 8 \end{bmatrix} - \begin{bmatrix} 4 & 6 & -1 \\ 2 & 1 & 0 \end{bmatrix}$

Solve each matrix equation.

3. $\begin{bmatrix} 6 & 1 \\ 4 & -2 \end{bmatrix} + X = \begin{bmatrix} 3 & 5 \\ -1 & 9 \end{bmatrix}$

4. $X - \begin{bmatrix} 2 & 0 \\ 5 & -1 \end{bmatrix} = \begin{bmatrix} 4 & 10 \\ 8 & -3 \end{bmatrix}$

Do you UNDERSTAND? MATHEMATICAL PRACTICES

5. Vocabulary Are the two matrices equal? Explain.

$\begin{bmatrix} \frac{1}{2} & \frac{3}{8} \\ 0.2 & \sqrt[3]{27} \end{bmatrix}$ and $\begin{bmatrix} 0.5 & 0.375 \\ \frac{1}{5} & 3 \end{bmatrix}$

6. Error Analysis Describe and correct the error made in subtracting the two matrices.

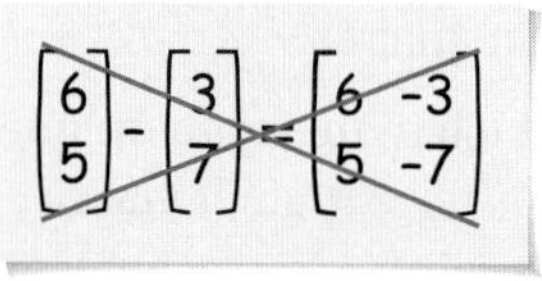

Practice and Problem-Solving Exercises MATHEMATICAL PRACTICES

A Practice

Find each sum or difference.

See Problem 1.

7. $\begin{bmatrix} 5 & 4 & 3 \\ 1 & -2 & 6 \end{bmatrix} + \begin{bmatrix} 1 & 1 & 1 \\ 1 & 1 & 1 \end{bmatrix}$

8. $\begin{bmatrix} 2 & 1 & 2 \\ 1 & 2 & 1 \end{bmatrix} - \begin{bmatrix} 2 & 3 & 2 \\ 3 & 2 & 3 \end{bmatrix}$

9. $\begin{bmatrix} 6.4 & -1.9 \\ -6.4 & 0.8 \end{bmatrix} + \begin{bmatrix} -2.5 & -0.4 \\ 5.8 & 8.3 \end{bmatrix}$

10. $\begin{bmatrix} 1.5 & -1.9 \\ 0 & 4.6 \end{bmatrix} - \begin{bmatrix} 8.3 & -3.2 \\ 2.1 & 5.6 \end{bmatrix}$

Solve each matrix equation.

See Problem 2.

11. $\begin{bmatrix} 1 & 2 \\ 2 & 1 \\ -3 & 4 \end{bmatrix} + X = \begin{bmatrix} 5 & -6 \\ 1 & 0 \\ 8 & 5 \end{bmatrix}$

12. $\begin{bmatrix} 2 & 1 & -1 \\ 0 & 2 & 1 \end{bmatrix} - X = \begin{bmatrix} 11 & 3 & -13 \\ 15 & -9 & 8 \end{bmatrix}$

13. $X - \begin{bmatrix} 1 & 4 \\ -2 & 3 \end{bmatrix} = \begin{bmatrix} 5 & -2 \\ 1 & 0 \end{bmatrix}$

14. $X + \begin{bmatrix} 6 & 1 \\ -2 & 3 \end{bmatrix} = \begin{bmatrix} 2 & 0 \\ -3 & 1 \end{bmatrix}$

Find each sum.

See Problem 3.

15. $\begin{bmatrix} 2 & -3 & 4 \\ 5 & 6 & -7 \end{bmatrix} + \begin{bmatrix} 0 & 0 & 0 \\ 0 & 0 & 0 \end{bmatrix}$

16. $\begin{bmatrix} 6 & -3 \\ -7 & 2 \end{bmatrix} + \begin{bmatrix} -6 & 3 \\ 7 & -2 \end{bmatrix}$

Find the value of each variable.

See Problem 4.

17. $\begin{bmatrix} 2 & 2 \\ -1 & 6 \end{bmatrix} - \begin{bmatrix} 4 & -1 \\ 0 & 5 \end{bmatrix} = \begin{bmatrix} x & y \\ -1 & z \end{bmatrix}$

18. $\begin{bmatrix} 2 & 4 \\ 8 & 4.5 \end{bmatrix} = \begin{bmatrix} 4x - 6 & -10t + 5 \\ 4x & 15t + 1.5x \end{bmatrix}$

B Apply

Find each matrix sum or difference if possible. If not possible, explain why.

$A = \begin{bmatrix} 3 & 4 \\ 6 & -2 \\ 1 & 0 \end{bmatrix}$ $B = \begin{bmatrix} -3 & 1 \\ 2 & -4 \\ -1 & 5 \end{bmatrix}$ $C = \begin{bmatrix} 1 & 2 \\ -3 & 1 \end{bmatrix}$ $D = \begin{bmatrix} 5 & 1 \\ 0 & 2 \end{bmatrix}$

19. $A + B$ **20.** $B + D$ **21.** $C + D$ **22.** $B - A$ **23.** $C - D$

24. Think About a Plan The table shows the number of beach balls produced during one shift at two manufacturing plants. Plant 1 has two shifts per day and Plant 2 has three shifts per day. Write matrices to represent one day's total output at the two plants. Then find the difference between daily production totals at the two plants.

- How can you use the number of shifts to find the total daily production totals at each plant?
- What matrix equation can you use to solve this problem?

Beach Ball Production Per Shift

	1-color		3-color	
	Plastic	Rubber	Plastic	Rubber
Plant 1	500	700	1300	1900
Plant 2	400	1200	600	1600

25. Sports The modern pentathlon is a grueling all-day competition. Each member of a team competes in five events: target shooting, fencing, swimming, horseback riding, and cross-country running. Here are scores for the U.S. women at the 2004 Olympic Games.

a. Write two 5×1 matrices to represent each woman's scores for each event.

b. Find the total score for each athlete.

U.S. Women's Pentathlon Scores, 2004 Olympics

Event	Anita Allen	Mary Beth Iagorashvili
Shooting	952	760
Fencing	720	832
Swimming	1108	1252
Riding	1172	1144
Running	1044	1064

SOURCE: Athens 2004 Olympic Games

26. Data Analysis Refer to the table at the right.

a. Add two matrices to find the total number of people participating in each activity.

b. Subtract two matrices to find the difference between the numbers of males and females in each activity.

c. Reasoning In part (b), does the order of the matrices matter? Explain.

U.S. Participation (millions) in Selected Leisure Activities

Activity	Male	Female
Movies	59.2	65.4
Exercise Programs	54.3	59.0
Sports Events	40.5	31.1
Home Improvement	45.4	41.8

SOURCE: U.S. National Endowment for the Arts

27. Writing Given a matrix A, explain how to find a matrix B such that $A + B = 0$.

Solve each equation for each variable.

28. $\begin{bmatrix} 4b+2 & -3 & 4d \\ -4a & 2 & 3 \\ 2f-1 & -14 & 1 \end{bmatrix} = \begin{bmatrix} 11 & 2c-1 & 0 \\ -8 & 2 & 3 \\ 0 & 3g-2 & 1 \end{bmatrix}$

29. $\begin{bmatrix} 4c & 2-d & 5 \\ -3 & -1 & 2 \\ 0 & -10 & 15 \end{bmatrix} = \begin{bmatrix} 2c+5 & 4d & g \\ -3 & h & f-g \\ 0 & -4c & 15 \end{bmatrix}$

Challenge

30. Find the sum of $E = \begin{bmatrix} 3 \\ 4 \\ 7 \end{bmatrix}$ and the additive inverse of $G = \begin{bmatrix} -2 \\ 0 \\ 5 \end{bmatrix}$.

31. Prove that matrix addition is commutative for 2×2 matrices.

32. Prove that matrix addition is associative for 2×2 matrices.

Concept Byte

For Use With Lesson A-1

TECHNOLOGY

Working with Matrices

Content Standard

N.VM.8 Add, subtract, and multiply matrices of appropriate dimensions.

MATHEMATICAL PRACTICES

You can use a graphing calculator to work with matrices. First you need to know how to enter a matrix into the calculator.

Example 1

Enter matrix $A = \begin{bmatrix} -3 & 4 \\ 7 & -5 \\ 0 & -2 \end{bmatrix}$ **into your graphing calculator.**

Select the **EDIT** option of the matrix feature to edit matrix **[A]**. Specify a 3×2 matrix by pressing 3 enter 2 enter. Enter the matrix elements one row at a time, pressing enter after each element. Then use the quit feature to return to the main screen.

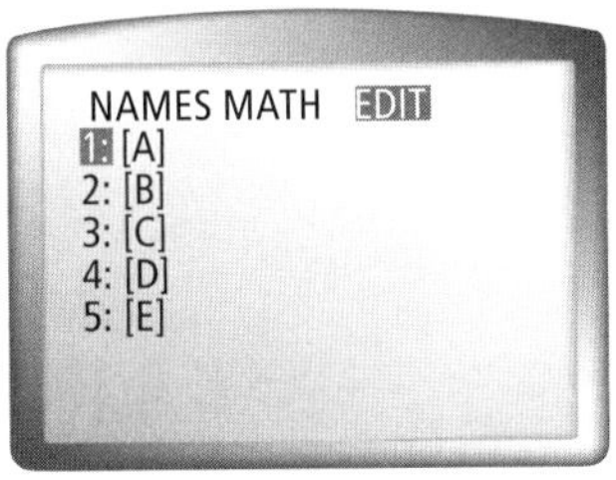

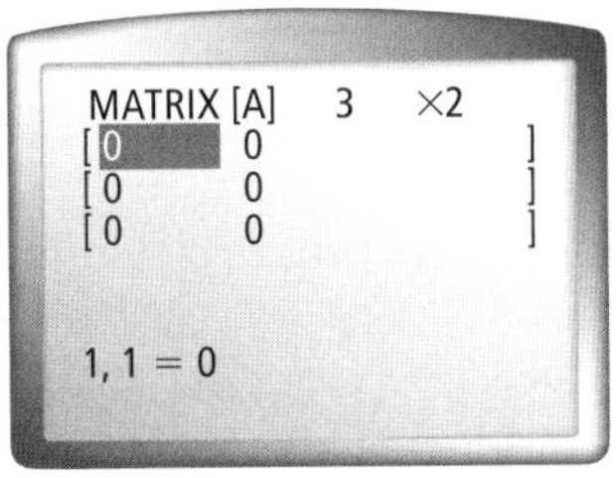

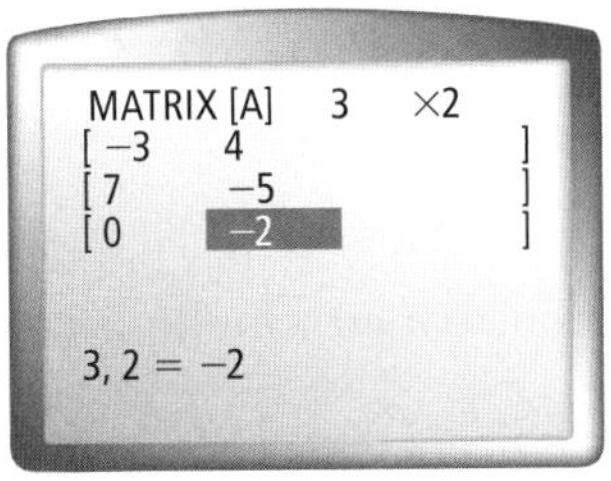

Example 2

Given $A = \begin{bmatrix} -3 & 4 \\ 7 & -5 \\ 0 & -2 \end{bmatrix}$ **and** $B = \begin{bmatrix} 10 & -7 \\ 4 & -3 \\ -12 & 11 \end{bmatrix}$**, find** $A + B$ **and** $A - B$**.**

Enter both matrices into the calculator. Use the **NAMES** option of the matrix feature to select each matrix. Press enter to see the sum. Repeat the corresponding steps to find the difference $A - B$.

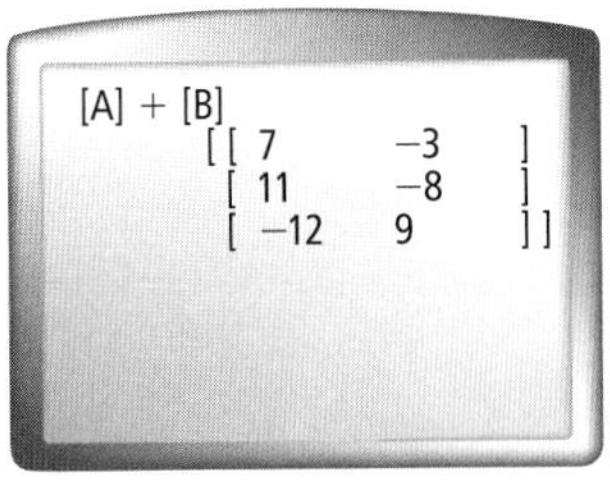

Exercises

Find each sum or difference.

1. $\begin{bmatrix} 0 & -3 \\ 5 & -7 \end{bmatrix} - \begin{bmatrix} -5 & 3 \\ 4 & 10 \end{bmatrix}$

2. $\begin{bmatrix} 3 & 5 & -7 \\ 0 & -2 & 0 \end{bmatrix} - \begin{bmatrix} -1 & 6 & 2 \\ -9 & 4 & 0 \end{bmatrix}$

3. $\begin{bmatrix} 3 \\ 5 \end{bmatrix} - \begin{bmatrix} -6 \\ 7 \end{bmatrix}$

4. $\begin{bmatrix} 3 & 5 & -8 \end{bmatrix} + \begin{bmatrix} -6 & 4 & 1 \end{bmatrix}$

5. $\begin{bmatrix} 17 & 8 & 0 \\ 3 & -5 & 2 \end{bmatrix} - \begin{bmatrix} 4 & 6 & 5 \\ 2 & -2 & 9 \end{bmatrix}$

6. $\begin{bmatrix} -9 & 6 & 4 \end{bmatrix} + \begin{bmatrix} -3 & 8 & 4 \end{bmatrix}$

A-2 Matrix Multiplication

Content Standards

N.VM.6 Use matrices to represent and manipulate data . . .

N.VM.7 Multiply matrices by scalars to produce new matrices . . .

Also N.VM.8, N.VM.9

Objective To multiply matrices using scalar and matrix multiplication

SOLVE IT! Getting Ready!

The values in the chart are the recommended 100% daily allowances.

In a family of five, the parents are on a 2000-calorie diet. The three children are on a 2500-calorie diet. For a dessert, the family shares a 500-g cake with 20% fat content. What percentage of the entire family daily fat allowance is in the cake?

	Calories	2,000	2,500
Total Fat	Less than	65 g	80 g
Sat Fat	Less than	20 g	25 g
Cholesterol	Less than	300 mg	300 mg
Sodium	Less than	2,400 mg	2,400 mg
Total Carbohydrate		300 g	375 g
Dietary Fiber		25 g	30 g

MATHEMATICAL PRACTICES

In the Solve It, you may have found the sum of products. Finding the sum of products is essential to matrix multiplication.

Lesson Vocabulary
- scalar
- scalar multiplication

Essential Understanding The product of two matrices is a matrix. To find an element in the product matrix, you multiply the elements of a row from the first matrix by the corresponding elements of a column from the second matrix. Then add the products.

Before you learn how to multiply two matrices, however, you should learn a simpler type of multiplication. This type of multiplication allows you to scale, or resize, the elements of the matrix.

$$3\begin{bmatrix} 5 & -1 \\ 3 & 7 \end{bmatrix} = \begin{bmatrix} 3(5) & 3(-1) \\ 3(3) & 3(7) \end{bmatrix} = \begin{bmatrix} 15 & -3 \\ 9 & 21 \end{bmatrix}$$

The real number factor (such as 3 in the example) is a **scalar**. Multiplication of a matrix A by a scalar c is **scalar multiplication**. To find the resulting matrix cA, you multiply each element of A by c.

take note

Key Concept Scalar Multiplication

To multiply a matrix by a scalar c, multiply each element of the matrix by c.

$$A = \begin{bmatrix} a_{11} & a_{12} & a_{13} \\ a_{21} & a_{22} & a_{23} \end{bmatrix} \quad cA = \begin{bmatrix} ca_{11} & ca_{12} & ca_{13} \\ ca_{21} & ca_{22} & ca_{23} \end{bmatrix}$$

Problem 1 Using Scalar Products

If $A = \begin{bmatrix} 2 & 8 & -3 \\ -1 & 5 & 2 \end{bmatrix}$ and $B = \begin{bmatrix} -1 & 0 & 5 \\ 0 & 3 & -2 \end{bmatrix}$, what is $4A + 3B$?

Think

What operation should you do first?
You should first multiply by the scalars, 4 and 3.

$$4A + 3B = 4\begin{bmatrix} 2 & 8 & -3 \\ -1 & 5 & 2 \end{bmatrix} + 3\begin{bmatrix} -1 & 0 & 5 \\ 0 & 3 & -2 \end{bmatrix}$$

$$= \begin{bmatrix} 8 & 32 & -12 \\ -4 & 20 & 8 \end{bmatrix} + \begin{bmatrix} -3 & 0 & 15 \\ 0 & 9 & -6 \end{bmatrix}$$

$$= \begin{bmatrix} 5 & 32 & 3 \\ -4 & 29 & 2 \end{bmatrix}$$

Got It? **1.** Using matrices A and B from Problem 1, what is $3A - 2B$?

take note

Properties Scalar Multiplication

If A and B are $m \times n$ matrices, c and d are scalars, and O is the $m \times n$ zero matrix, then

Example	Property
cA is an $m \times n$ matrix	Closure Property
$(cd)A = c(dA)$	Associative Property of Multiplication
$c(A + B) = cA + cB$ $(c + d)A = cA + dA$	Distributive Properties
$1 \cdot A = A$	Multiplicative Identity Property
$0 \cdot A = O$ and $cO = O$	Multiplicative Properties of Zero

Problem 2 Solving a Matrix Equation With Scalars

What is the solution of $2X + 3\begin{bmatrix} 2 & -1 \\ 3 & 4 \end{bmatrix} = \begin{bmatrix} 8 & 5 \\ 11 & 0 \end{bmatrix}$?

Think

Where have you seen problems that look like this before?
You saw problems like this when you solved one variable equations like $2x + 3(5) = 20$.

$2X + \begin{bmatrix} 6 & -3 \\ 9 & 12 \end{bmatrix} = \begin{bmatrix} 8 & 5 \\ 11 & 0 \end{bmatrix}$ Multiply by the scalar 3.

$2X = \begin{bmatrix} 8 & 5 \\ 11 & 0 \end{bmatrix} - \begin{bmatrix} 6 & -3 \\ 9 & 12 \end{bmatrix}$ Subtract $\begin{bmatrix} 6 & -3 \\ 9 & 12 \end{bmatrix}$ from each side.

$2X = \begin{bmatrix} 2 & 8 \\ 2 & -12 \end{bmatrix}$ Simplify.

$X = \begin{bmatrix} 1 & 4 \\ 1 & -6 \end{bmatrix}$ Multiply each side by $\frac{1}{2}$ and simplify.

Got It? **2.** What is the solution of $3X - 2\begin{bmatrix} -1 & 5 \\ 7 & 0 \end{bmatrix} = \begin{bmatrix} 17 & -13 \\ -7 & 0 \end{bmatrix}$?

The product of two matrices is a matrix. To find an element in the product matrix, multiply the elements of a row from the first matrix by the corresponding elements of a column from the second matrix. Then add the products.

take note

Key Concept Matrix Multiplication

To find element c_{ij} of the product matrix AB, multiply each element in the ith row of A by the corresponding element in the jth column of B. Then add the products.

$$AB = \begin{bmatrix} a_{11} & a_{12} \\ a_{21} & a_{22} \end{bmatrix}\begin{bmatrix} b_{11} & b_{12} \\ b_{21} & b_{22} \end{bmatrix} = \begin{bmatrix} a_{11}b_{11} + a_{12}b_{21} & a_{11}b_{12} + a_{12}b_{22} \\ a_{21}b_{11} + a_{22}b_{21} & a_{21}b_{12} + a_{22}b_{22} \end{bmatrix}$$

Problem 3 Multiplying Matrices

Think

What relationship must exist between the numbers of elements in a row of *A* and a column of *B*?

They must be equal.

If $A = \begin{bmatrix} 2 & 1 \\ -3 & 0 \end{bmatrix}$ and $B = \begin{bmatrix} -1 & 3 \\ 0 & 4 \end{bmatrix}$, what is AB?

Step 1 Multiply the elements in the first row of A by the elements in the first column of B. Add the products and place the sum in the first row, first column of AB.

$$\begin{bmatrix} 2 & 1 \\ -3 & 0 \end{bmatrix}\begin{bmatrix} -1 & 3 \\ 0 & 4 \end{bmatrix} = \begin{bmatrix} -2 & \_ \\ \_ & \_ \end{bmatrix}$$

$2(-1) + 1(0) = -2$

Step 2 Multiply the elements in the first row of A by the elements in the second column of B. Add the products and place the sum in the first row, second column of AB.

$$\begin{bmatrix} 2 & 1 \\ -3 & 0 \end{bmatrix}\begin{bmatrix} -1 & 3 \\ 0 & 4 \end{bmatrix} = \begin{bmatrix} -2 & 10 \\ \_ & \_ \end{bmatrix}$$

$2(3) + 1(4) = 10$

Repeat Steps 1 and 2 with the second row of A to fill in row two of the product matrix.

Step 3

$$\begin{bmatrix} 2 & 1 \\ -3 & 0 \end{bmatrix}\begin{bmatrix} -1 & 3 \\ 0 & 4 \end{bmatrix} = \begin{bmatrix} -2 & 10 \\ 3 & \_ \end{bmatrix}$$

$(-3)(-1) + 0(0) = 3$

Step 4

$$\begin{bmatrix} 2 & 1 \\ -3 & 0 \end{bmatrix}\begin{bmatrix} -1 & 3 \\ 0 & 4 \end{bmatrix} = \begin{bmatrix} -2 & 10 \\ 3 & -9 \end{bmatrix}$$

$(-3)(3) + 0(4) = -9$

The product of $\begin{bmatrix} 2 & 1 \\ -3 & 0 \end{bmatrix}$ and $\begin{bmatrix} -1 & 3 \\ 0 & 4 \end{bmatrix}$ is $\begin{bmatrix} -2 & 10 \\ 3 & -9 \end{bmatrix}$.

Got It? 3. If $A = \begin{bmatrix} 2 & -1 \\ 3 & 4 \end{bmatrix}$ and $B = \begin{bmatrix} -3 & 1 \\ 0 & 2 \end{bmatrix}$, what are the following products?

a. AB

b. BA

c. Reasoning Is matrix multiplication commutative? Explain.

Problem 4 Applying Matrix Multiplication

Sports **In 1966, Washington and New York (Giants) played the highest scoring game in National Football League history. The table summarizes the scoring. A touchdown (TD) is worth 6 points, a field goal (FG) is worth 3 points, a safety (S) is worth 2 points, and a point after touchdown (PAT) is worth 1 point. Using matrix multiplication, what was the final score?**

	TD	FG	S	PAT
WASHINGTON	10	1	0	9
NEW YORK	6	0	0	5

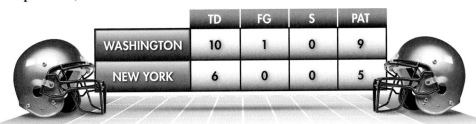

Know
- The number of each type of score
- The point value of each score

Need
The scoring summary and point values as matrices

Plan
Multiply the matrices to find each team's final score.

Think
What is the meaning of each number in matrix *P*?
They are the point values for each type of score.

Step 1 Enter the information in matrices.

$$S = \begin{bmatrix} 10 & 1 & 0 & 9 \\ 6 & 0 & 0 & 5 \end{bmatrix} \qquad P = \begin{bmatrix} 6 \\ 3 \\ 2 \\ 1 \end{bmatrix}$$

Step 2 Use matrix multiplication. The final score is the product SP.

$$SP = \begin{bmatrix} 10 & 1 & 0 & 9 \\ 6 & 0 & 0 & 5 \end{bmatrix} \begin{bmatrix} 6 \\ 3 \\ 2 \\ 1 \end{bmatrix}$$

$$= \begin{bmatrix} 10(6) + 1(3) + 0(2) + 9(1) \\ 6(6) + 0(3) + 0(2) + 5(1) \end{bmatrix} = \begin{bmatrix} 72 \\ 41 \end{bmatrix}$$

Step 3 Interpret the product matrix.

The first row of SP shows scoring for Washington, so the final score was Washington 72, New York 41.

Got It? **4.** There are three ways to score in a basketball game: three-point field goals, two-point field goals, and one-point free throws. In 1994, suppose a high school player scored 36 two-point field goals and 28 free throws. In 2006, suppose a high school player scored 7 three-point field goals, 21 two-point field goals, and 18 free throws. Using matrix multiplication, how many points did each player score?

You can multiply two matrices A and B only if the number of columns of A is equal to the number of rows of B.

take note — Property: Dimensions of a Product Matrix

If A is an $m \times n$ matrix and B is an $n \times p$ matrix, then the product matrix AB is an $m \times p$ matrix.

$$\text{matrix } A \cdot \text{matrix } B$$

$$\underset{\text{3 rows, 2 columns}}{\begin{bmatrix} 1 & 2 \\ 3 & 4 \\ 5 & 6 \end{bmatrix}} \quad \underset{\text{2 rows, 4 columns}}{\begin{bmatrix} 7 & 8 & 9 & 10 \\ 11 & 12 & 13 & 14 \end{bmatrix}}$$

3 rows

2 columns

2 rows

4 columns

equal

dimensions of product matrix

Product matrix AB is a 3×4 matrix.

Problem 5 Determining Whether Product Matrices Exist

Does either product AB or BA exist?

$$A = \begin{bmatrix} -2 & 1 \\ 3 & -2 \\ 0 & 1 \end{bmatrix} \qquad B = \begin{bmatrix} -1 & 0 & 2 & 1 \\ 2 & 0 & 0 & 3 \end{bmatrix}$$

Think

How can you tell if a product matrix exists without computing it?
Compare the dimensions of the matrices.

AB

$(3 \times 2)(2 \times 4) \rightarrow 3 \times 4$ product matrix

equal

Product AB exists.

BA

$(2 \times 4)(3 \times 2) \rightarrow$ no product

not equal

Got It? **5.** Do the following products exist?

$$A = \begin{bmatrix} 1 & 4 \\ -3 & 5 \end{bmatrix} \qquad B = \begin{bmatrix} -1 & 1 \end{bmatrix} \qquad C = \begin{bmatrix} 4 & 2 & 0 \\ 1 & 3 & 5 \end{bmatrix}$$

a. AB **b.** BA **c.** AC **d.** CA **e.** BC

Matrix multiplication of square $(n \times n)$ matrices has some of the properties of real number multiplication.

take note — Properties: Matrix Multiplication

If A, B, and C are $n \times n$ matrices, and O is the $n \times n$ zero matrix, then

Example	Property
AB is an $n \times n$ matrix	**Closure Property**
$(AB)C = A(BC)$	**Associative Property of Multiplication**
$A(B + C) = AB + AC$ $(B + C)A = BA + CA$	**Distributive Property**
$OA = AO = O$	**Multiplicative Property of Zero**

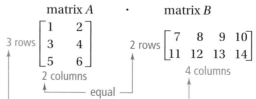

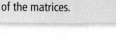

Lesson Check

Do you know HOW?

Let $A = \begin{bmatrix} 3 & -1 \\ 2 & 0 \end{bmatrix}$ and $B = \begin{bmatrix} 1 & 3 \\ -2 & 2 \end{bmatrix}$.

Find each of the following.

1. $2A$

2. $3B - 2A$

3. AB

4. BA

Do you UNDERSTAND? MATHEMATICAL PRACTICES

5. Vocabulary Which type of multiplication, *scalar* or *matrix*, can help you with a repeated matrix addition problem? Explain.

6. Error Analysis Your friend says there is a right order and a wrong order when multiplying A (a 2×4 matrix) and B (a 3×6 matrix). Explain your friend's error.

Practice and Problem-Solving Exercises

MATHEMATICAL PRACTICES

A Practice

Use matrices A, B, C, and D. Find each product, sum, or difference.

See Problem 1.

$A = \begin{bmatrix} 3 & 4 \\ 6 & -2 \\ 1 & 0 \end{bmatrix}$ $B = \begin{bmatrix} -3 & 1 \\ 2 & -4 \\ -1 & 5 \end{bmatrix}$ $C = \begin{bmatrix} 1 & 2 \\ -3 & 1 \end{bmatrix}$ $D = \begin{bmatrix} 5 & 1 \\ 0 & 2 \end{bmatrix}$

7. $3A$

8. $4B$

9. $-3C$

10. $-D$

11. $A - 2B$

12. $3A + 2B$

13. $4C + 3D$

14. $2A - 5B$

Solve each matrix equation. Check your answers.

See Problem 2.

15. $3\begin{bmatrix} 2 & 0 \\ -1 & 5 \end{bmatrix} - 2X = \begin{bmatrix} -10 & 5 \\ 0 & 17 \end{bmatrix}$

16. $4X + \begin{bmatrix} 1 & 3 \\ -7 & 9 \end{bmatrix} = \begin{bmatrix} -3 & 11 \\ 5 & -7 \end{bmatrix}$

17. $\frac{1}{2}X + \begin{bmatrix} 4 & -3 \\ 12 & 1 \end{bmatrix} = \begin{bmatrix} 2 & 1 \\ 1 & 2 \end{bmatrix}$

18. $5X - \begin{bmatrix} 1.5 & -3.6 \\ -0.3 & 2.8 \end{bmatrix} = \begin{bmatrix} 0.2 & 1.3 \\ -5.6 & 1.7 \end{bmatrix}$

Find each product.

See Problem 3.

19. $\begin{bmatrix} -3 & 4 \\ 5 & 2 \end{bmatrix}\begin{bmatrix} 1 & 0 \\ 2 & -3 \end{bmatrix}$

20. $\begin{bmatrix} 1 & 0 \\ 2 & -3 \end{bmatrix}\begin{bmatrix} -3 & 4 \\ 5 & 2 \end{bmatrix}$

21. $\begin{bmatrix} 0 & 2 \\ -4 & 0 \end{bmatrix}\begin{bmatrix} 0 & 2 \\ -4 & 0 \end{bmatrix}$

22. $\begin{bmatrix} -3 & 5 \end{bmatrix}\begin{bmatrix} -3 \\ 5 \end{bmatrix}$

23. $\begin{bmatrix} -3 & 5 \end{bmatrix}\begin{bmatrix} -3 & 0 \\ 5 & 0 \end{bmatrix}$

24. $\begin{bmatrix} -3 & 5 \end{bmatrix}\begin{bmatrix} 0 & -3 \\ 0 & 5 \end{bmatrix}$

25. $\begin{bmatrix} 0 & -3 \\ 0 & 5 \end{bmatrix}\begin{bmatrix} -3 & 0 \\ 5 & 0 \end{bmatrix}$

26. $\begin{bmatrix} 1 & 0 \\ -1 & -5 \\ 0 & 3 \end{bmatrix}\begin{bmatrix} -1 & 0 \\ 0 & -1 \end{bmatrix}$

27. $\begin{bmatrix} -1 & 3 & -3 \\ 2 & -2 & 1 \end{bmatrix}\begin{bmatrix} 5 \\ 4 \\ 3 \end{bmatrix}$

28. Business A florist makes three special floral arrangements. One uses three lilies. The second uses three lilies and four carnations. The third uses four daisies and three carnations. Lilies cost \$2.15 each, carnations cost \$.90 each, and daisies cost \$1.30 each.

See Problem 4.

a. Write a matrix to show the number of each type of flower in each arrangement.

b. Write a matrix to show the cost of each type of flower.

c. Find the matrix showing the cost of each floral arrangement.

Determine whether the product exists.

See Problem 5.

$F = \begin{bmatrix} 2 & 3 \\ 6 & 9 \end{bmatrix}$ $\quad G = \begin{bmatrix} -3 & 6 \\ 2 & -4 \end{bmatrix}$ $\quad H = \begin{bmatrix} -5 \\ 6 \end{bmatrix}$ $\quad J = \begin{bmatrix} 0 & 7 \end{bmatrix}$

29. FG **30.** GF **31.** FH **32.** HG **33.** JH

B Apply

34. Think About a Plan A hardware store chain sells hammers for \$3, flashlights for \$5, and lanterns for \$7. The store manager tracks the daily purchases at three of the chain's stores in a 3 × 3 matrix. What is the total gross revenue from the flashlights sold at all three stores?

Number of Items Sold

	Store A	Store B	Store C
Hammers	10	9	8
Flashlights	3	14	6
Lanterns	2	5	7

- How can you use matrix multiplication to solve this problem?
- What does the product matrix represent?

35. Sports Two teams are competing in a two-team track meet. Points for individual events are awarded as follows: 5 points for first place, 3 points for second place, and 1 point for third place. Points for team relays are awarded as follows: 5 points for first place and no points for second place.

a. Use matrix operations to determine the score in the track meet.

	Individual Events			Relays	
Team	First	Second	Third	First	Second
West River	8	5	2	8	5
River's Edge	6	9	12	6	9

b. Who would win if the scoring was changed to 5 points for first place, 2 points for second place, and 1 point for third place in each individual event and 5 points for first place and 0 points for second place in a relay?

For Exercises 36–43, use matrices *D*, *E*, and *F*. Perform the indicated operations if they are defined. If an operation is not defined, label it *undefined*.

$D = \begin{bmatrix} 1 & 2 & -1 \\ 0 & 3 & 1 \\ 2 & -1 & -2 \end{bmatrix}$ $\quad E = \begin{bmatrix} 2 & -5 & 0 \\ 1 & 0 & -2 \\ 3 & 1 & 1 \end{bmatrix}$ $\quad F = \begin{bmatrix} -3 & 2 \\ -5 & 1 \\ 2 & 4 \end{bmatrix}$

36. DE **37.** $-3F$ **38.** $(DE)F$ **39.** $D(EF)$

40. $D - 2E$ **41.** $(E - D)F$ **42.** $(DD)E$ **43.** $(2D)(3F)$

44. Writing Suppose A is a 2 × 3 matrix and B is a 3 × 2 matrix with elements not all being equal. Are AB and BA equal? Explain your reasoning. Include examples.

Challenge For Exercises 45–48, use matrices P, Q, R, S, and I. Determine whether the two expressions in each pair are equal.

$$P = \begin{bmatrix} 3 & 4 \\ 1 & 2 \end{bmatrix} \quad Q = \begin{bmatrix} 1 & 0 \\ 3 & -2 \end{bmatrix} \quad R = \begin{bmatrix} 1 & 4 \\ -2 & 1 \end{bmatrix} \quad S = \begin{bmatrix} 0 & 1 \\ 2 & 0 \end{bmatrix} \quad I = \begin{bmatrix} 1 & 0 \\ 0 & 1 \end{bmatrix}$$

45. $(P + Q)R$ and $PR + QR$

46. $(P + Q)I$ and $PI + QI$

47. $(P + Q)(R + S)$ and $(P + Q)R + (P + Q)S$

48. $(P + Q)(R + S)$ and $PR + PS + QR + QS$

Concept Byte

For Use With Lesson A-2

Networks

Content Standard

N.VM.6 Use matrices to represent and manipulate data . . .

A finite graph is a set of points, called vertices, connected by curves, or paths.

You can use a matrix to describe a finite graph. The digit "1" indicates a path between two vertices or one vertex and itself. The digit "0" indicates that no path exists between two vertices or from one vertex to itself.

Example 1

Write a matrix A to represent the finite graph. Explain the significance of element a_{41}.

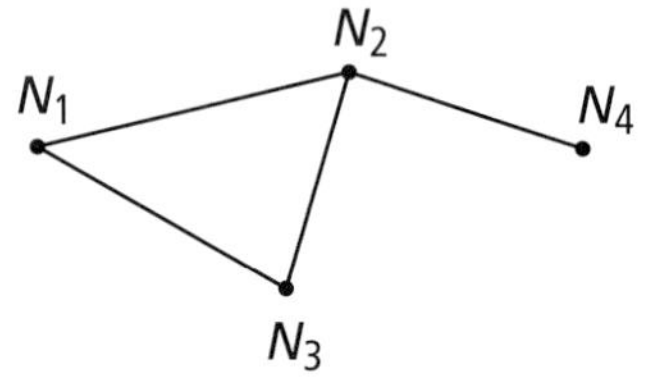

$$A = \begin{array}{c} \\ N_1 \\ N_2 \\ N_3 \\ N_4 \end{array} \begin{array}{c} \begin{array}{cccc} N_1 & N_2 & N_3 & N_4 \end{array} \\ \begin{bmatrix} 0 & 1 & 1 & 0 \\ 1 & 0 & 1 & 1 \\ 1 & 1 & 0 & 0 \\ 0 & 1 & 0 & 0 \end{bmatrix} \end{array}$$

There is a path from N_2 to N_4.

Element a_{41} is 0. It indicates that there is no path between N_4 and N_1.

Directed graphs are finite graphs that indicate the direction of a path. The directed graph below represents the information in the map.

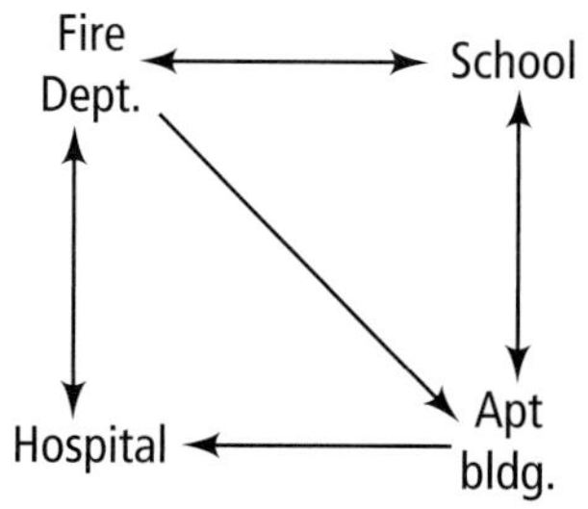

You can use a matrix to represent the information in a directed graph.

Example 2

Write a matrix B to represent the information from the directed graph. Compare elements b_{12} and b_{21}.

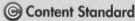

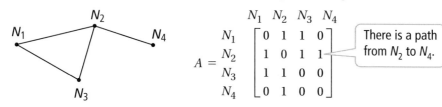

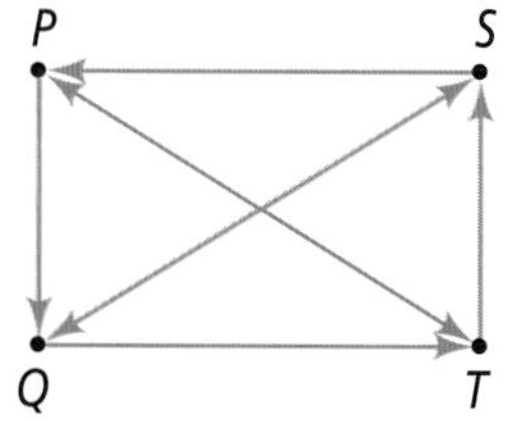

$$B = \begin{array}{r} \text{To} \rightarrow \\ \text{From} \rightarrow P \\ Q \\ S \\ T \end{array} \begin{array}{c} \begin{array}{cccc} P & Q & S & T \end{array} \\ \begin{bmatrix} 0 & 1 & 0 & 1 \\ 0 & 0 & 1 & 1 \\ 1 & 1 & 0 & 0 \\ 1 & 0 & 1 & 0 \end{bmatrix} \end{array}$$

Element b_{12} is 1 and b_{21} is 0. The path between P and Q is one way, from P to Q.

Example 3

Draw a directed graph to represent the information in the matrix.

$$\begin{array}{l} \text{To} \rightarrow \\ \text{From} \rightarrow \\ C = \\ \end{array} \begin{array}{c} \\ A \\ B \\ C \end{array} \begin{array}{c} \begin{array}{ccc} A & B & C \end{array} \\ \begin{bmatrix} 1 & 1 & 1 \\ 1 & 0 & 1 \\ 0 & 0 & 0 \end{bmatrix} \end{array}$$

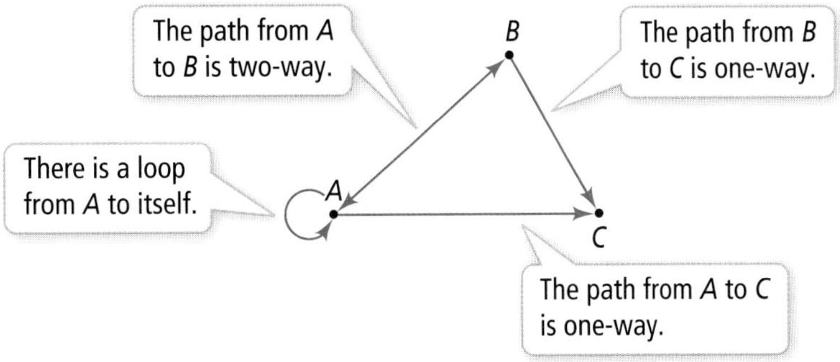

The path from A to B is two-way.
The path from B to C is one-way.
There is a loop from A to itself.
The path from A to C is one-way.
A
B
C

Exercises

Write a matrix to represent each finite or directed graph.

1. 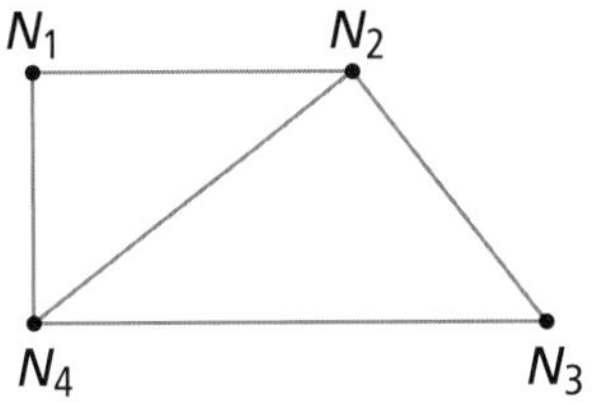

2. 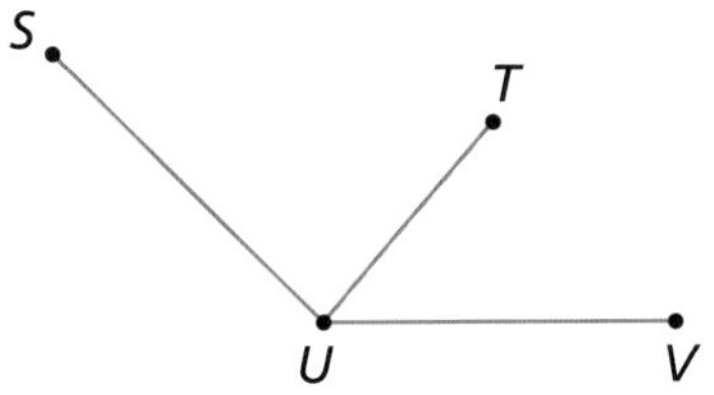

3. 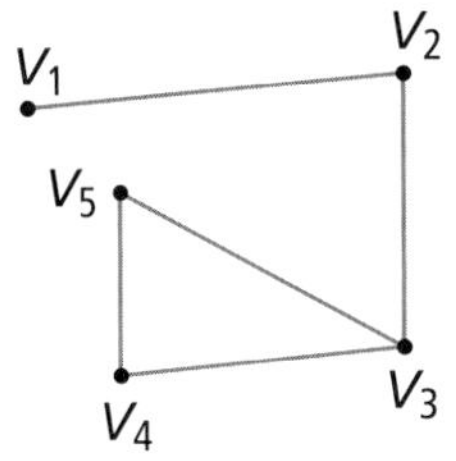

4. 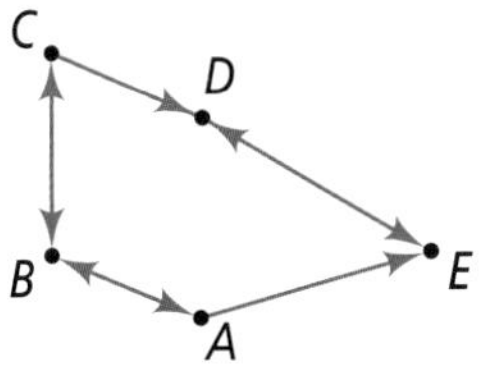

5. 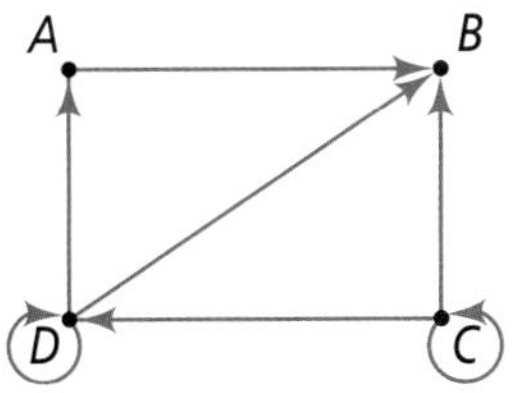

6. 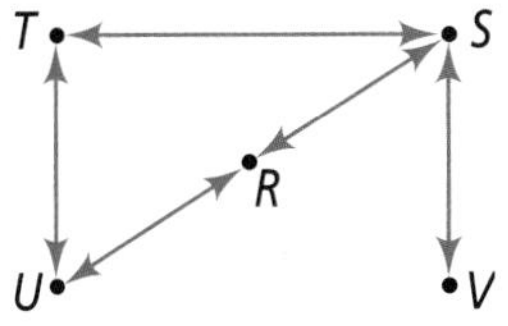

Draw a directed graph to represent the information in each matrix.

7.
$$\begin{array}{c} \\ J \\ K \\ L \\ M \end{array} \begin{array}{c} \begin{array}{cccc} J & K & L & M \end{array} \\ \begin{bmatrix} 0 & 0 & 0 & 1 \\ 0 & 0 & 1 & 1 \\ 0 & 1 & 0 & 1 \\ 1 & 1 & 1 & 0 \end{bmatrix} \end{array}$$

8.
$$\begin{array}{c} \\ A \\ B \\ C \\ D \end{array} \begin{array}{c} \begin{array}{cccc} A & B & C & D \end{array} \\ \begin{bmatrix} 0 & 0 & 1 & 1 \\ 1 & 1 & 0 & 0 \\ 0 & 1 & 0 & 1 \\ 1 & 0 & 1 & 0 \end{bmatrix} \end{array}$$

9.
$$\begin{array}{c} \\ N_1 \\ N_2 \\ N_3 \\ N_4 \end{array} \begin{array}{c} \begin{array}{cccc} N_1 & N_2 & N_3 & N_4 \end{array} \\ \begin{bmatrix} 1 & 1 & 1 & 1 \\ 0 & 0 & 1 & 1 \\ 1 & 0 & 0 & 0 \\ 0 & 0 & 1 & 0 \end{bmatrix} \end{array}$$

10. Travel Alice and Becky live on Parkway East, at the intersections of Owens Bridge and Bay Bridge, respectively. Carl and David live on Parkway West, at the intersections of Bay Bridge and Owens Bridge, respectively. Parkway East is a one-way street running east. Parkway West is one-way running west. Both bridges are two-way.

a. Draw a directed graph indicating road travel between the houses.

b. Write a matrix T to represent the information in the directed graph.

c. Writing Calculate T^2. What does the matrix model? Explain.

A-3 Determinants and Inverses

Content Standards

N.VM.10 . . . The determinant of a square matrix is nonzero if and only if the matrix has a multiplicative inverse.

N.VM.12 Work with 2 × 2 matrices as a transformation of the plane . . .

Objective To find the inverse of a matrix

MATHEMATICAL PRACTICES

SOLVE IT! **Getting Ready!**

What is the area of the triangle? Explain how you found your answer.

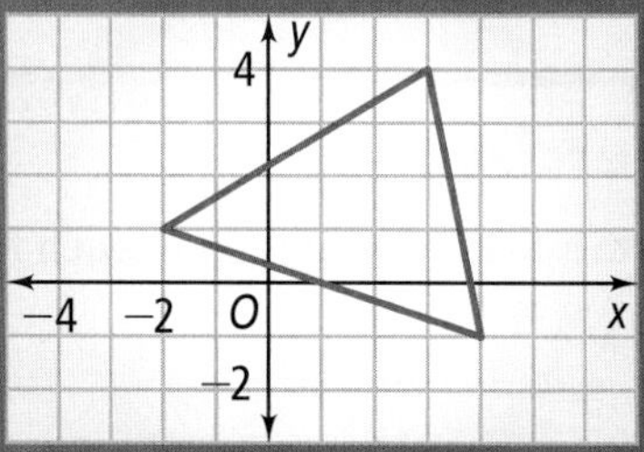

Lesson Vocabulary
- square matrix
- multiplicative identity matrix
- multiplicative inverse matrix
- determinant
- singular matrix

This lesson will prepare you to use matrices to solve problems, including how to find the area of a triangle with vertices anywhere in the coordinate plane.

Essential Understanding The product of a matrix and its *multiplicative inverse matrix* is the *multiplicative identity matrix*. Not all matrices have inverse matrices.

A **square matrix** is a matrix with the same number of rows and columns. While there is a multiplicative identity matrix for any square matrix, not all square matrices have multiplicative inverses.

take note — Key Concepts Identity and Multiplicative Inverse Matrices

For an $n \times n$ matrix, the **multiplicative identity matrix** is an $n \times n$ matrix I, or I_n, with 1's along the main diagonal and 0's elsewhere.

$$I_2 = \begin{bmatrix} 1 & 0 \\ 0 & 1 \end{bmatrix}, \quad I_3 = \begin{bmatrix} 1 & 0 & 0 \\ 0 & 1 & 0 \\ 0 & 0 & 1 \end{bmatrix}, \quad \text{and so forth.}$$

If A and B are square matrices and $AB = BA = I$, then B is the **multiplicative inverse matrix** of A, written A^{-1}.

Think

How do you determine whether *A* and *B* are inverses?
Find *AB* and *BA*. Each product must equal *I*.

Problem 1 Determining Whether Matrices are Inverses

For each of the following, are matrices A and B inverses?

A $A = \begin{bmatrix} 1 & 2 \\ 3 & 4 \end{bmatrix}$ $\quad B = \begin{bmatrix} -2 & 1 \\ \frac{3}{2} & -\frac{1}{2} \end{bmatrix}$

Since $AB = I$ and $BA = I$,
matrices A and B are inverses.

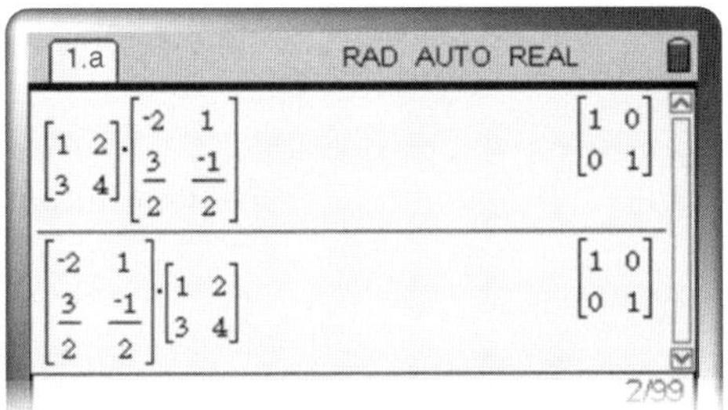

B $A = \begin{bmatrix} 1 & 0 & 2 \\ -2 & 1 & 1 \\ -1 & 1 & 2 \end{bmatrix}$ $\quad B = \begin{bmatrix} -1 & -2 & 2 \\ -3 & -4 & 5 \\ 1 & 1 & -1 \end{bmatrix}$

Since $AB = I$ and $BA = I$,
matrices A and B are inverses.

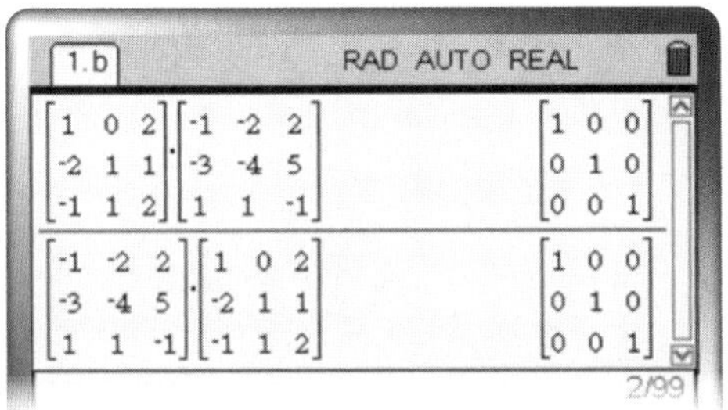

C $A = \begin{bmatrix} 2 & 4 \\ 2 & 2 \end{bmatrix}$ $\quad B = \begin{bmatrix} 2 & 5 \\ -1 & -3 \end{bmatrix}$

Since $AB \neq I$ (and $BA \neq I$),
matrices A and B are not inverses.

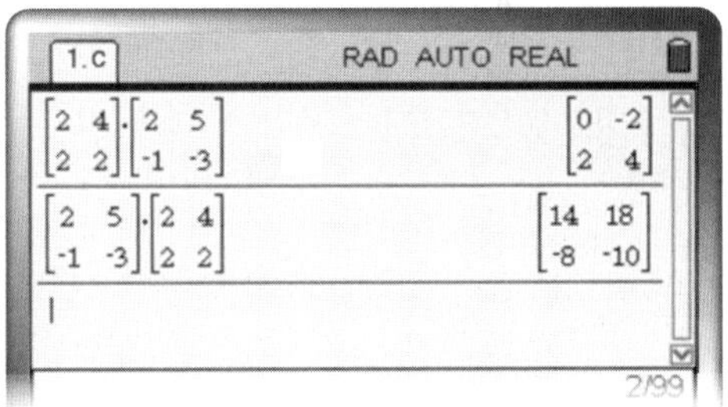

Got It? 1. For each of the following, are A and B inverses?

a. $A = \begin{bmatrix} 1 & 1 \\ 5 & 4 \end{bmatrix}$ $\quad B = \begin{bmatrix} -4 & 1 \\ 5 & -1 \end{bmatrix}$

b. $A = \begin{bmatrix} 3 & 2 \\ 5 & 4 \end{bmatrix}$ $\quad B = \begin{bmatrix} 2 & -1 \\ -\frac{5}{2} & \frac{3}{2} \end{bmatrix}$

c. Reasoning Does the matrix $\begin{bmatrix} 0 & 0 \\ 0 & 0 \end{bmatrix}$ have an inverse? Explain.

Every square matrix with real-number elements has a number associated with it. The number is its *determinant*. Given $A = \begin{bmatrix} a & b \\ c & d \end{bmatrix}$,

Write	**Read**	**Evaluate**
↓	↓	↓
det A	the determinant of A	$\det \begin{bmatrix} a & b \\ c & d \end{bmatrix} = ad - bc$

Key Concept Determinants of 2 × 2 and 3 × 3 Matrices

The **determinant** of a 2×2 matrix $\begin{bmatrix} a & b \\ c & d \end{bmatrix}$ is det $\begin{bmatrix} a & b \\ c & d \end{bmatrix} = ad - bc$.

The determinant of a 3×3 matrix $\begin{bmatrix} a_1 & b_1 & c_1 \\ a_2 & b_2 & c_2 \\ a_3 & b_3 & c_3 \end{bmatrix}$ is

$$a_1 b_2 c_3 + b_1 c_2 a_3 + c_1 a_2 b_3 - (a_3 b_2 c_1 + b_3 c_2 a_1 + c_3 a_2 b_1)$$

a copy of the first two columns

Visualize the pattern this way:

$$\begin{bmatrix} a_1 & b_1 & c_1 \\ a_2 & b_2 & c_2 \\ a_3 & b_3 & c_3 \end{bmatrix} \begin{matrix} a_1 & b_1 \\ a_2 & b_2 \\ a_3 & b_3 \end{matrix}$$

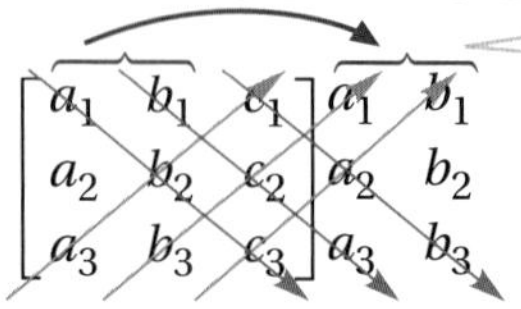

© **Problem 2** Evaluating the Determinants of Matrices

What can you do first to evaluate a 3 × 3 determinant?

Copy the first two columns to the right of the matrix.

$$\begin{bmatrix} 1 & 0 & -2 \\ 0 & 4 & -1 \\ 3 & 5 & 2 \end{bmatrix} \begin{matrix} 1 & 0 \\ 0 & 4 \\ 3 & 5 \end{matrix}$$

What are the following determinants?

A det $\begin{bmatrix} 3 & -1 \\ 2 & 5 \end{bmatrix} = (3)(5) - (-1)(2) = 15 - (-2) = 17$

B det $\begin{bmatrix} 1 & 0 & -2 \\ 0 & 4 & -1 \\ 3 & 5 & 2 \end{bmatrix} = (1)(4)(2) + (0)(-1)(3) + (-2)(0)(5)$

$$- [(3)(4)(-2) + (5)(-1)(1) + (2)(0)(0)]$$

$$= 8 + 0 + 0 - (-24 - 5 + 0)$$

$$= 37$$

Check Use a graphing calculator.

1.1 RAD AUTO REAL

det $\begin{bmatrix} 1 & 0 & -2 \\ 0 & 4 & -1 \\ 3 & 5 & 2 \end{bmatrix}$ 37

1/99

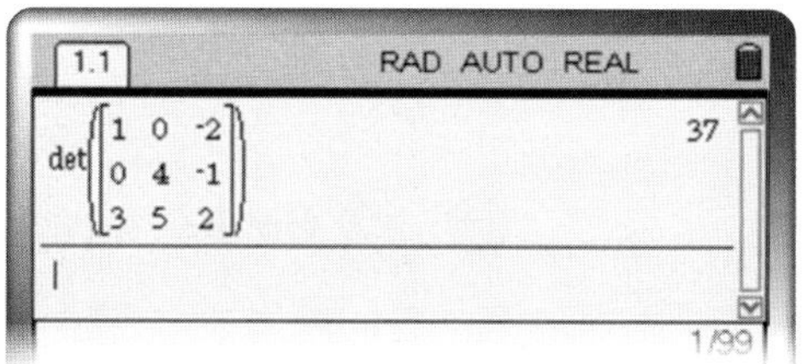

✓ **Got It? 2.** What are the determinants of the following matrices?

a. $\begin{bmatrix} 3 & 6 \\ 2 & 5 \end{bmatrix}$ **b.** $\begin{bmatrix} -2 & 0 \\ 3 & 0 \end{bmatrix}$ **c.** $\begin{bmatrix} 1 & 0 & 3 \\ 2 & 4 & 6 \\ 5 & -1 & 3 \end{bmatrix}$

You can use determinants to find the areas of polygons. Since all polygons can be divided into triangles, all you need is a way to find the area of a triangle.

Key Concept Area of a Triangle

The area of a triangle with vertices (x_1, y_1), (x_2, y_2), and (x_3, y_3) is

Area $= \frac{1}{2} |\det A|$ where $A = \begin{bmatrix} x_1 & y_1 & 1 \\ x_2 & y_2 & 1 \\ x_3 & y_3 & 1 \end{bmatrix}$

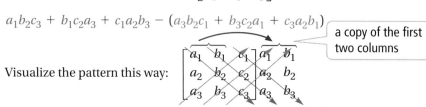

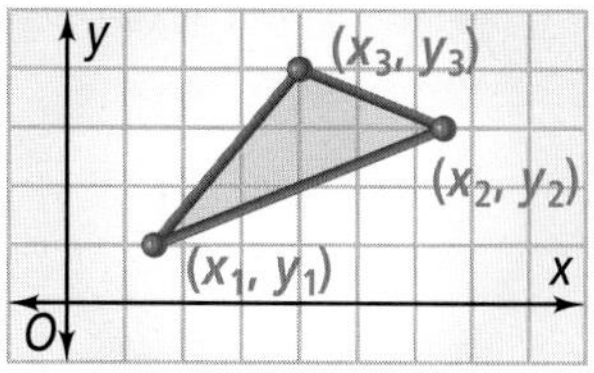

Problem 3 Finding the Area of a Polygon

Land **One factor in flood safety along a levee is the area that will absorb water should the levee break. The coordinates shown are in miles. What is the area in the pictured California community?**

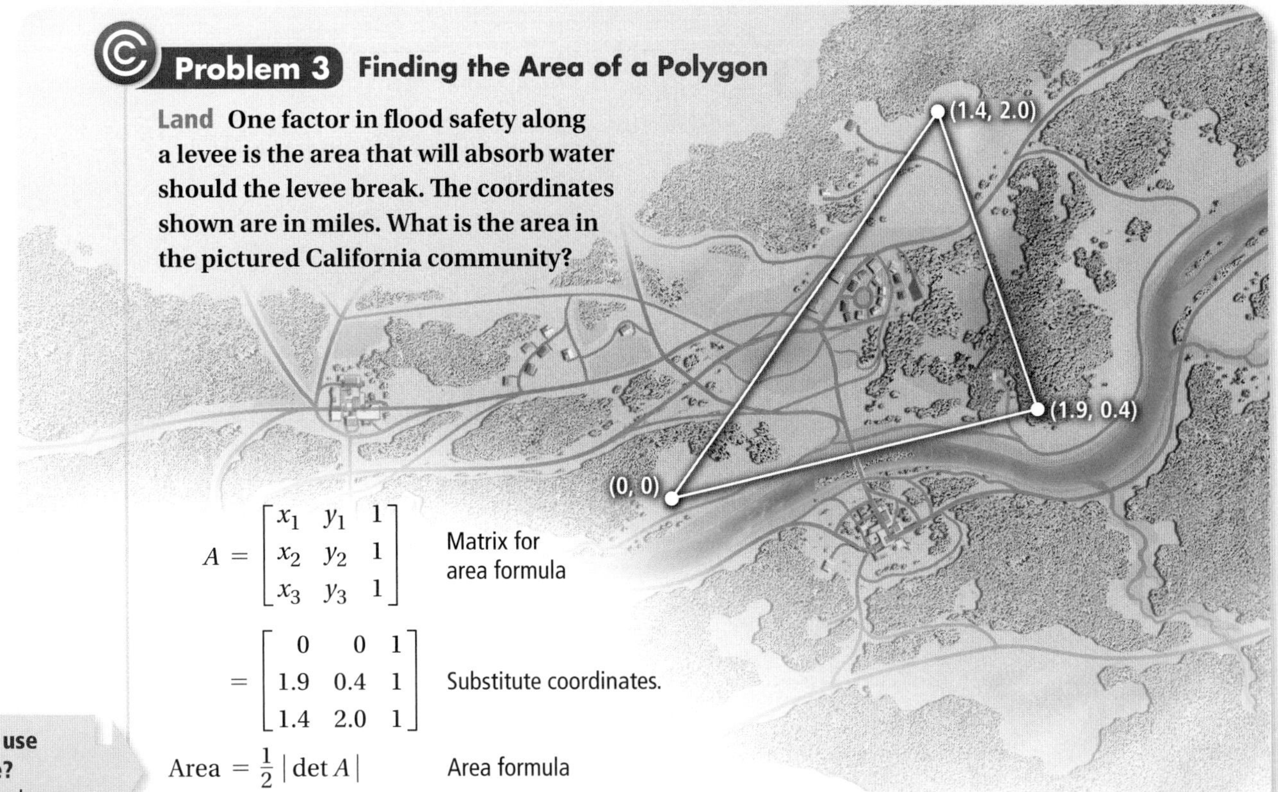

$$A = \begin{bmatrix} x_1 & y_1 & 1 \\ x_2 & y_2 & 1 \\ x_3 & y_3 & 1 \end{bmatrix}$$ Matrix for area formula

$$= \begin{bmatrix} 0 & 0 & 1 \\ 1.9 & 0.4 & 1 \\ 1.4 & 2.0 & 1 \end{bmatrix}$$ Substitute coordinates.

$$\text{Area} = \frac{1}{2}\,|\det A|$$ Area formula

$$= 1.62$$ Use a calculator to evaluate.

Think

Why must you use absolute value?
A determinant can be positive or negative. Area must be positive.

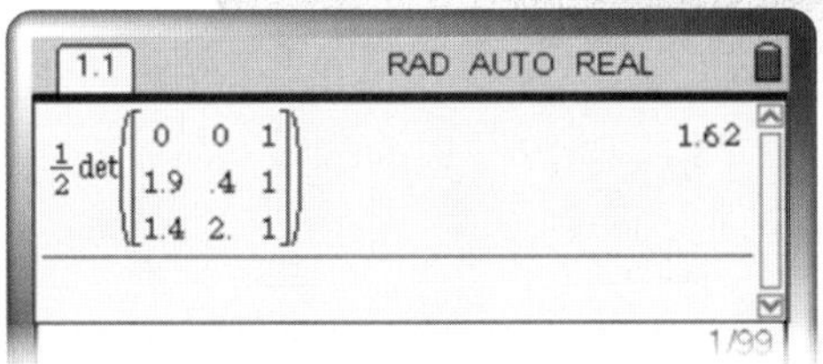

The area of the triangle is 1.62 mi^2.

Check for Reasonableness The area is approximately one-half the area of a 1.9 by 2 rectangle. Thus, an area of about 1.6 units^2 is reasonable.

Got It? **3.** What is the area of the triangle with the given vertices?

a. (1, 3), (−3, 0), (5, 0) **b.** (1, 3), (5, 8), (9, −1)

The determinant of a matrix can help you determine whether the matrix has an inverse and, if it exists, to find the inverse.

take note

Key Concept Inverse of a 2 × 2 Matrix

Let $A = \begin{bmatrix} a & b \\ c & d \end{bmatrix}$.

If $\det A = 0$, then A is a **singular matrix** and has no inverse.

If $\det A \neq 0$, then the inverse of A, written A^{-1}, is

$$A^{-1} = \frac{1}{\det A}\begin{bmatrix} d & -b \\ -c & a \end{bmatrix} = \frac{1}{ad - bc}\begin{bmatrix} d & -b \\ -c & a \end{bmatrix}.$$

Problem 4 Finding the Inverse of a Matrix

Does the matrix $A = \begin{bmatrix} -3 & 6 \\ -1 & 3 \end{bmatrix}$ have an inverse? If it does, what is A^{-1}?

Think	Write
Evaluate det A. If det $A \neq 0$, the matrix has an inverse.	$\det A = ad - bc$ $= (-3)(3) - (6)(-1)$ $= -9 - (-6)$ $= -9 + 6$ $= -3$ det $A \neq 0$, so A has an inverse.
Find A^{-1}. Switch elements on the main diagonal. Change signs on the other diagonal.	$A^{-1} = \frac{1}{\det A}\begin{bmatrix} d & -b \\ -c & a \end{bmatrix}$
From above, det $A = -3$. For A, $a = -3$, $b = 6$, $c = -1$, and $d = 3$.	$= \frac{1}{-3}\begin{bmatrix} 3 & -6 \\ 1 & -3 \end{bmatrix}$
Multiply by the scalar and simplify the fractions.	$= \begin{bmatrix} \frac{3}{-3} & \frac{-6}{-3} \\ \frac{1}{-3} & \frac{-3}{-3} \end{bmatrix}$ $= \begin{bmatrix} -1 & 2 \\ -\frac{1}{3} & 1 \end{bmatrix}$

Check Use a graphing calculator.

Method 1

Check that $AA^{-1} = I$.

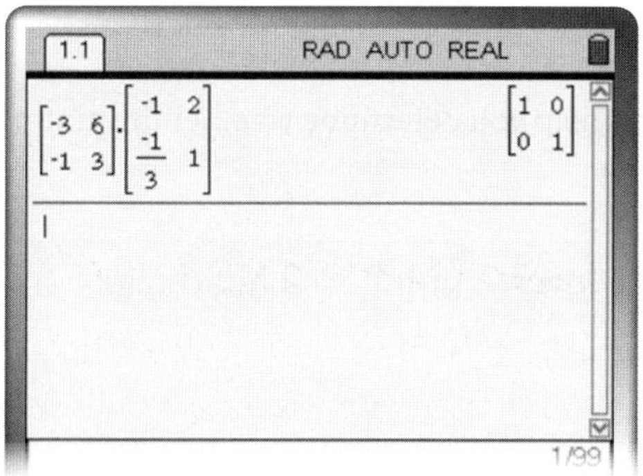

Method 2

Find A^{-1}.

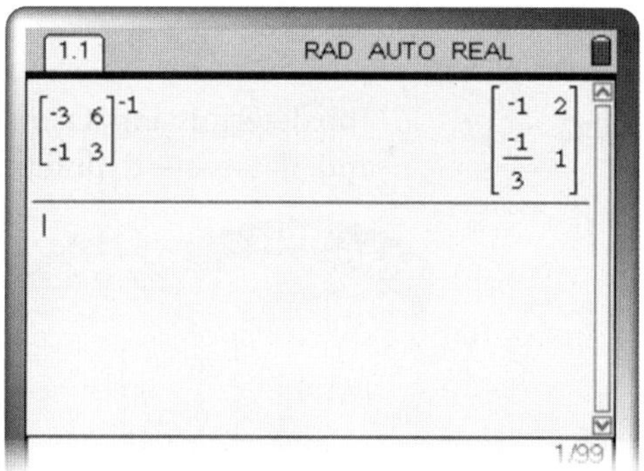

Got It? 4. Does the matrix have an inverse? If so, what is it?

a. $A = \begin{bmatrix} 4 & 2 \\ 3 & 2 \end{bmatrix}$ **b.** $B = \begin{bmatrix} 2 & 5 \\ -4 & -10 \end{bmatrix}$ **c.** $C = \begin{bmatrix} 7 & 4 \\ 5 & 3 \end{bmatrix}$

Problem 5 Encoding and Decoding With Matrices

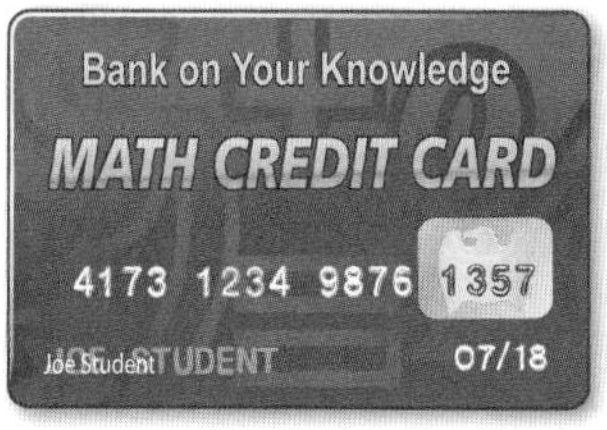

A **How can you use matrix multiplication to encode the account number from the credit card?**

Plan

What size array should you use for the card information? Since the coding matrix has two columns, the information matrix must have two rows, so they can be multiplied.

Step 1 Select a coding matrix. $C = \begin{bmatrix} 2 & -1 \\ 3 & 5 \end{bmatrix}$

Step 2 Place the card information in a matrix with appropriate dimensions for multiplication by the coding matrix.

$$A = \begin{bmatrix} 4 & 1 & 7 & 3 & 1 & 2 & 3 & 4 \\ 9 & 8 & 7 & 6 & 1 & 3 & 5 & 7 \end{bmatrix}$$

Step 3 Multiply the coding matrix and the information matrix to encode the information. Use a calculator.

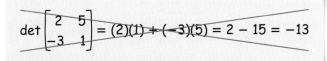

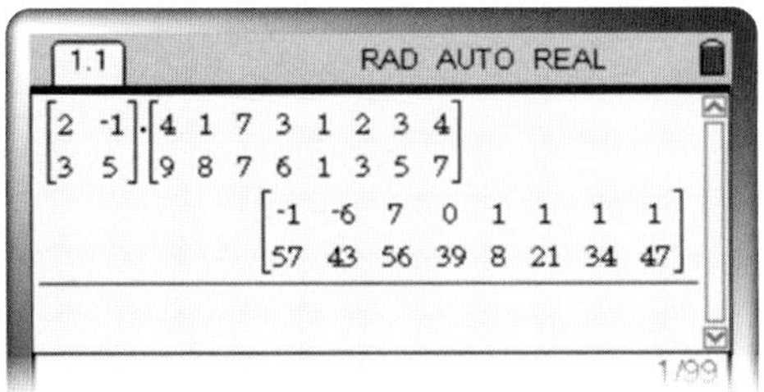

1.1
RAD AUTO REAL
[2 -1; 3 5]·[4 1 7 3 1 2 3 4; 9 8 7 6 1 3 5 7]
[-1 -6 7 0 1 1 1 1; 57 43 56 39 8 21 34 47]
1/99

$$CA = \begin{bmatrix} 2 & -1 \\ 3 & 5 \end{bmatrix}\begin{bmatrix} 4 & 1 & 7 & 3 & 1 & 2 & 3 & 4 \\ 9 & 8 & 7 & 6 & 1 & 3 & 5 & 7 \end{bmatrix}$$

$$= \begin{bmatrix} -1 & -6 & 7 & 0 & 1 & 1 & 1 & 1 \\ 57 & 43 & 56 & 39 & 8 & 21 & 34 & 47 \end{bmatrix}$$

Step 4 The coded account number is
$-1, -6, 7, 0, 1, 1, 1, 1, 57, 43, 56, 39, 8, 21, 34, 47$.

B **How do you use a decoding matrix to recover the account number?**

Multiply the coded information by the inverse of the coding matrix.

$$\begin{bmatrix} 2 & -1 \\ 3 & 5 \end{bmatrix}^{-1}\begin{bmatrix} -1 & -6 & 7 & 0 & 1 & 1 & 1 & 1 \\ 57 & 43 & 56 & 39 & 8 & 21 & 34 & 47 \end{bmatrix} = \begin{bmatrix} 4 & 1 & 7 & 3 & 1 & 2 & 3 & 4 \\ 9 & 8 & 7 & 6 & 1 & 3 & 5 & 7 \end{bmatrix}$$

Got It? **5. a.** How can you use matrix multiplication and the coding matrix $\begin{bmatrix} 4 & 8 \\ -2 & 4 \end{bmatrix}$ to encode the credit card account number in Problem 5?

b. How can you use the inverse of the coding matrix to recover the credit card number?

Lesson Check

Do you know HOW?

Evaluate the determinant of each matrix.

1. $\begin{bmatrix} 4 & -1 \\ 8 & 2 \end{bmatrix}$

2. $\begin{bmatrix} 1 & 0 & 0 \\ -1 & 2 & 3 \\ 4 & -1 & 2 \end{bmatrix}$

Find the inverse of each matrix, if it exists.

3. $\begin{bmatrix} 4 & 2 \\ 10 & 5 \end{bmatrix}$

4. $\begin{bmatrix} 5 & 2 \\ 7 & 3 \end{bmatrix}$

Do you UNDERSTAND? MATHEMATICAL PRACTICES

5. Error Analysis What mistake did the student make when finding the determinant of $\begin{bmatrix} 2 & 5 \\ -3 & 1 \end{bmatrix}$?

$$\det \begin{bmatrix} 2 & 5 \\ -3 & 1 \end{bmatrix} = (2)(1) + (-3)(5) = 2 - 15 = -13$$

6. Reasoning Explain why a 2×3 matrix does not have a multiplicative inverse.

Practice and Problem-Solving Exercises

MATHEMATICAL PRACTICES

A Practice

Determine whether the matrices are multiplicative inverses. See Problem 1.

7. $\begin{bmatrix} 3 & 2 \\ 4 & 3 \end{bmatrix}, \begin{bmatrix} 3 & -2 \\ -4 & 3 \end{bmatrix}$

8. $\begin{bmatrix} -3 & 7 \\ -2 & 5 \end{bmatrix}, \begin{bmatrix} -5 & 7 \\ -2 & 3 \end{bmatrix}$

9. $\begin{bmatrix} \frac{1}{5} & -\frac{1}{10} \\ 0 & \frac{1}{4} \end{bmatrix}, \begin{bmatrix} 5 & 2 \\ 0 & 4 \end{bmatrix}$

10. $\begin{bmatrix} 1 & 2 & -1 \\ -1.5 & -3 & 1.75 \\ 0 & -1 & 0.5 \end{bmatrix}, \begin{bmatrix} 1 & 0 & 2 \\ 3 & 2 & -1 \\ 6 & 4 & 0 \end{bmatrix}$

11. $\begin{bmatrix} 2 & 2 & 2 \\ -2 & 2 & -2 \\ -2 & -2 & -2 \end{bmatrix}, \begin{bmatrix} 2 & 2 & 2 \\ -2 & 2 & -2 \\ -2 & -2 & -2 \end{bmatrix}$

Evaluate the determinant of each matrix. See Problems 2, 3, and 4.

12. $\begin{bmatrix} 7 & 2 \\ 0 & -3 \end{bmatrix}$

13. $\begin{bmatrix} 6 & 2 \\ -6 & -2 \end{bmatrix}$

14. $\begin{bmatrix} 0 & 0.5 \\ 1.5 & 2 \end{bmatrix}$

15. $\begin{bmatrix} \frac{1}{2} & \frac{2}{3} \\ \frac{3}{5} & \frac{1}{4} \end{bmatrix}$

16. $\begin{bmatrix} -1 & 3 \\ 5 & 2 \end{bmatrix}$

17. $\begin{bmatrix} 5 & 3 \\ -2 & 1 \end{bmatrix}$

18. $\begin{bmatrix} 2 & -1 \\ 5 & -4 \end{bmatrix}$

19. $\begin{bmatrix} -4 & 3 \\ 2 & 0 \end{bmatrix}$

20. $\begin{bmatrix} 1 & 2 & 5 \\ 3 & 1 & 0 \\ 1 & 2 & 1 \end{bmatrix}$

21. $\begin{bmatrix} 1 & 4 & 0 \\ 2 & 3 & 5 \\ 0 & 1 & 0 \end{bmatrix}$

22. $\begin{bmatrix} -2 & 4 & 1 \\ 3 & 0 & -1 \\ 1 & 2 & 1 \end{bmatrix}$

23. $\begin{bmatrix} 2 & 3 & 0 \\ 1 & 2 & 5 \\ 7 & 0 & 1 \end{bmatrix}$

Graphing Calculator **Evaluate the determinant of each 3 × 3 matrix.**

24. $\begin{bmatrix} 1 & 0 & 0 \\ 0 & 1 & 0 \\ 0 & 0 & 1 \end{bmatrix}$

25. $\begin{bmatrix} 0 & -2 & -3 \\ 1 & 2 & 4 \\ -2 & 0 & 1 \end{bmatrix}$

26. $\begin{bmatrix} 12.2 & 13.3 & 9 \\ 1 & -4 & -17 \\ 21.4 & -15 & 0 \end{bmatrix}$

27. Use the map to determine the approximate area of the Bermuda Triangle.

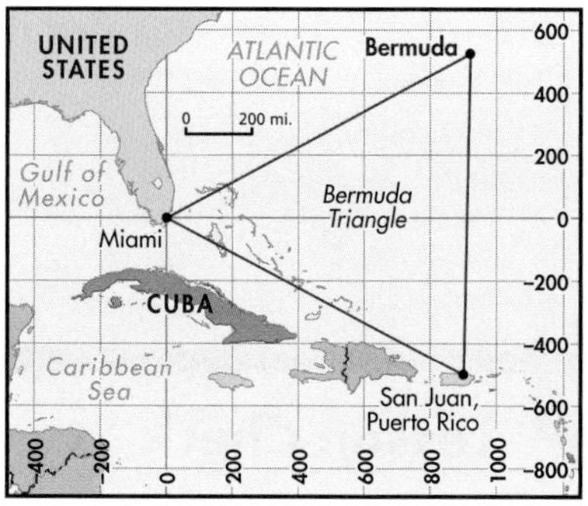

Determine whether each matrix has an inverse. If an inverse matrix exists, find it.

28. $\begin{bmatrix} 2 & -1 \\ 1 & 0 \end{bmatrix}$

29. $\begin{bmatrix} 2 & 3 \\ 1 & 1 \end{bmatrix}$

30. $\begin{bmatrix} 2 & 3 \\ 2 & 4 \end{bmatrix}$

31. $\begin{bmatrix} 1 & 3 \\ 2 & 0 \end{bmatrix}$

32. $\begin{bmatrix} 6 & -8 \\ -3 & 4 \end{bmatrix}$

33. $\begin{bmatrix} 4 & 8 \\ -3 & -2 \end{bmatrix}$

34. $\begin{bmatrix} -1.5 & 3 \\ 2.5 & -0.5 \end{bmatrix}$

35. $\begin{bmatrix} 1 & -2 \\ 3 & 0 \end{bmatrix}$

36. Error Analysis A student wrote $\begin{bmatrix} 1 & \frac{1}{2} \\ \frac{1}{3} & \frac{1}{4} \end{bmatrix}$ as the inverse of $\begin{bmatrix} 1 & 2 \\ 3 & 4 \end{bmatrix}$. What mistake did the student make? Explain your reasoning.

37. Use the coding matrix in Problem 5 to encode the phone number (555) 358-0001. See Problem 5.

B Apply

Evaluate each determinant.

38. $\begin{bmatrix} 4 & 5 \\ -4 & 4 \end{bmatrix}$ **39.** $\begin{bmatrix} -3 & 10 \\ 6 & 20 \end{bmatrix}$ **40.** $\begin{bmatrix} -\frac{1}{2} & 2 \\ -2 & 8 \end{bmatrix}$ **41.** $\begin{bmatrix} 6 & 9 \\ 3 & 6 \end{bmatrix}$

42. $\begin{bmatrix} 0 & 2 & -3 \\ 1 & 2 & 4 \\ -2 & 0 & 1 \end{bmatrix}$ **43.** $\begin{bmatrix} 5 & 1 & 0 \\ 0 & 2 & -1 \\ -2 & -3 & 1 \end{bmatrix}$ **44.** $\begin{bmatrix} 4 & 6 & -1 \\ 2 & 3 & 2 \\ 1 & -1 & 1 \end{bmatrix}$ **45.** $\begin{bmatrix} -3 & 2 & -1 \\ 2 & 5 & 2 \\ 1 & -2 & 0 \end{bmatrix}$

46. Think About a Plan Use matrices to find the area of the figure at the right.
- What shapes do you know how to find the area of?
- Can the polygon be broken into these shapes?
- How many shapes will you need to break the polygon into?

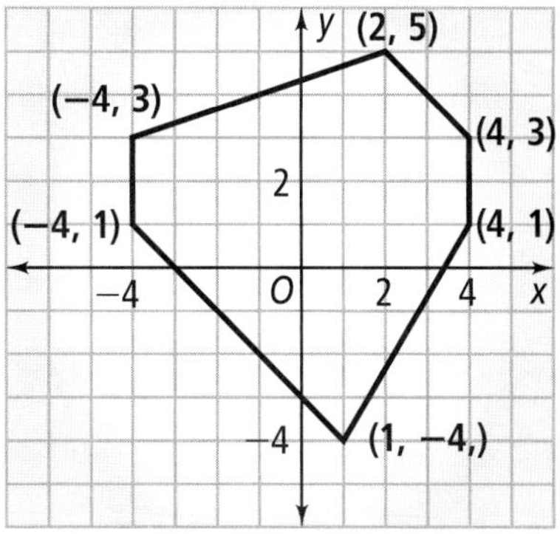

47. Writing Suppose $A = \begin{bmatrix} a & b \\ c & d \end{bmatrix}$ has an inverse. In your own words, describe how to switch or change the elements of A to write A^{-1}.

48. If matrix A has an inverse, what must be true?

I. $AA^{-1} = I$ II. $A^{-1}A = I$ III. $A^{-1}I = A^{-1}$

(A) I only (C) I and II only

(B) II only (D) I, II, and III

49. Geometry Use matrices to find the area of the figure at the right. Check your result by using standard area formulas.

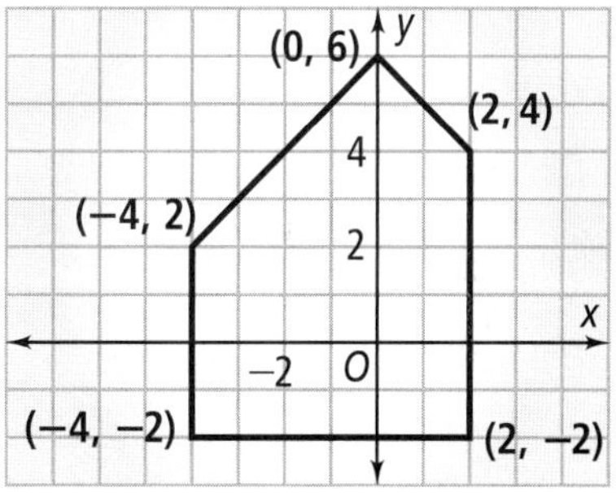

Determine whether each matrix has an inverse. If an inverse matrix exists, find it. If it does not exist, explain why not.

50. $\begin{bmatrix} 1 & 4 \\ 1 & 3 \end{bmatrix}$ **51.** $\begin{bmatrix} 4 & 7 \\ 3 & 5 \end{bmatrix}$ **52.** $\begin{bmatrix} -3 & 11 \\ 2 & -7 \end{bmatrix}$ **53.** $\begin{bmatrix} 2 & 0 \\ 0 & 2 \end{bmatrix}$

54. $\begin{bmatrix} -2 & 1 & -1 \\ 2 & 0 & 4 \\ 0 & 2 & 5 \end{bmatrix}$ **55.** $\begin{bmatrix} 2 & 0 & -1 \\ -1 & -1 & 1 \\ 3 & 2 & 0 \end{bmatrix}$ **56.** $\begin{bmatrix} 0 & 0 & 2 \\ 1 & 4 & -2 \\ 3 & -2 & 1 \end{bmatrix}$ **57.** $\begin{bmatrix} 1 & 2 & 6 \\ 1 & -1 & 0 \\ 1 & 0 & 2 \end{bmatrix}$

58. Writing Evaluate the determinant of each matrix. Describe any patterns.

a. $\begin{bmatrix} 1 & 2 & 3 \\ 1 & 2 & 3 \\ 1 & 2 & 3 \end{bmatrix}$ **b.** $\begin{bmatrix} -1 & -2 & -3 \\ -3 & -2 & -1 \\ -1 & -2 & -3 \end{bmatrix}$ **c.** $\begin{bmatrix} 1 & 2 & 3 \\ 2 & 3 & 1 \\ 1 & 2 & 3 \end{bmatrix}$ **d.** $\begin{bmatrix} -1 & 2 & -3 \\ 2 & -3 & -1 \\ -1 & 2 & -3 \end{bmatrix}$

59. Reasoning For what value of x will matrix A have no inverse? $A = \begin{bmatrix} 1 & 2 \\ 3 & x \end{bmatrix}$

Challenge

60. Reasoning Suppose $A = \begin{bmatrix} a & b \\ c & d \end{bmatrix}$. For what values of a, b, c, and d will A be its own inverse? (*Hint:* There is more than one correct answer.)

61. Let $M = \begin{bmatrix} a & b \\ c & d \end{bmatrix}$ and $N = \begin{bmatrix} e & f \\ g & h \end{bmatrix}$. Prove that the product of the determinants of M and N equals the determinant of the matrix product MN.

A-4 Inverse Matrices and Systems

Content Standard

N.VM.8 Add, subtract, and multiply matrices of appropriate dimensions.

Objective To solve systems of equations using matrix inverses and multiplication

SOLVE IT!

Getting Ready!

The machine counted your nickels and dimes. How many of each coin did you have? Explain.

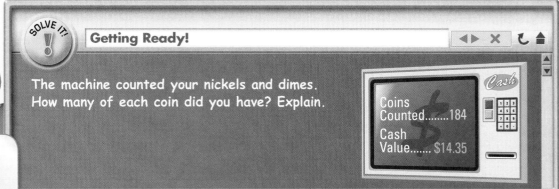

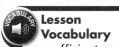

You know how to solve this one! The lesson will give you another method.

MATHEMATICAL PRACTICES In this lesson, you will solve systems of equations by solving a matrix equation.

Lesson Vocabulary
- coefficient matrix
- variable matrix
- constant matrix

Essential Understanding You can solve some matrix equations $AX = B$ by multiplying each side of the equation by A^{-1}, the inverse of matrix A.

If matrix A has an inverse, you can use it to solve the matrix equation $AX = B$. Multiply each side of the equation by A^{-1} to find X.

$$AX = B$$

$$A^{-1}AX = A^{-1}B \quad \text{Multiply each side by } A^{-1}.$$

$$IX = A^{-1}B \quad A^{-1}A = I\text{, the identity matrix.}$$

$$X = A^{-1}B \quad IX = X$$

Problem 1 Solving a Matrix Equation Using an Inverse Matrix

Think

How do you know the equation has a solution?
Check det A. If det $A \neq 0$, you can solve the equation.

What is the solution of each matrix equation?

A $\begin{bmatrix} 5 & 3 \\ 3 & 2 \end{bmatrix} X = \begin{bmatrix} 1 \\ -3 \end{bmatrix}$

Step 1 Evaluate det A and find A^{-1}.

$$\det A = (5)(2) - (3)(3) = 1$$

$$A^{-1} = \frac{1}{\det A}\begin{bmatrix} d & -b \\ -c & a \end{bmatrix} = \frac{1}{1}\begin{bmatrix} 2 & -3 \\ -3 & 5 \end{bmatrix} = \begin{bmatrix} 2 & -3 \\ -3 & 5 \end{bmatrix}$$

Think

Does it matter if you multiply by A^{-1} on the left or right side of A?
Even though $A^{-1}A = AA^{-1} = I$, you must multiply each side of the equation by A^{-1} on the left.

Step 2 Multiply each side of the equation by A^{-1}.

$$\begin{bmatrix} 2 & -3 \\ -3 & 5 \end{bmatrix}\begin{bmatrix} 5 & 3 \\ 3 & 2 \end{bmatrix}X = \begin{bmatrix} 2 & -3 \\ -3 & 5 \end{bmatrix}\begin{bmatrix} 1 \\ -3 \end{bmatrix}$$

$$\begin{bmatrix} (2)(5) + (-3)(3) & (2)(3) + (-3)(2) \\ (-3)(5) + (5)(3) & (-3)(3) + (5)(2) \end{bmatrix}X = \begin{bmatrix} (2)(1) + (-3)(-3) \\ (-3)(1) + (5)(-3) \end{bmatrix}$$

$$\begin{bmatrix} 1 & 0 \\ 0 & 1 \end{bmatrix}X = \begin{bmatrix} 11 \\ -18 \end{bmatrix}$$

$$X = \begin{bmatrix} 11 \\ -18 \end{bmatrix}$$

Check

Method 1

Use paper and pencil.

$$\begin{bmatrix} 5 & 3 \\ 3 & 2 \end{bmatrix}X \stackrel{?}{=} \begin{bmatrix} 1 \\ -3 \end{bmatrix}$$

$$\begin{bmatrix} 5 & 3 \\ 3 & 2 \end{bmatrix}\begin{bmatrix} 11 \\ -18 \end{bmatrix} \stackrel{?}{=} \begin{bmatrix} 1 \\ -3 \end{bmatrix}$$

$$\begin{bmatrix} (5)(11) + (3)(-18) \\ (3)(11) + (2)(-18) \end{bmatrix} \stackrel{?}{=} \begin{bmatrix} 1 \\ -3 \end{bmatrix}$$

$$\begin{bmatrix} 1 \\ -3 \end{bmatrix} = \begin{bmatrix} 1 \\ -3 \end{bmatrix} \checkmark$$

Method 2

Use a calculator.

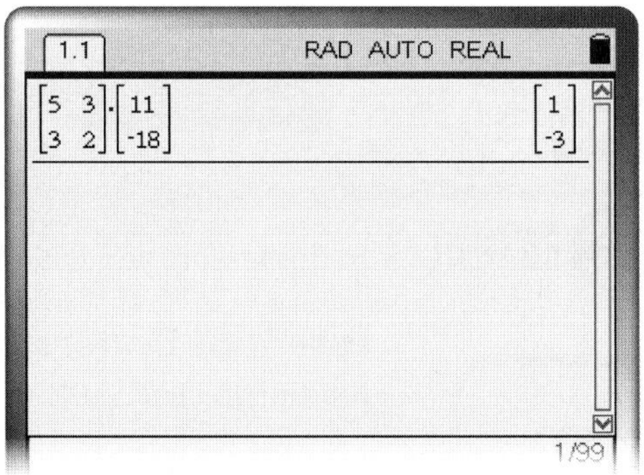

B $\begin{bmatrix} 3 & -9 \\ -2 & 6 \end{bmatrix}X = \begin{bmatrix} 2 \\ 5 \end{bmatrix}$

Evaluate det A.

$\det A = (3)(6) - (-2)(-9) = 18 - 18 = 0.$

Matrix A has no inverse. The matrix equation has no solution.

Got It? 1. What is the solution of each matrix equation?

a. $\begin{bmatrix} 4 & 3 \\ 2 & 2 \end{bmatrix}X = \begin{bmatrix} -5 \\ 2 \end{bmatrix}$ **b.** $\begin{bmatrix} 7 & 5 \\ 4 & 3 \end{bmatrix}X = \begin{bmatrix} -3 & 0 \\ 1 & 4 \end{bmatrix}$ **c.** $\begin{bmatrix} 2 & 3 \\ 4 & 6 \end{bmatrix}X = \begin{bmatrix} 3 \\ -7 \end{bmatrix}$

You can write a system of equations as a matrix equation $AX = B$, using a **coefficient matrix**, a **variable matrix**, and a **constant matrix**.

System of Equations

$$\begin{cases} 2x + 3y = 1 \\ 5x - 2y = 13 \end{cases}$$

Matrix Equation

$$\begin{bmatrix} 2 & 3 \\ 5 & -2 \end{bmatrix}\begin{bmatrix} x \\ y \end{bmatrix} = \begin{bmatrix} 1 \\ 13 \end{bmatrix}$$

coefficient matrix, A variable matrix, X constant matrix, B

Problem 2 Writing a System as a Matrix Equation

What is the matrix equation that corresponds to each system?

A $\begin{cases} 4x + 7y = 6 \\ -5x + 3y = 1 \end{cases}$

Step 1 Identify the coefficient, variable, and constant matrices.

coefficient matrix, A $\begin{bmatrix} 4 & 7 \\ -5 & 3 \end{bmatrix}$ variable matrix, X $\begin{bmatrix} x \\ y \end{bmatrix}$ constant matrix, B $\begin{bmatrix} 6 \\ 1 \end{bmatrix}$

Step 2 Write the matrix equation.

$$\begin{bmatrix} 4 & 7 \\ -5 & 3 \end{bmatrix}\begin{bmatrix} x \\ y \end{bmatrix} = \begin{bmatrix} 6 \\ 1 \end{bmatrix}$$

B $\begin{cases} 3a + 5b - 12c = 6 \\ 7b + 2c = 8 \\ 5a = 3c + 1 \end{cases}$

Plan

How is this system different from the one in part A?
There are three variables. Some terms have coefficients of 0, and the third equation has a variable on the right side of the = sign.

Step 1 Rewrite the system so the variables are in the same order in each equation.

$$\begin{cases} 3a + 5b - 12c = 6 \\ 7b + 2c = 8 \\ 5a = 3c + 1 \end{cases} \rightarrow \begin{cases} 3a + 5b - 12c = 6 \\ 7b + 2c = 8 \\ 5a - 3c = 1 \end{cases}$$

Step 2 Identify the coefficient, variable, and constant matrices.

coefficient matrix, A $\begin{bmatrix} 3 & 5 & -12 \\ 0 & 7 & 2 \\ 5 & 0 & -3 \end{bmatrix}$ variable matrix, X $\begin{bmatrix} a \\ b \\ c \end{bmatrix}$ constant matrix, B $\begin{bmatrix} 6 \\ 8 \\ 1 \end{bmatrix}$

Step 3 Write the matrix equation.

$$\begin{bmatrix} 3 & 5 & -12 \\ 0 & 7 & 2 \\ 5 & 0 & -3 \end{bmatrix}\begin{bmatrix} a \\ b \\ c \end{bmatrix} = \begin{bmatrix} 6 \\ 8 \\ 1 \end{bmatrix}$$

Got It? 2. What is the matrix equation that corresponds to each system?

a. $\begin{cases} 3x - 7y = 8 \\ 5x + y = -2 \end{cases}$ **b.** $\begin{cases} x + 3y + 5z = 12 \\ -2x + y - 4z = -2 \\ 7x - 2y = 7 \end{cases}$ **c.** $\begin{cases} 2x + 3 = 8y \\ -x + y = -4 \end{cases}$

If the coefficient matrix has an inverse, you can use it to find a unique solution to a system of equations.

Problem 3 Solving a System of Two Equations

What is the solution of the system $\begin{cases} 5x - 4y = 4 \\ 3x - 2y = 3 \end{cases}$? Solve using matrices.

Think

Write the system as a matrix equation. Write the coefficient, variable, and constant matrices.

Write

$$A \quad X \quad = B$$

$$\begin{bmatrix} 5 & -4 \\ 3 & -2 \end{bmatrix}\begin{bmatrix} x \\ y \end{bmatrix} = \begin{bmatrix} 4 \\ 3 \end{bmatrix}$$

You need to find A^{-1}. Since det $A = 2$, A^{-1} exists.

$$A^{-1} = \frac{1}{\det A}\begin{bmatrix} -2 & 4 \\ -3 & 5 \end{bmatrix}$$

$$= \frac{1}{(5)(-2) - (3)(-4)}\begin{bmatrix} -2 & 4 \\ -3 & 5 \end{bmatrix}$$

$$= \frac{1}{2}\begin{bmatrix} -2 & 4 \\ -3 & 5 \end{bmatrix}$$

$$= \begin{bmatrix} -1 & 2 \\ -\frac{3}{2} & \frac{5}{2} \end{bmatrix}$$

Multiply each side of the matrix equation by A^{-1} on the left.

$$\begin{bmatrix} -1 & 2 \\ -\frac{3}{2} & \frac{5}{2} \end{bmatrix}\begin{bmatrix} 5 & -4 \\ 3 & -2 \end{bmatrix}\begin{bmatrix} x \\ y \end{bmatrix} = \begin{bmatrix} -1 & 2 \\ -\frac{3}{2} & \frac{5}{2} \end{bmatrix}\begin{bmatrix} 4 \\ 3 \end{bmatrix}$$

Solve for $\begin{bmatrix} x \\ y \end{bmatrix}$ and check.

$$\begin{bmatrix} x \\ y \end{bmatrix} = \begin{bmatrix} (-1)(4) + (2)(3) \\ \left(-\frac{3}{2}\right)(4) + \left(\frac{5}{2}\right)(3) \end{bmatrix} = \begin{bmatrix} 2 \\ \frac{3}{2} \end{bmatrix}$$

The solution is $x = 2$, $y = \frac{3}{2}$.

$5(2) - 4\left(\frac{3}{2}\right) = 4$ ✔

$3(2) - 2\left(\frac{3}{2}\right) = 3$ ✔

Got It? 3. What is the solution of each system of equations? Solve using matrices.

a. $\begin{cases} 9x + 2y = 3 \\ 3x + y = -6 \end{cases}$ **b.** $\begin{cases} 4x - 6y = 9 \\ -10x + 15y = 8 \end{cases}$

The system $\begin{cases} -6x + 3y = 8 \\ 4x - 2y = 10 \end{cases}$ has coefficient matrix A with det $A = 0$. There is no inverse matrix and the system has no unique solution. Recall that this means the system either has no solutions (graphs are parallel lines in the 2×2 case) or infinitely many solutions (graphs are the same line in the 2×2 case). For the system above, the lines are parallel.

You can use a graphing calculator to solve a system of three equations.

Problem 4 Solving a System of Three Equations

Multiple Choice **On a new exercise program, your friend plans to do a run-jog-walk routine every other day for 40 min. She would like to burn 310 calories during each session. The table shows how many calories a person your friend's age and weight burns per minute of each type of exercise.**

Calories Burned

Running (8 mi/h)	Jogging (5 mi/h)	Walking (3.5 mi/h)
12.5 cal/min	7.5 cal/min	3.5 cal/min

If your friend plans on jogging twice as long as she runs, how many minutes should she exercise at each rate?

Ⓐ run 10, jog 5, walk 25

Ⓑ run 30, jog 15, walk 5

Ⓒ run 5, jog 10, walk 25

Ⓓ run 10, jog 20, walk 10

Think
How many equations do you need to solve this problem?
Since there are three variables you need three equations.

Step 1 Define the variables.

Let x = number of minutes running.

y = number of minutes jogging.

z = number of minutes walking.

Step 2 Write a system of equations for the problem.

$$\begin{cases} 12.5x + 7.5y + 3.5z = 310 \\ x + y + z = 40 \\ 2x = y \end{cases} \rightarrow \begin{cases} 12.5x + 7.5y + 3.5z = 310 \\ x + y + z = 40 \\ 2x - y + 0z = 0 \end{cases}$$

Step 3 Write the system as a matrix equation.

$$\begin{bmatrix} 12.5 & 7.5 & 3.5 \\ 1 & 1 & 1 \\ 2 & -1 & 0 \end{bmatrix} \begin{bmatrix} x \\ y \\ z \end{bmatrix} = \begin{bmatrix} 310 \\ 40 \\ 0 \end{bmatrix}$$

Step 4 Use a calculator. Solve for the variable matrix.

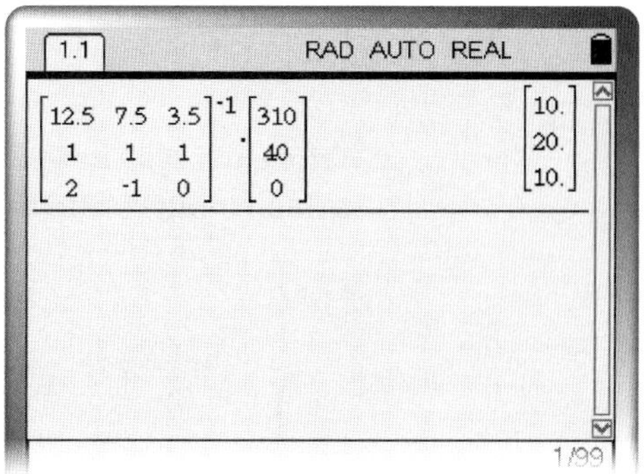

Step 5 Interpret the solution.

Your friend should run for 10 min, jog for 20 min, and walk for 10 min.
The correct answer is D.

Got It? **4.** After following her exercise program from Problem 4 for a month, your friend plans to increase the calories she burns with each session. She still wants to exercise for 40 min every other day, but now she wants to burn 460 calories during each session. If she only runs and jogs, how many minutes of each exercise type should she do now?

Lesson Check

Do you know HOW?

Write each system as a matrix equation.

1. $\begin{cases} -6x + 3y = 8 \\ 4x - 2y = 10 \end{cases}$

2. $\begin{cases} 2x + 3y = 12 \\ x - 2y + z = 9 \\ 6y - 4z = 8 \end{cases}$

Solve each system using a matrix equation. Check your answer.

3. $\begin{cases} x + 2y = 11 \\ x + 4y = 17 \end{cases}$

4. $\begin{cases} 2x - 3y = 6 \\ x + y = -12 \end{cases}$

Do you UNDERSTAND? MATHEMATICAL PRACTICES

5. Error Analysis A student is trying to use the matrix equation below to solve a system of equations. What error did the student make? What matrix equation should the student use?

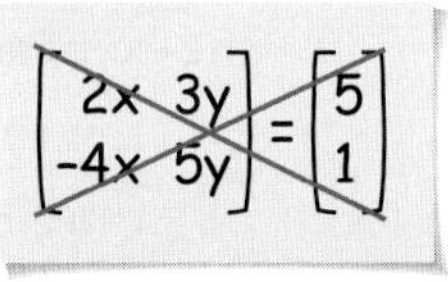

6. Reasoning Explain how to write the matrix equation $\begin{bmatrix} -2 & 3 \\ 4 & 1 \end{bmatrix}\begin{bmatrix} p \\ q \end{bmatrix} = \begin{bmatrix} 2 \\ -5 \end{bmatrix}$ as a system of linear equations.

Practice and Problem-Solving Exercises

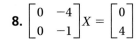

MATHEMATICAL PRACTICES

A Practice

Solve each matrix equation. If an equation cannot be solved, explain why. See Problem 1.

7. $\begin{bmatrix} 12 & 7 \\ 5 & 3 \end{bmatrix}X = \begin{bmatrix} 2 & -1 \\ 3 & 2 \end{bmatrix}$

8. $\begin{bmatrix} 0 & -4 \\ 0 & -1 \end{bmatrix}X = \begin{bmatrix} 0 \\ 4 \end{bmatrix}$

9. $\begin{bmatrix} 5 & 1 & 4 \\ 2 & -3 & -5 \\ 7 & 2 & -6 \end{bmatrix}X = \begin{bmatrix} 5 \\ 2 \\ 5 \end{bmatrix}$

10. $\begin{bmatrix} 6 & 10 & 13 \\ 4 & -2 & 7 \\ 0 & 9 & -8 \end{bmatrix}X = \begin{bmatrix} 84 \\ 18 \\ 56 \end{bmatrix}$

Write each system as a matrix equation. Identify the coefficient matrix, the variable matrix, and the constant matrix. See Problem 2.

11. $\begin{cases} x + y = 5 \\ x - 2y = -4 \end{cases}$

12. $\begin{cases} y = 3x - 7 \\ x = 2 \end{cases}$

13. $\begin{cases} 3a + 5b = 0 \\ a + b = 2 \end{cases}$

14. $\begin{cases} x + 3y - z = 2 \\ x + 2z = 8 \\ 2y - z = 1 \end{cases}$

15. $\begin{cases} r - s + t = 150 \\ 2r + t = 425 \\ s + 3t = 0 \end{cases}$

16. $\begin{cases} x + 2y = 11 \\ 2x + 3y = 18 \end{cases}$

Solve each system of equations using a matrix equation. Check your answers. See Problem 3.

17. $\begin{cases} x + 3y = 5 \\ x + 4y = 6 \end{cases}$ **18.** $\begin{cases} p - 3q = -1 \\ -5p + 16q = 5 \end{cases}$ **19.** $\begin{cases} 300x - y = 130 \\ 200x + y = 120 \end{cases}$

20. $\begin{cases} x + 5y = -4 \\ x + 6y = -5 \end{cases}$ **21.** $\begin{cases} 2x + 3y = 12 \\ x + 2y = 7 \end{cases}$ **22.** $\begin{cases} 2x + 3y = 5 \\ x + 2y = 6 \end{cases}$

23. $\begin{cases} x + y + z = 4 \\ 4x + 5y = 3 \\ y - 3z = -10 \end{cases}$ **24.** $\begin{cases} 9y + 2z = 18 \\ 3x + 2y + z = 5 \\ x - y = -1 \end{cases}$ **25.** $\begin{cases} 9y + 2z = 14 \\ 3x + 2y + z = 5 \\ x - y = -1 \end{cases}$

26. Fitness Your classmate is starting a new fitness program. He is planning to ride his bicycle 60 minutes every day. He burns 7 Calories per minute bicycling at 11 mph and 11.75 Calories per minute bicycling at 15 mph. How long should he bicycle at each speed to burn 600 calories per hour? See Problem 4.

B Apply

27. Think About a Plan Suppose you want to fill nine 1-lb tins with a snack mix. You plan to buy almonds for $2.45/lb, peanuts for $1.85/lb, and raisins for $.80/lb. You want the mix to contain twice as much nuts as raisins by weight. If you spend exactly $15, how much of each ingredient should you buy?

- How many equations do you need to represent this situation?
- How can you represent this system using a matrix equation?

28. Nutrition Suppose you are making a trail mix for your friends and want to fill three 1-lb bags. Almonds cost $2.25/lb, peanuts cost $1.30/lb, and raisins cost $.90/lb. You want each bag to contain twice as much nuts as raisins by weight. If you spent $4.45, how much of each ingredient did you buy?

Solve each system.

29. $\begin{cases} -3x + 4y = 2 \\ x - y = -1 \end{cases}$ **30.** $\begin{cases} x + 2y = 10 \\ 3x + 5y = 26 \end{cases}$ **31.** $\begin{cases} x - 3y = -1 \\ -6x + 19y = 6 \end{cases}$

32. $\begin{cases} x = 5 - y \\ 3y = z \\ x + z = 7 \end{cases}$ **33.** $\begin{cases} -x = -4 - z \\ 2y = z - 1 \\ x = 6 - y - z \end{cases}$ **34.** $\begin{cases} -b + 2c = 4 \\ a + b - c = -10 \\ 2a + 3c = 1 \end{cases}$

35. $\begin{cases} x + y + z = 4 \\ 4x + 5y = 4 \\ y - 3z = -9 \end{cases}$ **36.** $\begin{cases} x + y + z = 4 \\ 4x + 5y = 3 \\ y - 3z = -10 \end{cases}$

37. $\begin{cases} -2w + x + y = 0 \\ -w + 2x - y + z = 1 \\ -2w + 3x + 3y + 2z = 6 \\ w + x + 2y + z = 5 \end{cases}$ **38.** $\begin{cases} -2w + x + y = -2 \\ -w + 2x - y + z = -4 \\ -2w + 3x + 3y + 2z = 2 \\ w + x + 2y + z = 6 \end{cases}$

Solve each matrix equation. If the coefficient matrix has no inverse, write *no unique solution.*

39. $\begin{bmatrix} 1 & 1 \\ 1 & 2 \end{bmatrix}\begin{bmatrix} x \\ y \end{bmatrix} = \begin{bmatrix} 8 \\ 10 \end{bmatrix}$ **40.** $\begin{bmatrix} 2 & -3 \\ -4 & 6 \end{bmatrix}\begin{bmatrix} a \\ b \end{bmatrix} = \begin{bmatrix} 1 \\ -2 \end{bmatrix}$ **41.** $\begin{bmatrix} 2 & 1 \\ 4 & 3 \end{bmatrix}\begin{bmatrix} x \\ y \end{bmatrix} = \begin{bmatrix} 10 \\ -2 \end{bmatrix}$

Determine whether each system has a unique solution. If it has a unique solution, find it.

42. $\begin{cases} 20x + 5y = 240 \\ y = 20x \end{cases}$

43. $\begin{cases} 20x + 5y = 145 \\ 30x - 5y = 125 \end{cases}$

44. $\begin{cases} y = 2000 - 65x \\ y = 500 + 55x \end{cases}$

45. $\begin{cases} y = \frac{2}{3}x - 3 \\ y = -x + 7 \end{cases}$

46. $\begin{cases} 3x + 2y = 10 \\ 6x + 4y = 16 \end{cases}$

47. $\begin{cases} x + 2y + z = 4 \\ y = x - 3 \\ z = 2x \end{cases}$

48. Coordinate Geometry The coordinates (x, y) of a point in a plane are the solution of the system $\begin{cases} 2x + 3y = 13 \\ 5x + 7y = 31 \end{cases}$. Find the coordinates of the point.

49. Geometry A rectangle is twice as long as it is wide. The perimeter is 840 ft. Find the dimensions of the rectangle.

50. Reasoning Substitute each point $(-3, 5)$ and $(2, -1)$ into the slope-intercept form of a linear equation to write a system of equations. Then use the system to find the equation of the line containing the two points. Explain your reasoning.

Challenge **Solve each matrix equation.**

51. $-2\begin{bmatrix} -2 & 0 \\ 0 & -1 \end{bmatrix} + \begin{bmatrix} 0 & -3 \\ 5 & -4 \end{bmatrix}X + \begin{bmatrix} 0 & -3 \\ 5 & -4 \end{bmatrix} = \begin{bmatrix} 19 & -27 \\ 10 & -24 \end{bmatrix}$

52. $\begin{bmatrix} 0 & -6 \\ 1 & 2 \end{bmatrix} - \begin{bmatrix} 5 & 2 \\ 4 & 3 \end{bmatrix}X - \begin{bmatrix} 2 & -26 \\ 3 & -18 \end{bmatrix} = \begin{bmatrix} 3 & 25 \\ 2 & 24 \end{bmatrix}$

53. $\begin{bmatrix} 7 & -5 & 3 \\ 0 & 1 & 3 \\ 8 & 4 & -2 \end{bmatrix}X + \begin{bmatrix} 5 \\ -9 \\ 0 \end{bmatrix} = \begin{bmatrix} 54 \\ -12 \\ 96 \end{bmatrix}$

54. $\begin{bmatrix} -1 & 0 & 2 \\ -6 & -5 & 0 \\ 1 & 4 & 1 \end{bmatrix} - \begin{bmatrix} -4 & 0 & 2 \\ 0 & 3 & 6 \\ 0 & 5 & 0 \end{bmatrix}X = \begin{bmatrix} -21 & 10 & 26 \\ -54 & 1 & -15 \\ 1 & 4 & -24 \end{bmatrix}$

Open-Ended **Complete each system for the given number of solutions.**

55. infinitely many

$\begin{cases} x + y = 7 \\ 2x + 2y = \blacksquare \end{cases}$

56. one solution

$\begin{cases} x + y + z = 7 \\ y + z = \blacksquare \\ z = \blacksquare \end{cases}$

57. no solution

$\begin{cases} x + y + z = 7 \\ y + z = \blacksquare \\ y + z = \blacksquare \end{cases}$

58. Nutrition A caterer combines ingredients to make a paella, a Spanish fiesta dish. The paella weighs 18 lb, costs \$29.50, and supplies 850 g of protein.

a. Write a system of three equations to find the weight of each ingredient that the caterer uses.

b. Solve the system. How many pounds of each ingredient did she use?

Paella Nutrition Chart

Food	Cost/lb	Protein/lb
Chicken	\$1.50	100 g
Rice	\$.40	20 g
Shellfish	\$6.00	50 g

A-5 Geometric Transformations

Content Standards

G.CO.5 Given a geometric figure and a rotation, reflection, or translation, draw the transformed figure . . . Specify a sequence of transformations . . .

Also G.CO.2, N.VM.6, N.VM.7, N.VM.8

Objective To transform geometric figures using matrix operations

SOLVE IT! Getting Ready!

The first column in R is the point (1, 0).

MATHEMATICAL PRACTICES

The matrix R contains the 10 points that define the red figure.

$$R = \begin{bmatrix} 1 & 3 & 2 & 2 & 3 & 1 & 2 & 3 & 1 & 3 \\ 0 & 0 & 2 & 4 & 4 & 6 & 6 & 6 & 8 & 8 \end{bmatrix}$$

Find the matrix B that contains the 10 corresponding points of the blue figure. What is the matrix T for which R + T = B? Explain your reasoning.

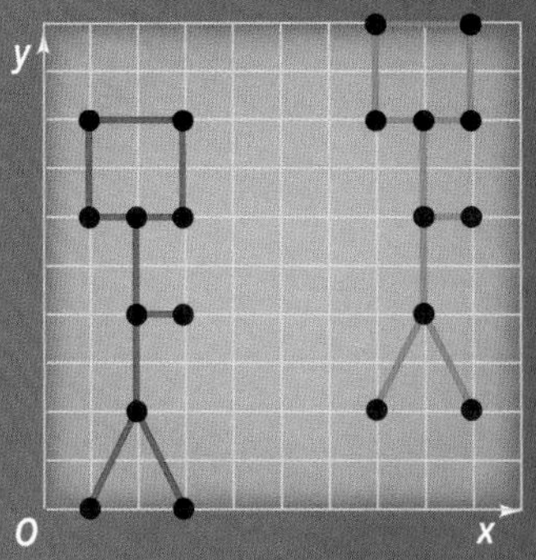

Dynamic Activity
Translations
Dilations

Lesson Vocabulary
- image
- preimage
- dilation
- rotation
- center of rotation

Matrix T in the Solve It *translates* the figure. Other transformations *dilate, rotate,* and *reflect* such geometric figures.

Essential Understanding You can multiply a 2×1 matrix representing a point by a 2×2 matrix to rotate the point about the origin or reflect the point across a line.

You can write the n points that define a figure as a $2 \times n$ matrix. For example, you can represent the four vertices of kite $ABCD$ with the 2×4 matrix shown.

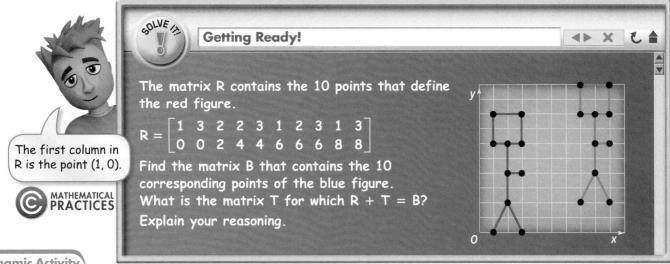

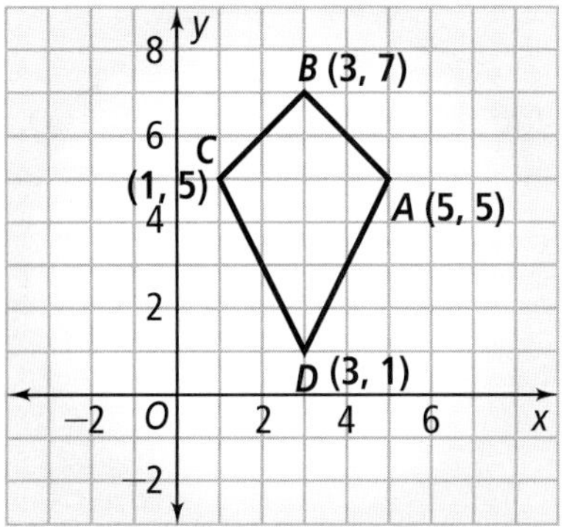

$$\begin{matrix} & A & B & C & D \\ x\text{-coordinate} & \\ y\text{-coordinate} & \end{matrix} \begin{bmatrix} 5 & 3 & 1 & 3 \\ 5 & 7 & 5 & 1 \end{bmatrix}$$

A change to a figure is a transformation of the figure. The transformed figure is the **image**. The original figure is the **preimage**. In the Solve It, the red figure is the preimage. The blue figure is the image.

The transformation of the figure in the Solve It is a translation—moving a figure to a new location without changing its size, shape, or orientation. You can use matrix addition to translate all the vertices of a figure in one step.

Problem 1 Translating a Figure

Kite $ABCD$ has vertices (5, 5), (3, 7), (1, 5), and (3, 1). If you translate it 8 units to the right and 5 units down, what are the coordinates of the vertices of its image $A'B'C'D'$? Use matrix addition. Draw $ABCD$ and its image.

Think

To translate 8 units to the right, what must you do to each x-coordinate?
Add 8 to each x-coordinate to translate 8 units to the right.

Preimage Vertices | **Translation Matrix** | **Image Vertices**

Add 8 to each x-coordinate.

Subtract 5 from each y-coordinate.

$$\begin{matrix} A & B & C & D \end{matrix} \qquad\qquad\qquad\qquad \begin{matrix} A' & B' & C' & D' \end{matrix}$$

$$\begin{bmatrix} 5 & 3 & 1 & 3 \\ 5 & 7 & 5 & 1 \end{bmatrix} + \begin{bmatrix} 8 & 8 & 8 & 8 \\ -5 & -5 & -5 & -5 \end{bmatrix} = \begin{bmatrix} 13 & 11 & 9 & 11 \\ 0 & 2 & 0 & -4 \end{bmatrix}$$

The vertices of the preimage, $A(5, 5)$, $B(3, 7)$, $C(1, 5)$, and $D(3, 1)$ translate to the vertices $A'(13, 0)$, $B'(11, 2)$, $C'(9, 0)$, and $D'(11, -4)$ of the image.

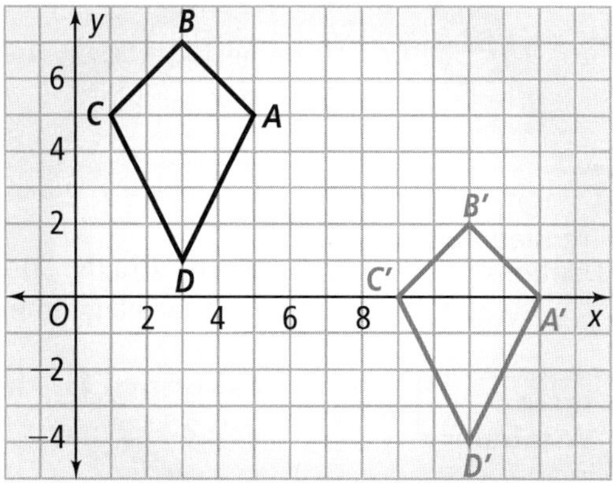

Got It? 1. a. Reasoning How would you translate the kite image $A'B'C'D'$ to the kite preimage $ABCD$?

b. A pentagon has vertices $(0, -5)$, $(-1, -1)$, $(-5, 0)$, $(1, 3)$, and $(4, 0)$. Use matrix addition to translate the pentagon 3 units left and 2 units up. What are the vertices of the image? Graph the preimage and the image.

You enlarge or reduce a figure with a **dilation**. You use scalar multiplication to dilate a figure with center of dilation at the origin. In this book, dilations have their centers at the origin.

$$\begin{matrix} A & B & C \end{matrix} \qquad\qquad \begin{matrix} A' & B' & C' \end{matrix}$$

$$2\begin{bmatrix} -1 & 3 & 2 \\ 0 & 2 & -1 \end{bmatrix} = \begin{bmatrix} -2 & 6 & 4 \\ 0 & 4 & -2 \end{bmatrix}$$

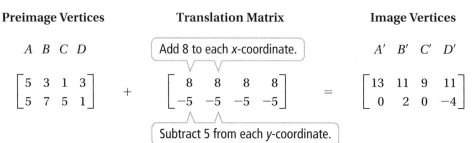

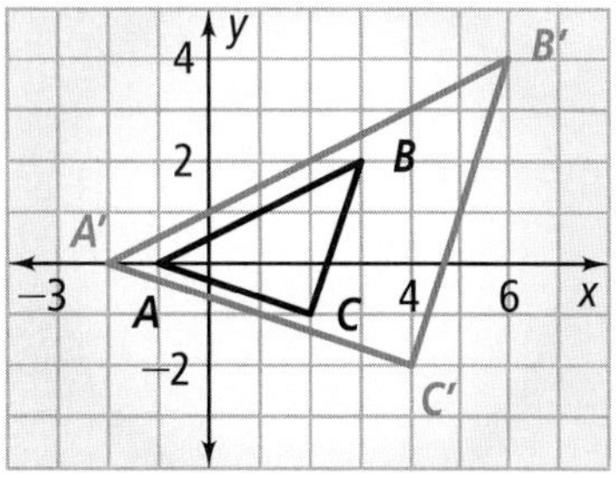

Problem 2 Dilating a Figure STEM

Digital Media **The width of the digital picture is presently 800 pixels (approximately 11.1 in.). Its height is 600 pixels (approximately 8.3 in.). You want to reduce its width as shown. This will allow the picture to fit on any computer screen without scrolling. Using a dilation, what are the coordinates of the vertices of the reduced image?**

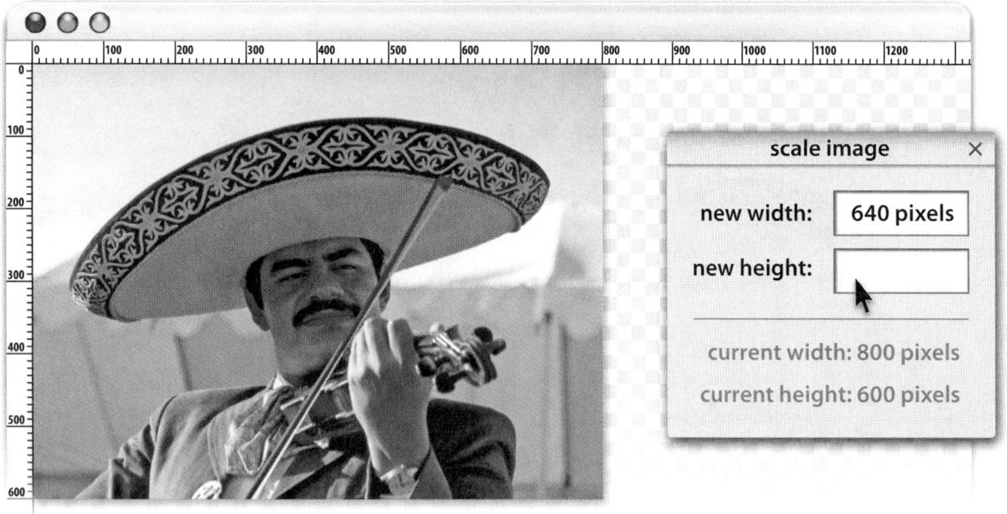

Know
- Current picture size
- Dilated picture width

Need
- Scale factor
- Dilated picture height

Plan
- Find the scale factor.
- Write a preimage matrix of the photo coordinates.
- Use scalar multiplication.

Step 1 Find the scale factor.

Dilated picture width: 640 pixels

Current picture width: 800 pixels

Scale factor $= \frac{\text{Dilated Width}}{\text{Current Width}} = \frac{640}{800}$, or 0.8.

Step 2 Multiply the preimage matrix by the scale factor, 0.8.

$$0.8\begin{bmatrix} 0 & 800 & 800 & 0 \\ 0 & 0 & 600 & 600 \end{bmatrix} = \begin{bmatrix} 0 & 640 & 640 & 0 \\ 0 & 0 & 480 & 480 \end{bmatrix}$$

The coordinates of the vertices of the reduced image are (0, 0), (640, 0), (640, 480), and (0, 480).

Got It? **2.** You are to enlarge a picture by the factor 2. The preimage is 5 in. by 3 in.

a. Write a matrix of coordinates of the preimage vertices. Make one vertex (0, 0).

b. What are the coordinates of the vertices of the image? Show the multiplication that you used for the dilation.

c. **Reasoning** You enlarged the picture by the factor 2. By what factor did you increase its area?

A **rotation** turns a figure about a fixed point—the **center of rotation**. You can multiply a figure's vertex matrix by a rotation matrix to find the vertices of the rotation image. In this book, rotations are counterclockwise about the origin.

The matrix $\begin{bmatrix} 0 & -1 \\ 1 & 0 \end{bmatrix}$ rotates a figure 90°. A 90° rotation followed by another 90° rotation, or

$$\begin{bmatrix} 0 & -1 \\ 1 & 0 \end{bmatrix}\begin{bmatrix} 0 & -1 \\ 1 & 0 \end{bmatrix} = \begin{bmatrix} 0 & -1 \\ 1 & 0 \end{bmatrix}^2 = \begin{bmatrix} -1 & 0 \\ 0 & -1 \end{bmatrix},$$

is a 180° rotation. Rotate another 90° for a 270° rotation.

take note

Properties **Rotation Matrices for the Coordinate Plane**

90° Rotation	180° Rotation	270° Rotation	360° Rotation
$\begin{bmatrix} 0 & -1 \\ 1 & 0 \end{bmatrix}$	$\begin{bmatrix} -1 & 0 \\ 0 & -1 \end{bmatrix}$	$\begin{bmatrix} 0 & 1 \\ -1 & 0 \end{bmatrix}$	$\begin{bmatrix} 1 & 0 \\ 0 & 1 \end{bmatrix}$

Problem 3 Rotating a Figure

Rotate the triangle with vertices $A(1, 1)$, $B(5, 2)$, and $C(-2, 3)$ by the indicated amount. What are the vertices of the image? Graph the preimage and the image in the same coordinate plane.

Plan

How do you rotate the triangle?
Multiply the 2 × 3 triangle matrix by the appropriate rotation matrix to get the 2 × 3 image matrix.

A 90°

$$\begin{bmatrix} 0 & -1 \\ 1 & 0 \end{bmatrix}\begin{bmatrix} 1 & 5 & -2 \\ 1 & 2 & 3 \end{bmatrix} = \begin{bmatrix} -1 & -2 & -3 \\ 1 & 5 & -2 \end{bmatrix}$$

The vertices of the image are $(-1, 1)$, $(-2, 5)$, and $(-3, -2)$.

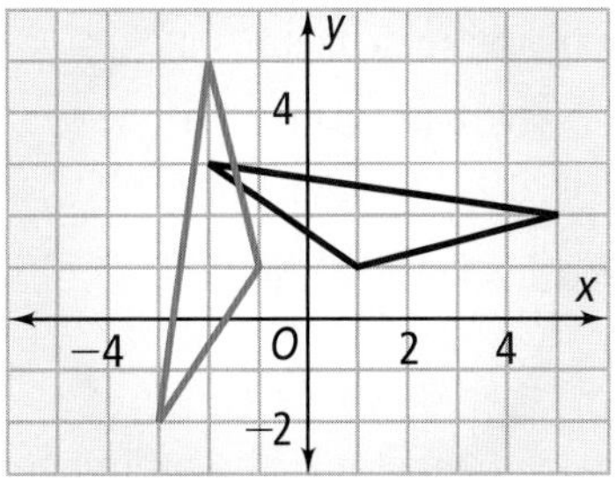

B 180°

$$\begin{bmatrix} -1 & 0 \\ 0 & -1 \end{bmatrix}\begin{bmatrix} 1 & 5 & -2 \\ 1 & 2 & 3 \end{bmatrix} = \begin{bmatrix} -1 & -5 & 2 \\ -1 & -2 & -3 \end{bmatrix}$$

The vertices of the image are $(-1, -1)$, $(-5, -2)$, and $(2, -3)$.

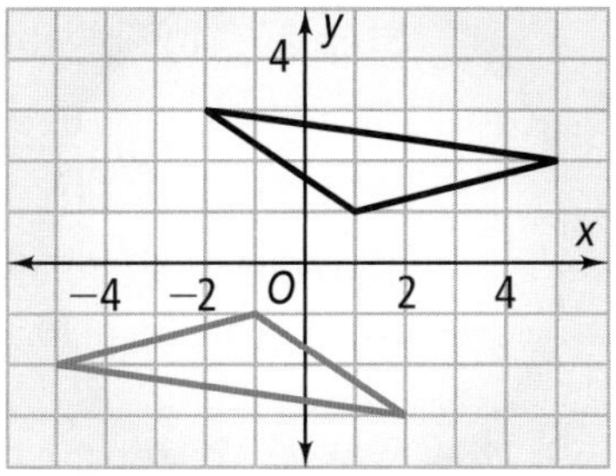

Got It? 3. Rotate the triangle with vertices $D(-3, 0)$, $E(-4, 4)$, and $F(1, 1)$ the indicated amount. What are the vertices of the image? Graph the preimage and the image in the same coordinate plane.

a. 270° **b.** 360°

A *reflection* maps a point or figure in the coordinate plane to its mirror image using a specific line as its line of reflection. In this book, the lines of reflection are $y = 0$ (the x-axis), $x = 0$ (the y-axis), $y = x$, and $y = -x$.

take note

Properties Reflection Matrices for the Coordinate Plane

across x-axis	across y-axis	across $y = x$	across $y = -x$
$\begin{bmatrix} 1 & 0 \\ 0 & -1 \end{bmatrix}$	$\begin{bmatrix} -1 & 0 \\ 0 & 1 \end{bmatrix}$	$\begin{bmatrix} 0 & 1 \\ 1 & 0 \end{bmatrix}$	$\begin{bmatrix} 0 & -1 \\ -1 & 0 \end{bmatrix}$

Problem 4 Reflecting a Figure

Reflect the quadrilateral with vertices $A(2, 1)$, $B(8, 1)$, $C(8, 4)$, and $D(5, 5)$ across the indicated line. What are the vertices of the image? Graph the preimage and the image in the same coordinate plane.

Think

Does it matter what order you list the points in the preimage matrix?
Yes; you should list them in order as you move around the outside of the figure.

A y-axis

$$\begin{bmatrix} -1 & 0 \\ 0 & 1 \end{bmatrix}\begin{bmatrix} 2 & 8 & 8 & 5 \\ 1 & 1 & 4 & 5 \end{bmatrix} = \begin{bmatrix} -2 & -8 & -8 & -5 \\ 1 & 1 & 4 & 5 \end{bmatrix}$$

The vertices of the image are $(-2, 1)$, $(-8, 1)$, $(-8, 4)$, and $(-5, 5)$.

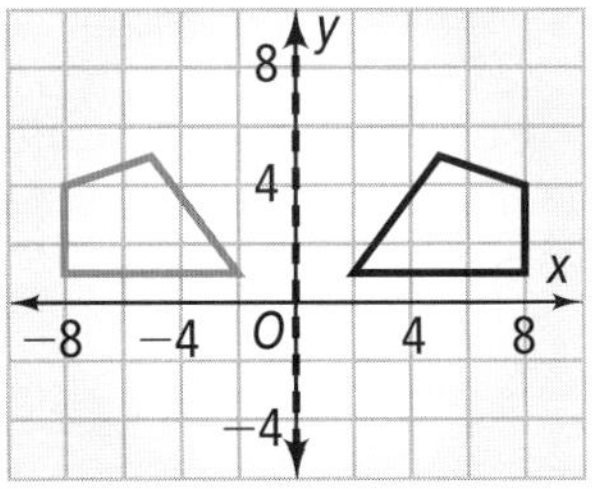

B $y = -x$

$$\begin{bmatrix} 0 & -1 \\ -1 & 0 \end{bmatrix}\begin{bmatrix} 2 & 8 & 8 & 5 \\ 1 & 1 & 4 & 5 \end{bmatrix} = \begin{bmatrix} -1 & -1 & -4 & -5 \\ -2 & -8 & -8 & -5 \end{bmatrix}$$

The vertices of the image are $(-1, -2)$, $(-1, -8)$, $(-4, -8)$, and $(-5, -5)$.

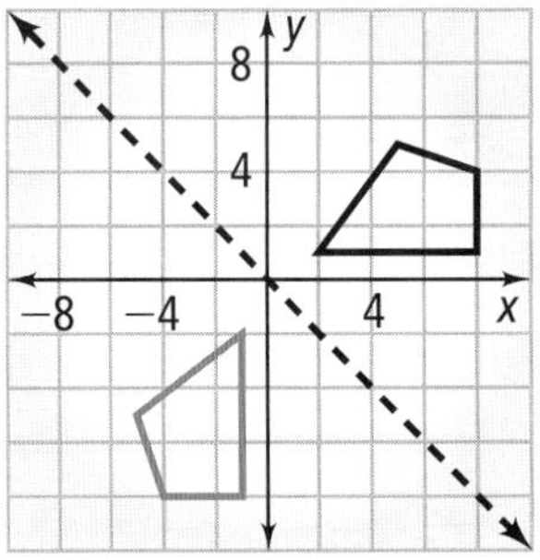

Got It? 4. Reflect the quadrilateral with vertices $E(1, 1)$, $F(3, 1)$, $G(6, 4)$, and $H(1, 3)$ across the indicated line. What are vertices of the image? Graph the preimage and the image in the same coordinate plane.

a. x-axis **b.** $y = x$

Lesson Check

Do you know HOW?

Use matrices to perform the following transformations on the triangle with vertices $A(1, 1)$, $B(2, 4)$, and $C(4, -1)$. State the coordinates of the vertices of the image.

1. Reduce by a factor of $\frac{1}{2}$.

2. Rotate 270°.

3. Reflect across the line $y = x$.

Do you UNDERSTAND? MATHEMATICAL PRACTICES

4. Reasoning Which transformations, translation, dilation, rotation, or reflection, leave the size of a figure unchanged? Explain.

5. Writing Describe two ways that the point (3, 7) can be transformed to the point (7, 3).

6. Reasoning What is true about $\begin{bmatrix} -3 & 0 \\ 0 & -3 \end{bmatrix}\begin{bmatrix} 1 & -2 & 4 \\ 1 & -1 & 2 \end{bmatrix}$ and $-3\begin{bmatrix} 1 & -2 & 4 \\ 1 & -1 & 2 \end{bmatrix}$? Explain.

Practice and Problem-Solving Exercises MATHEMATICAL PRACTICES

A Practice

Use matrix addition to find the coordinates of each image after a translation 3 units left and 5 units up. If possible, graph each pair of figures on the same coordinate plane. See Problem 1.

7. $A(1, -3)$, $B(1, 1)$, $C(5, 1)$, $D(5, -3)$

8. $G(0, 0)$, $H(4, 4)$, $I(8, 0)$, $J(4, -4)$

9. $J(-10, 2)$, $K(-16, 1)$, $L(12, -5)$

10. $R(9, 3)$, $S(3, 6)$, $T(3, 3)$, $U(6, -3)$

Find the coordinates of each image after the given dilation. See Problem 2.

11. $\begin{bmatrix} 0 & 2 & 5 & 8 \\ 0 & 4 & 5 & 1 \end{bmatrix}$, 2

12. $\begin{bmatrix} -7 & -3 & 4 \\ -5 & 4 & 0 \end{bmatrix}$, 0.5

13. $\begin{bmatrix} -8 & 2 & 3 & 1 & -2 \\ 6 & 4 & 0 & -4 & 0 \end{bmatrix}$, 1.5

Graph each figure and its image after the given rotation. See Problem 3.

14. $\begin{bmatrix} 0 & -3 & 5 \\ 0 & 1 & 2 \end{bmatrix}$; 90°

15. $\begin{bmatrix} -1 & 0 & 5 \\ -1 & 5 & 0 \end{bmatrix}$; 180°

16. $\begin{bmatrix} -5 & 6 & 0 \\ -1 & 2 & 4 \end{bmatrix}$; 90°

Find the coordinates of each image after the given rotation.

17. $\begin{bmatrix} 3 & 6 & 3 & 6 \\ -3 & 3 & 3 & -3 \end{bmatrix}$; 270°

18. $\begin{bmatrix} 0 & 4 & 8 & 6 \\ 0 & 4 & 4 & 2 \end{bmatrix}$; 360°

19. $\begin{bmatrix} 1 & 2 & 3 & 4 & 2.5 \\ 3 & 2 & 2 & 3 & 5 \end{bmatrix}$; 180°

Graph each figure and its image after reflection across the given line. See Problem 4.

20. $\begin{bmatrix} 0 & -3 & 5 \\ 0 & 1 & 2 \end{bmatrix}$; $y = x$

21. $\begin{bmatrix} -1 & 0 & 5 \\ -1 & 5 & 0 \end{bmatrix}$; y-axis

22. $\begin{bmatrix} -3 & -5 & -10 \\ 4 & 7 & 1 \end{bmatrix}$; x-axis

Find the coordinates of each image after reflection across the given line.

23. $\begin{bmatrix} 3 & 6 & 3 & 6 \\ -3 & 3 & 3 & -3 \end{bmatrix}$; $y = -x$

24. $\begin{bmatrix} 0 & 4 & 8 & 6 \\ 0 & 4 & 4 & 2 \end{bmatrix}$; x-axis

25. $\begin{bmatrix} 1 & 2 & 3 & 4 & 2.5 \\ 3 & 2 & 2 & 3 & 5 \end{bmatrix}$; $y = x$

B Apply

Geometry Each matrix represents the vertices of a polygon. Translate each figure 5 units left and 1 unit up. Express your answer as a matrix.

26. $\begin{bmatrix} -3 & -3 & 2 & 2 \\ -2 & -4 & -2 & -4 \end{bmatrix}$ **27.** $\begin{bmatrix} -3 & 0 & 3 & 0 \\ -9 & -6 & -9 & -12 \end{bmatrix}$ **28.** $\begin{bmatrix} 0 & 1 & -4 \\ 0 & 3 & 5 \end{bmatrix}$

For Exercises 29–32, use $\triangle ABC$. Write the coordinates of each image in matrix form.

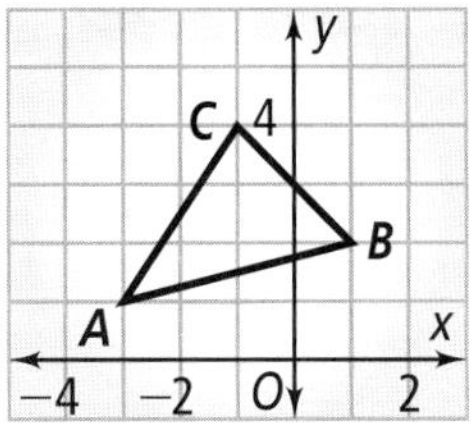

29. a translation 2 units left and 3 units down

30. a dilation half the original size

31. a rotation of 180°

32. a reflection across the x-axis

33. Think About a Plan In an upcoming cartoon, the hero is a gymnast. In one scene he swings around a high bar. Describe the rotation matrices that would be needed so four frames of the movie would show the illustrated motion (below), one frame after the other.

- What do you need to do first to describe the motion?
- Can you use just one rotation matrix, or do you need three?

Frame 1 Frame 2 Frame 3 Frame 4

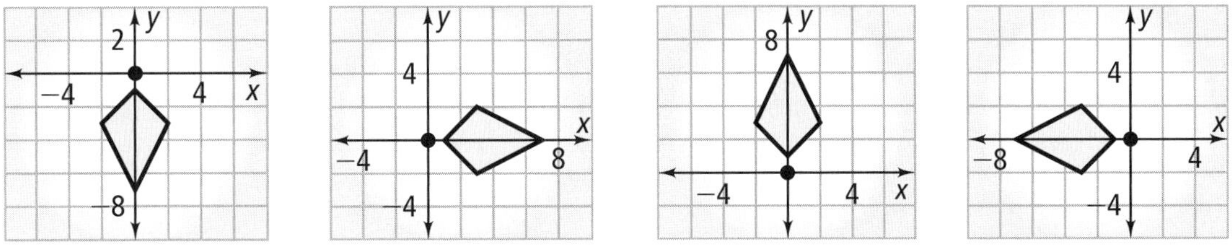

34. Animation Suppose you want the cartoon of the gymnast in the previous exercise to show two revolutions around the bar. What rotation matrices are needed so eight frames of the movie would show the illustrated motion, one frame after the other.

35. Writing Explain why you might want to represent a transformation as a matrix.

Use matrices to represent the vertices of graph f and graph g. Name each transformation.

36.

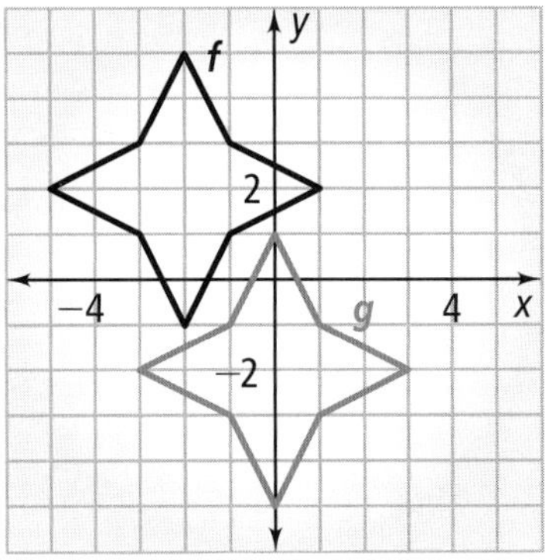

37.

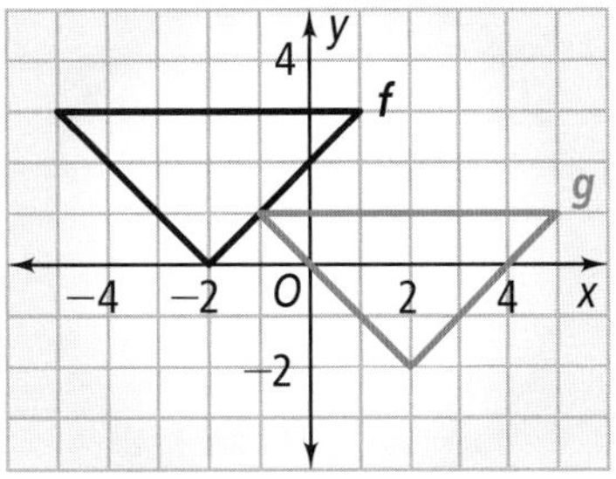

38.

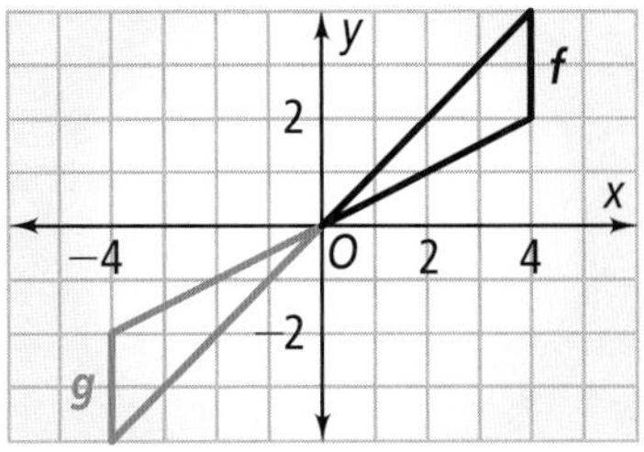

Challenge **Geometry** **Each matrix represents the vertices of a transformed polygon. Write a matrix to represent the vertices of the image before each transformation.**

39. $\begin{bmatrix} -3 & 0.5 & -5 \\ 0 & 3 & 3 \end{bmatrix}$; dilation of 2

40. $\begin{bmatrix} 3 & 4.5 & 5 & 3.5 \\ 3 & 1.5 & 2 & 4 \end{bmatrix}$; rotation of 90°

41. Writing Explain why a reflection of a matrix of points from a function table across the line $y = x$ is equivalent to finding the inverse of the function.

A-6 Vectors

Content Standards

N.VM.5a Represent scalar multiplication graphically by scaling vectors . . . perform scalar multiplication component-wise.

N.VM.11 Multiply a vector . . . by a matrix of suitable dimension to produce another vector.

Also N.VM.1-4, N.VM.5b, N.VM.12

Objective To use basic vector operations and the dot product

1 knot is a speed of 1 nautical mile (about 6076 ft) per hour. 1 knot is faster than 1 mi/h.

MATHEMATICAL PRACTICES

SOLVE IT! Getting Ready!

A young sailor maintains a constant speed of 12 knots. Starting from a pier, she sails for 20 min on the heading shown. Then she turns and sails for 15 min on the next heading. On her next turn, the sailboat capsizes. The Coast Guard immediately sends a rescue boat, traveling at 50 knots, from the same pier. How long does it take the rescue boat to reach her? Explain.

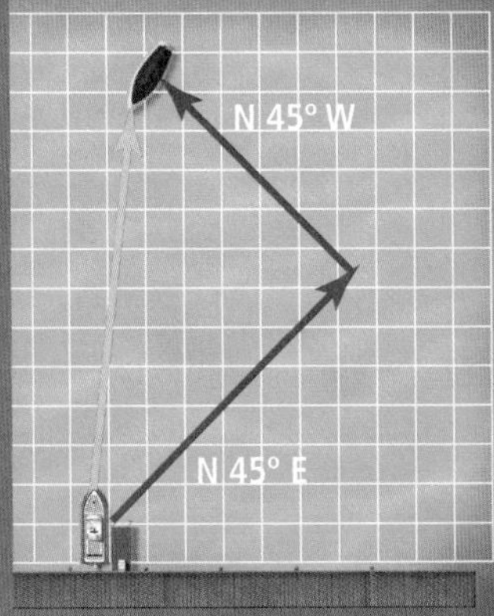

Lesson Vocabulary
- vector
- magnitude
- initial point
- terminal point
- dot product
- normal vectors

In the Solve It, the Coast Guard had to know both distance and direction to rescue the sailor.

Essential Understanding A *vector* is a mathematical object that has both *magnitude* (size) and direction.

take note — Key Concept Vectors in Two Dimensions

A vector has magnitude and direction. You can describe a vector as a directed line segment with initial and terminal points. Two such segments with the same magnitude and direction represent the same vector.

$\mathbf{v} = \overrightarrow{PQ}$ where $P = (1, 1)$ and $Q = (3, 4)$ and

$\mathbf{v} = \overrightarrow{RS}$ where $R = (-1, 2)$ and $S = (1, 5)$

represent the same vector.

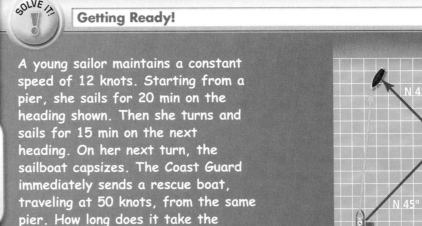

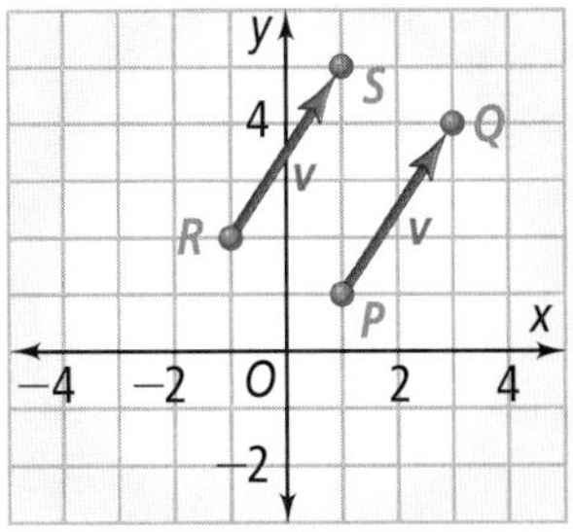

A **vector** has both magnitude and direction. You often use an arrow to represent a vector. The **magnitude** of a vector **v** is the length of the arrow. You can denote it as $|\mathbf{v}|$. You show the direction of the vector by the **initial point** and the **terminal point** of the arrow.

The position of a vector is not important. For this reason, a vector **v** in standard position has initial point (0, 0) and is completely determined by its terminal point (a, b). You can represent **v** in component form as $\langle a, b \rangle$. Use the Pythagorean theorem to find the magnitude of **v**, $|\mathbf{v}| = \sqrt{a^2 + b^2}$.

Problem 1 Representing a Vector

What is the component form of the vector $\mathbf{v} = \overrightarrow{PQ}$ shown here?

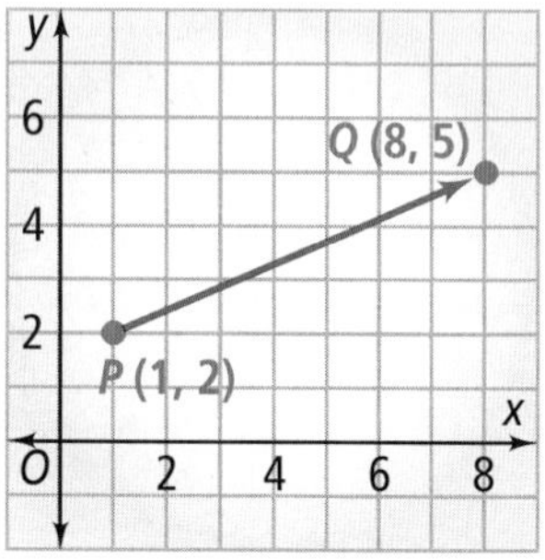

Think	Write
For component form, the initial point must be at the origin. You need to move it 1 unit left and 2 units down.	$(1 - 1, 2 - 2) = (0, 0)$
You must move the terminal point in the same way.	$(8 - 1, 5 - 2) = (7, 3)$
The new terminal point is the component form.	$\mathbf{v} = \langle 7, 3 \rangle$

Got It? **1.** What are the component forms of the two vectors shown here?

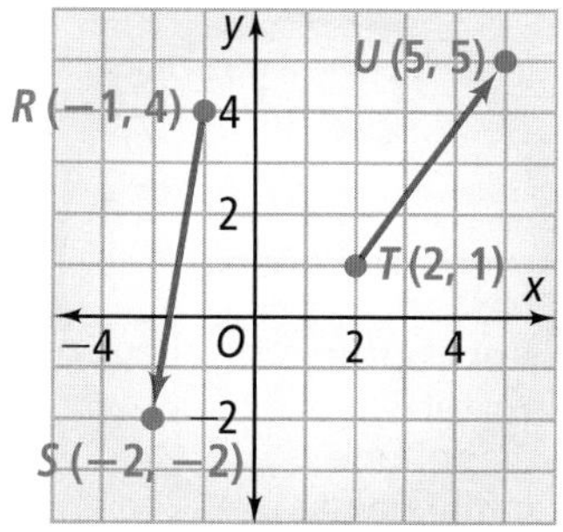

You can also write a vector $\mathbf{v} = \langle a, b \rangle$ in matrix form, $\mathbf{v} = \begin{bmatrix} a \\ b \end{bmatrix}$. By writing in matrix form, you can use matrix transformations to transform a vector.

Problem 2 Rotating a Vector

Rotate the vector $\mathbf{w} = \langle 3, -2 \rangle$ by 90°. What is the component form of the resulting vector?

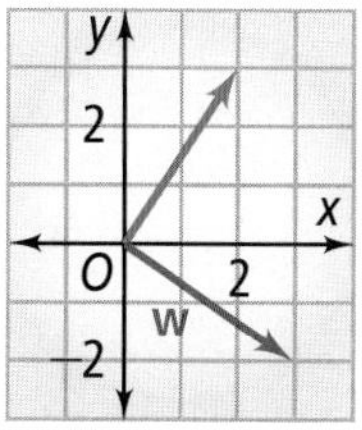

Think

How can you rotate points in the coordinate plane? You can multiply by a rotation matrix.

Step 1 Write the vector in matrix form. $\begin{bmatrix} 3 \\ -2 \end{bmatrix}$

Step 2 Multiply the vector by the 90° rotation matrix.

$$\begin{bmatrix} 0 & -1 \\ 1 & 0 \end{bmatrix}\begin{bmatrix} 3 \\ -2 \end{bmatrix} = \begin{bmatrix} 2 \\ 3 \end{bmatrix}$$

Step 3 The resulting vector is $\langle 2, 3 \rangle$.

Got It? **2. a.** Rotate the vector $\mathbf{v} = \langle -3, 5 \rangle$ by 270°. What is the component form of the resulting vector?

b. Reasoning What other matrix transformations can you apply to vectors in matrix form?

You can use real number operations to define operations involving vectors.

take note — Properties Operations With Vectors

Given $\mathbf{v} = \langle v_1, v_2 \rangle$, $\mathbf{w} = \langle w_1, w_2 \rangle$, and any real number k:

$$\mathbf{v} + \mathbf{w} = \langle v_1 + w_1, v_2 + w_2 \rangle$$
$$\mathbf{v} - \mathbf{w} = \langle v_1 - w_1, v_2 - w_2 \rangle$$
$$k\mathbf{v} = \langle kv_1, kv_2 \rangle$$

Note that
$\mathbf{w} + (\mathbf{v} - \mathbf{w}) = \mathbf{v}$
and $(\mathbf{v} - \mathbf{w}) + \mathbf{w} = \mathbf{v}$.

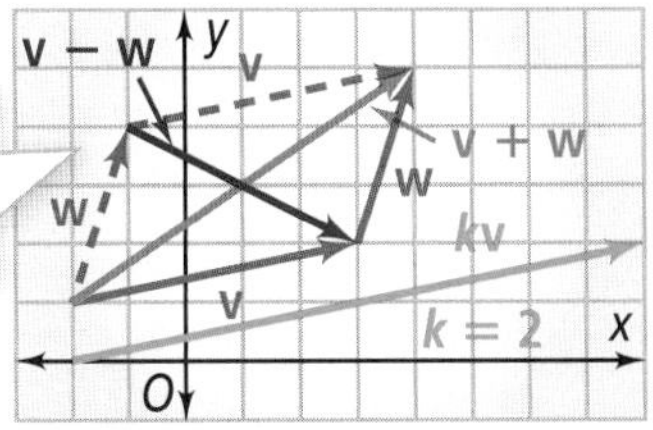

Problem 3 Adding and Subtracting Vectors

GRIDDED RESPONSE

Let $\mathbf{u} = \langle -2, 3 \rangle$ and $\mathbf{v} = \langle 5, -2 \rangle$. What is $|\mathbf{u} + \mathbf{v}|$, rounded to the nearest hundredth?

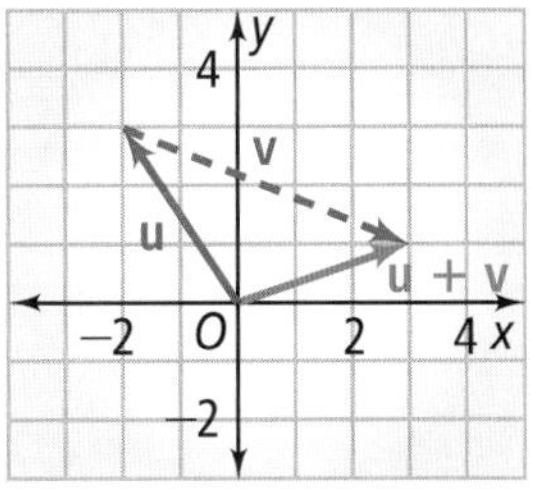

To find $\mathbf{u} + \mathbf{v}$, use the tip-to-tail method shown above.

Think
How do you draw v with initial point (−2, 3)?
Use $(-2 + 5, 3 - 2) = (3, 1)$ for the terminal point.

Step 1 Draw $\mathbf{u} = \langle -2, 3 \rangle$ in standard position.

Step 2 At the tip of $\mathbf{u}$, draw $\mathbf{v} = \langle 5, -2 \rangle$ from $(-2, 3)$ to $(3, 1)$.

Step 3 Draw $\mathbf{u} + \mathbf{v}$ to have the initial point of $\mathbf{u}$ and the terminal point of $\mathbf{v}$.

Step 4 Express $\mathbf{u} + \mathbf{v}$ in component form. $\mathbf{u} + \mathbf{v} = \langle 3, 1 \rangle$

Step 5 $|\mathbf{u} + \mathbf{v}| = \sqrt{3^2 + 1^2} = \sqrt{10} \approx 3.16$

Check $\mathbf{u} + \mathbf{v} = \langle -2, 3 \rangle + \langle 5, -2 \rangle = \langle -2 + 5, 3 + (-2) \rangle = \langle 3, 1 \rangle$

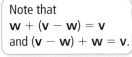

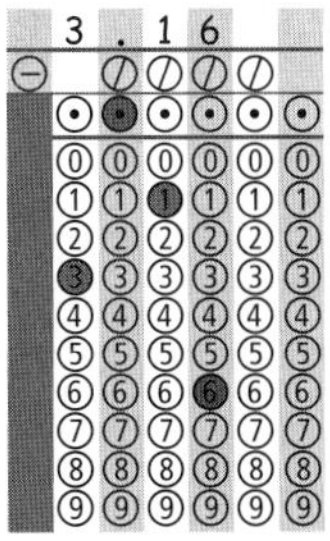

Got It? **3.** Using the vectors given in Problem 3, what is $|\mathbf{u} - \mathbf{v}|$?

Scalar multiplication of a vector by a positive number (other than 1) changes only the magnitude. Multiplication by a negative number (other than −1) changes the magnitude and reverses the direction of the vector.

Problem 4 Scalar Multiplication

Plan

How should you start?
Begin by finding the component form of the scaled vectors.

For $\mathbf{v} = \langle 1, -2 \rangle$ and $\mathbf{w} = \langle 2, 3 \rangle$, what are the graphs of the following vectors?

A $\mathbf{v}$ and $3\mathbf{v}$

$$3\mathbf{v} = 3\langle 1, -2 \rangle = \langle 3(1), 3(-2) \rangle = \langle 3, -6 \rangle$$

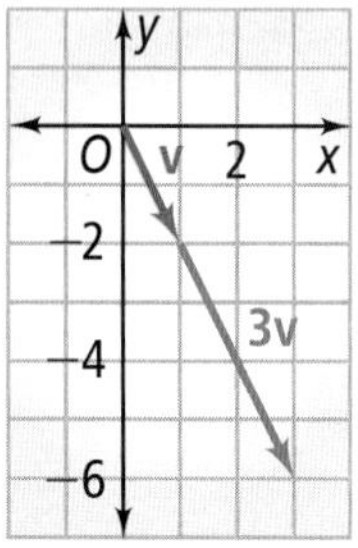

B $\mathbf{w}$ and $-2\mathbf{w}$

$$-2\mathbf{w} = -2\langle 2, 3 \rangle = \langle -2(2), -2(3) \rangle = \langle -4, -6 \rangle$$

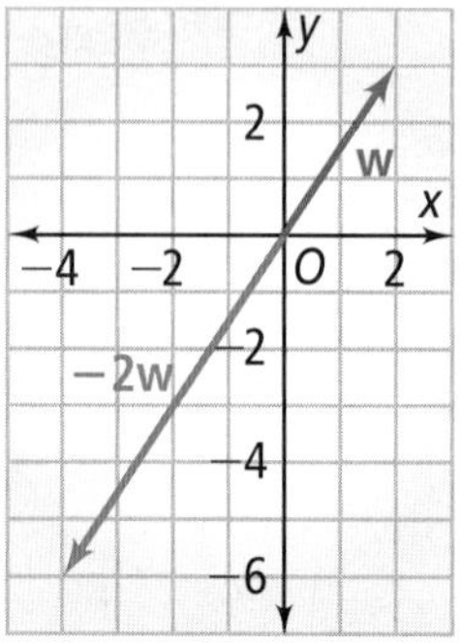

Got It? 4. Given $\mathbf{u} = \langle -2, 4 \rangle$, what are the graphs of the following vectors?

a. $-\mathbf{u}$

b. $\frac{1}{2}\mathbf{u}$

If $\mathbf{v} = \langle v_1, v_2 \rangle$ and $\mathbf{w} = \langle w_1, w_2 \rangle$, the **dot product** $\mathbf{v} \cdot \mathbf{w}$ is $v_1w_1 + v_2w_2$. If $\mathbf{v} \cdot \mathbf{w} = 0$, the two vectors are **normal**, or perpendicular, to each other.

Problem 5 Finding Dot Products

Think

How can you check your results?
If the slopes of the lines containing the vectors are negative reciprocals, the vectors are normal.

Are the following vectors normal?

A $\mathbf{t} = \langle 2, -5 \rangle, \mathbf{u} = \langle 7, 3 \rangle$

$$\mathbf{t} \cdot \mathbf{u} = (2)(7) + (-5)(3) = 14 + (-15) = -1$$

t and **u** are not normal.

Check

$$m_{\mathbf{t}} = \frac{-5 - 0}{2 - 0} = -\frac{5}{2}$$

$$m_{\mathbf{u}} = \frac{3 - 0}{7 - 0} = \frac{3}{7}$$

not perpendicular ✔

B $\mathbf{v} = \langle 10, -4 \rangle, \mathbf{w} = \langle 2, 5 \rangle$

$$\mathbf{v} \cdot \mathbf{w} = (10)(2) + (-4)(5) = 20 - 20 = 0$$

v and **w** are normal.

Check

$$m_{\mathbf{v}} = \frac{-4 - 0}{10 - 0} = -\frac{2}{5}$$

$$m_{\mathbf{w}} = \frac{5 - 0}{2 - 0} = \frac{5}{2}$$

perpendicular ✔

Got It? 5. Are the following vectors normal?

a. $\langle -2, 6 \rangle, \langle -9, -18 \rangle$

b. $\left\langle 3, \frac{5}{6} \right\rangle, \left\langle -\frac{10}{9}, 4 \right\rangle$

Lesson Check

Do you know HOW?

Let $P = (-2, 2)$, $Q = (3, 4)$, $R = (-2, 5)$, and $S = (2, -8)$. What are the component forms of the following vectors?

1. $\overrightarrow{PQ}$

2. $\overrightarrow{RS} + \overrightarrow{PQ}$

3. $\overrightarrow{RS} - \overrightarrow{RQ}$

4. $-5\overrightarrow{PR}$

Do you UNDERSTAND? MATHEMATICAL PRACTICES

5. Vocabulary Which of the following vectors has the greatest magnitude? Explain.

$\mathbf{a} = \langle 3, 4 \rangle$ $\mathbf{b} = \langle -4, 3 \rangle$ $\mathbf{c} = \langle 4, -3 \rangle$

6. Error Analysis Your friend says that the magnitude of vector $\langle 8, 3 \rangle$ is 4 times that of vector $\langle 2, 3 \rangle$ since 8 is 4 times 2. Explain why your friend's statement is incorrect.

Practice and Problem-Solving Exercises MATHEMATICAL PRACTICES

A Practice

Referring to the graph, what are the component forms of the following vectors?

See Problem 1.

7. u

8. v

9. w

10. f

11. g

12. h

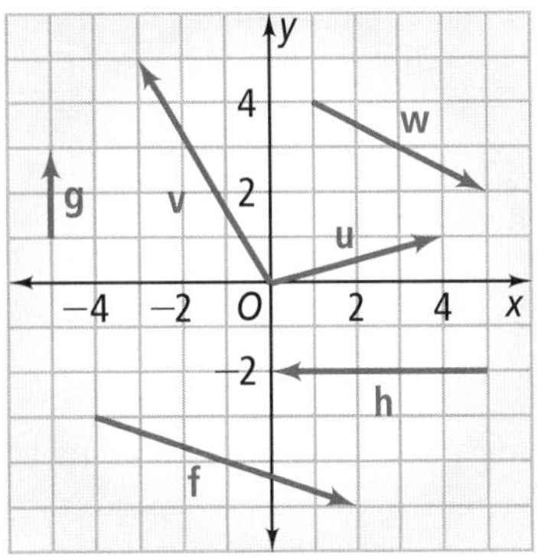

Transform each vector as described. Write the resulting vector in component form.

See Problem 2.

13. $\langle 5, 1 \rangle$; rotate 90°

14. $\langle -4, 3 \rangle$; rotate 180°

15. $\langle 0, 2 \rangle$; rotate 270°

16. $\langle 11, -4 \rangle$; reflect across x-axis

17. $\langle -3, 0 \rangle$; reflect across y-axis

18. $\langle 4, 5 \rangle$; reflect across $y = x$

19. $\langle 4, -3 \rangle$; reflect across $y = -x$

Let $\mathbf{u} = \langle -1, 3 \rangle$, $\mathbf{v} = \langle 2, 4 \rangle$, and $\mathbf{w} = \langle 2, -5 \rangle$. Find the component forms of the following vectors.

See Problems 3 and 4.

20. $\mathbf{u} + \mathbf{v}$

21. $\mathbf{v} + \mathbf{w}$

22. $\mathbf{u} - \mathbf{v}$

23. $\mathbf{u} - \mathbf{w}$

24. $2\mathbf{u}$

25. $-4\mathbf{w}$

26. $\frac{3}{2}\mathbf{v}$

27. $-3\mathbf{v}$

Determine whether the vectors in each pair are normal to each other.

See Problem 5.

28. $\langle 6, -3 \rangle$ and $\langle 2, 4 \rangle$

29. $\langle 8, -4 \rangle$ and $\langle -2, 4 \rangle$

30. $\begin{bmatrix} 1 \\ 8 \end{bmatrix}$ and $\begin{bmatrix} 4 \\ -2 \end{bmatrix}$

31. $\begin{bmatrix} 0.8 \\ -0.6 \end{bmatrix}$ and $\begin{bmatrix} 0.3 \\ 0.4 \end{bmatrix}$

B Apply

Let u $= \begin{bmatrix} -5 \\ 3 \end{bmatrix}$, v $= \begin{bmatrix} 4 \\ -3 \end{bmatrix}$, and w $= \begin{bmatrix} 2 \\ 2 \end{bmatrix}$. Find the following vectors.

32. $2\mathbf{u} + 3\mathbf{v}$ **33.** $2\mathbf{v} - 4\mathbf{w}$ **34.** $-\mathbf{u} - \mathbf{w}$ **35.** $-3\mathbf{u} + \mathbf{v} - \frac{1}{2}\mathbf{w}$

36. Think About a Plan A ferry shuttles people from one side of a river to the other. The speed of the ferry in still water is 25 mi/h. The river flows directly south at 7 mi/h. If the ferry heads directly west, what is the ferry's resulting speed?

- How can a sketch help you solve this problem?
- What formula can you use to find the speed?

37. Aviation A twin-engine airplane has a speed of 300 mi/h in still air. Suppose the airplane heads south and encounters a wind blowing 50 mi/h due east. What is the resultant speed of the airplane?

38. Aviation A small airplane lands at a point 216 mi east and 76 mi north of the point from which it took off. How far did the airplane fly?

39. Consider the triangle with vertices at $A(2, 2)$, $B(5, 3)$, and $C(3, 6)$. Express the sides of the triangle as vectors $\overrightarrow{AB}$, $\overrightarrow{BC}$, and $\overrightarrow{CA}$.

Let a $= \langle 6, -1 \rangle$, b $= \langle -4, 3 \rangle$, and c $= \langle 2, 0 \rangle$. Solve each of the following for the unknown vector v.

40. $\mathbf{a} + \mathbf{v} = \mathbf{b}$ **41.** $\mathbf{c} - \mathbf{v} = \mathbf{b}$

42. $\mathbf{v} - \mathbf{b} = \mathbf{a} + \mathbf{c}$ **43.** $\mathbf{a} + \mathbf{b} + \mathbf{c} + \mathbf{v} = (0, 0)$

44. Navigation A fishing boat leaves its home port and travels 150 mi directly east. It then changes course and travels 40 mi due north. How long will the direct return trip take if the boat averages 23 mi/h?

45. Writing Subtract any vector from itself. The result is still a vector, but a unique one. Explain what this vector is, and what it means for vector addition.

Reasoning Do the following properties hold for vectors and scalars? Identify each property and make a diagram to support your answers.

46. $\mathbf{u} + \mathbf{v} = \mathbf{v} + \mathbf{u}$ **47.** $k(\mathbf{u} + \mathbf{v}) = k\mathbf{u} + k\mathbf{v}$

48. $\mathbf{u} - \mathbf{v} = \mathbf{v} - \mathbf{u}$ **49.** $(\mathbf{u} + \mathbf{v}) + \mathbf{w} = \mathbf{u} + (\mathbf{v} + \mathbf{w})$

C Challenge

50. Aviation A helicopter starts at (0, 0) and makes three legs of a flight represented by the vectors $\langle 10, 10 \rangle$, $\langle 5, -4 \rangle$, and $\langle -3, 5 \rangle$, in that order. If another helicopter starts at (0, 0) and flies the same three legs in a different order, would it end in the same place? Justify your answer.

51. Two vectors are parallel if the absolute value of their dot product is equal to the product of their magnitudes. Which of the following vectors are parallel? Which are perpendicular?

$\mathbf{a} = \begin{bmatrix} 0.9 \\ 1.2 \end{bmatrix}$ $\mathbf{b} = \begin{bmatrix} -2 \\ 1.5 \end{bmatrix}$ $\mathbf{c} = \begin{bmatrix} 6 \\ -8 \end{bmatrix}$ $\mathbf{d} = \begin{bmatrix} -4.5 \\ -6 \end{bmatrix}$

52. Given $\mathbf{u} = \langle -4, 3 \rangle$ and $\mathbf{v} = \langle 1, -2 \rangle$, find $\mathbf{w}$ if $\mathbf{u} \cdot \mathbf{w} = 7$ and $\mathbf{v} \cdot \mathbf{w} = -8$.

STEM **53.** **Physics** When an object is not moving, all the forces acting on it must sum to 0. The object is said to be *in equilibrium*. Two cables of different lengths hold a stoplight over an intersection. The force vectors being applied along the two cables are $\langle 20, 18 \rangle$ and $\langle -20, 12 \rangle$. The magnitude of each vector is measured in pounds. A third force vector in this situation is the force due to gravity, and is straight downward. How much does the stoplight weigh?

A Topic Review

A-1 Adding and Subracting Matrices

Quick Review

To perform matrix addition or subtraction, add or subtract the corresponding elements in the matrices.

Two matrices are **equal matrices** when they have the same dimensions and corresponding elements are equal. This principle is used to solve a **matrix equation**.

Example

If $A = \begin{bmatrix} 2 & 1 & -2 \\ 1 & 4 & 3 \\ -2 & -1 & 5 \end{bmatrix}$ and $B = \begin{bmatrix} 1 & -2 & 4 \\ -3 & -2 & 1 \\ 0 & 0 & 5 \end{bmatrix}$, what is $A + B$?

$$A + B = \begin{bmatrix} 2+1 & 1+(-2) & -2+4 \\ 1+(-3) & 4+(-2) & 3+1 \\ -2+0 & -1+0 & 5+5 \end{bmatrix}$$

$$= \begin{bmatrix} 3 & -1 & 2 \\ -2 & 2 & 4 \\ -2 & -1 & 10 \end{bmatrix}$$

Exercises

Find each sum or difference.

1. $\begin{bmatrix} 1 & 2 & -5 \\ 3 & -2 & 1 \end{bmatrix} + \begin{bmatrix} -2 & 7 & -3 \\ 1 & 2 & 5 \end{bmatrix}$

2. $\begin{bmatrix} 0 & 2 \\ -4 & -1 \end{bmatrix} - \begin{bmatrix} -5 & 6 \\ -9 & -1 \end{bmatrix}$

Solve each matrix equation.

3. $[2 \;\; -6 \;\; 8] + [-1 \;\; -2 \;\; 4] = X$

4. $\begin{bmatrix} 7 & -1 \\ 0 & 8 \end{bmatrix} + X = \begin{bmatrix} 4 & 9 \\ -3 & 11 \end{bmatrix}$

Find the value of each variable.

5. $\begin{bmatrix} x-5 & 9 \\ 4 & t+2 \end{bmatrix} = \begin{bmatrix} -7 & w+1 \\ 8-r & 1 \end{bmatrix}$

6. $\begin{bmatrix} -4+t & 2y \\ r & w+5 \end{bmatrix} = \begin{bmatrix} 2t & 11 \\ -2r+12 & 9 \end{bmatrix}$

A-2 Matrix Multiplication

Quick Review

To obtain the product of a matrix and a **scalar**, multiply each matrix element by the scalar. Matrix multiplication uses both multiplication and addition. The element in the ith row and the jth column of the product of two matrices is the sum of the products of each element of the ith row of the first matrix and the corresponding element of the jth column of the second matrix. The first matrix must have the same number of columns as the second has rows.

Example

If $A = \begin{bmatrix} 1 & -3 \\ -2 & 0 \end{bmatrix}$ and $B = \begin{bmatrix} 1 & 4 \\ 0 & 2 \end{bmatrix}$, what is AB?

$$AB = \begin{bmatrix} (1)(1)+(-3)(0) & (1)(4)+(-3)(2) \\ (-2)(1)+(0)(0) & (-2)(4)+(0)(2) \end{bmatrix}$$

$$= \begin{bmatrix} 1 & -2 \\ -2 & -8 \end{bmatrix}$$

Exercises

Use matrices *A*, *B*, *C*, and *D* to find each scalar product and sum, or difference, if possible. If an operation is not defined, label it *undefined*.

$A = \begin{bmatrix} 6 & 1 & 0 & 8 \\ -4 & 3 & 7 & 11 \end{bmatrix}$ $\quad B = \begin{bmatrix} 1 & 3 \\ -2 & 4 \end{bmatrix}$

$C = \begin{bmatrix} -2 & 1 \\ 4 & 0 \\ 2 & 2 \\ 1 & 1 \end{bmatrix}$ $\quad D = \begin{bmatrix} 5 & -2 \\ 3 & 6 \end{bmatrix}$

7. $3A$
8. $B - 2A$
9. AB
10. BA
11. $AC - BD$
12. $4B - 3D$

A-3 Determinants and Inverses

Quick Review

A **square matrix** with 1's along its main diagonal and 0's elsewhere is the **multiplicative identity matrix**, I. If A and X are square matrices such that $AX = I$, then X is the **multiplicative identity matrix** of A, A^{-1}.

You can use a calculator to find the inverse of a matrix. You can find the inverse of a 2×2 matrix

$A = \begin{bmatrix} a & b \\ c & d \end{bmatrix}$ by using its **determinant**.

$$A^{-1} = \frac{1}{\det A}\begin{bmatrix} d & -b \\ -c & a \end{bmatrix} = \frac{1}{ad - bc}\begin{bmatrix} d & -b \\ -c & a \end{bmatrix}$$

Example

What is the determinant of $\begin{bmatrix} 2 & -3 \\ 3 & -4 \end{bmatrix}$?

$$\det\begin{bmatrix} 2 & -3 \\ 3 & -4 \end{bmatrix} = (2)(-4) - (-3)(3)$$
$$= -8 - (-9) = 1$$

Exercises

Evaluate the determinant of each matrix and find the inverse, if possible.

13. $\begin{bmatrix} 6 & 1 \\ 0 & 4 \end{bmatrix}$

14. $\begin{bmatrix} 5 & -2 \\ 10 & -4 \end{bmatrix}$

15. $\begin{bmatrix} 10 & 1 \\ 8 & 5 \end{bmatrix}$

16. $\begin{bmatrix} 1 & 0 & 2 \\ -1 & 0 & 1 \\ -1 & -2 & 0 \end{bmatrix}$

A-4 Inverse Matrices and Systems

Quick Review

You can use inverse matrices to solve some matrix equations and systems of equations. When equations in a system are in standard form, the product of the **coefficient matrix** and the **variable matrix** equals the **constant matrix**. You solve the equation by multiplying both sides of the equation by the inverse of the coefficient matrix. If that inverse does not exist, the system does not have a unique solution.

Example

What is the matrix equation that corresponds to the following system? $\begin{cases} 2x - y = 12 \\ x + 4y = 15 \end{cases}$

Identify $A = \begin{bmatrix} 2 & -1 \\ 1 & 4 \end{bmatrix}$, $X = \begin{bmatrix} x \\ y \end{bmatrix}$, and $B = \begin{bmatrix} 12 \\ 15 \end{bmatrix}$.

The matrix equation is $AX = B$ or $\begin{bmatrix} 2 & -1 \\ 1 & 4 \end{bmatrix}\begin{bmatrix} x \\ y \end{bmatrix} = \begin{bmatrix} 12 \\ 15 \end{bmatrix}$.

Exercises

Use an inverse matrix to solve each equation or system.

17. $\begin{bmatrix} 3 & 5 \\ 6 & 2 \end{bmatrix} X = \begin{bmatrix} -2 & 6 \\ 4 & 12 \end{bmatrix}$

18. $\begin{cases} x - y = 3 \\ 2x - y = -1 \end{cases}$

19. $\begin{bmatrix} 4 & 1 \\ 2 & 1 \end{bmatrix}\begin{bmatrix} x \\ y \end{bmatrix} = \begin{bmatrix} 10 \\ 6 \end{bmatrix}$

20. $\begin{bmatrix} -6 & 0 \\ 7 & 1 \end{bmatrix} X = \begin{bmatrix} -12 & -6 \\ 17 & 9 \end{bmatrix}$

21. $\begin{cases} x + 2y = 15 \\ 2x + 4y = 30 \end{cases}$

22. $\begin{cases} a + 2b + c = 14 \\ b = c + 1 \\ a = -3c + 6 \end{cases}$

A-5 Geometric Transformations

Quick Review

A change made to a figure is a transformation. The original figure is the **preimage**, and the transformed figure is the **image**. A translation slides a figure without changing its size or shape. A **dilation** changes the size of a figure. You can use matrix addition to translate a figure and scalar multiplication to dilate a figure.

You can use multiplication by the appropriate matrix to perform transformations that are specific reflections or **rotations**. For example, to reflect a figure across the y-axis, multiply by $\begin{bmatrix} -1 & 0 \\ 0 & 1 \end{bmatrix}$.

Example

A triangle has vertices $A(3, 2)$, $B(1, -2)$, and $C(1, 2)$. What are the coordinates after a 90° rotation?

$$\begin{bmatrix} 0 & -1 \\ 1 & 0 \end{bmatrix}\begin{bmatrix} 3 & 1 & 1 \\ 2 & -2 & 2 \end{bmatrix} = \begin{bmatrix} -2 & 2 & -2 \\ 3 & 1 & 1 \end{bmatrix}$$

The coordinates are $(-2, 3)$, $(2, 1)$, and $(-2, 1)$.

Exercises

In matrix form, write the coordinates of each image of the triangle with vertices $A(3, 1)$, $B(-2, 0)$, and $C(1, 5)$.

23. a translation 3 units left and 4 units up

24. a reflection across the y-axis

25. a reflection across the line $y = x$

26. a dilation half the original size

27. a dilation twice the original size

28. a rotation of 270°

A-6 Vectors

Quick Review

A **vector** has both **magnitude** and **direction**. It is a directed line segment that you can describe using a pair of **initial** and **terminal** points. If a vector were in standard position with the initial point at (0, 0), the component form would be $\langle a, b\rangle$ and the magnitude $|\mathbf{v}| = \sqrt{a^2 + b^2}$ would give you the length.

Given two vectors $\mathbf{v} = \langle v_1, v_2\rangle$ and $\mathbf{w} = \langle w_1, w_2\rangle$, the **dot product** $\mathbf{v} \cdot \mathbf{w}$ is $v_1w_1 + v_2w_2$. If the dot product equals 0, then **v** and **w** are **normal**, or perpendicular, to each other.

Example

Are the vectors $\langle -1, 2\rangle$ and $\langle 4, 2\rangle$ normal?

$$\begin{aligned}\langle -1, 2\rangle \cdot \langle 4, 2\rangle &= (-1)(4) + (2)(2) \\ &= -4 + 4 = 0\end{aligned}$$

The vectors are normal.

Exercises

Let $\mathbf{u} = \langle -3, 4\rangle$, $\mathbf{v} = \langle 2, 4\rangle$, and $\mathbf{w} = \langle 4, -1\rangle$. Write each resulting vector in component form and find the magnitude.

29. $\mathbf{u} + \mathbf{v}$

30. $\mathbf{w} - \mathbf{u}$

31. $3\mathbf{u}$

32. $-2\mathbf{w} + 3\mathbf{v}$

33. $\frac{1}{2}\mathbf{v} + 3\mathbf{u}$

34. $-\mathbf{w} + 3\mathbf{v} + 2\mathbf{u}$

Find the dot product of each pair of vectors and determine whether they are normal.

35. $\langle 4, -3\rangle$ and $\langle -3, -4\rangle$

36. $\begin{bmatrix} 1 \\ 7 \end{bmatrix}$ and $\begin{bmatrix} 14 \\ -2 \end{bmatrix}$

A Pull It All Together

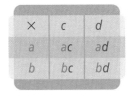

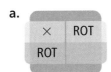

To solve these problems, you will pull together concepts and skills related to matrices.

BIG idea Data Representation

You can represent data in a variety of ways.

Performance Task 1

The first matrix represents inventory (how many there are) of four types of objects. The second matrix is a price matrix. The third matrix is the product of the first two matrices. Give an example of real inventory and real prices for which the product matrix makes sense. Explain the meaning of the product.

$$\begin{bmatrix} a_1 & a_2 \\ b_1 & b_2 \end{bmatrix} \begin{bmatrix} p_1 \\ p_2 \end{bmatrix} = \begin{bmatrix} r_1 \\ r_2 \end{bmatrix}$$

BIG idea Modeling

You can represent many real-world mathematical problems algebraically. These representations can lead to algebraic solutions.

Performance Task 2

Suppose the matrix equation $AX = B$ represents the system $\begin{cases} a_1x + a_2y = b_1 \\ a_3x + a_4y = b_2 \end{cases}$ and $\det A = 0$. Show that the system is either dependent (has many solutions) or inconsistent (has no solutions). (*Hint:* First show that a_3 and a_4 are proportional to a_1 and a_2.)

BIG idea Transformations

Translations, reflections, rotations, and dilations can help you understand relationships within objects and between objects.

Performance Task 3

Each entry in a multiplication table, as shown in the 2-by-2 table at the right, is the product of the factor shown at the left and the factor shown at the top.

×	c	d
a	ac	ad
b	bc	bd

Let $ROT = \{r_{90°}, r_{180°}, r_{270°}, r_{360°}\}$

$REF = \{R_{x\text{-axis}}, R_{y\text{-axis}}, R_{y=x}, R_{y=-x}\}$

be the sets of rotations and reflections, respectively, as described in Lesson A-5. Build each 4-by-4 multiplication table.

a.

×	ROT
ROT	

b.

×	REF
REF	

c.

×	ROT
REF	

d.

×	REF
ROT	

TOPIC

B

Reasoning and Proof

Big Ideas

Reasoning and Proof

Essential Question How can you make a conjecture and prove that it is true?

Domains

- Construct Viable Arguments
- Attend to precision

Topic B Preview

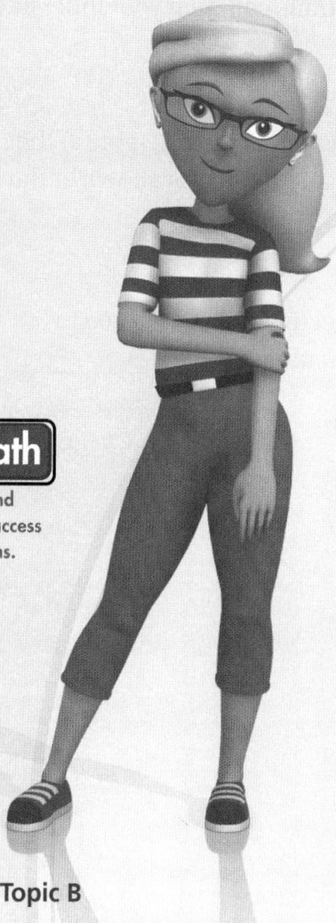

Vocabulary

English/Spanish Vocabulary Audio Online:

English	Spanish
biconditional, *p. H74*	bicondicional
conclusion, *p. H67*	conclusión
conditional, *p. H67*	condicional
conjecture, *p. H60*	conjetura
contrapositive, *p. H70*	contrapositivo
converse, *p. H70*	recíproco
deductive reasoning, *p. H82*	razonamiento deductivo
hypothesis, *p. H67*	hipótesis
inductive reasoning, *p. H59*	razonamiento inductivo
inverse, *p. H70*	inverso
negation, *p. H70*	negación

Interactive Digital Path

Log in to **pearsonsuccessnet.com** and click on Interactive Digital Path to access the Solve Its and animated Problems.

B-1 Patterns and Inductive Reasoning

Prepares for **G.CO.9** Prove theorems about lines and angles . . . Also prepares for **G.CO.10, G.CO.11**

Objective To use inductive reasoning to make conjectures

Solve It! Write your solution to the Solve It in the space below.

In the Solve It, you may have used inductive reasoning. **Inductive reasoning** is reasoning based on patterns you observe.

Essential Understanding You can observe patterns in some number sequences and some sequences of geometric figures to discover relationships.

Problem 1 Finding and Using a Pattern

Got It? What are the next two terms in each sequence?

a. 45, 40, 35, 30, . . .

b.

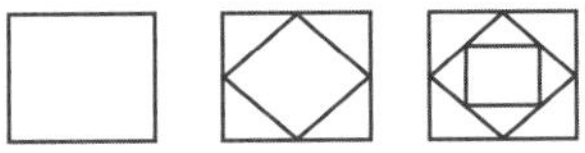

A Practice **Find a pattern for each sequence. Use the pattern to show the next two terms.**

1. $1, \frac{1}{2}, \frac{1}{4}, \frac{1}{8}, \ldots$

2. 

You may want to find the tenth or the one-hundredth term in a sequence. In this case, rather than find every previous term, you can look for a pattern and make a conjecture. A **conjecture** is a conclusion you reach using inductive reasoning.

Problem 2 Using Inductive Reasoning

Got It? What conjecture can you make about the twenty-first term in R, W, B, R, W, B, . . .?

Plan

Do you need to extend the sequence to 21 terms?

A Practice **Use the sequence and inductive reasoning to make a conjecture.**

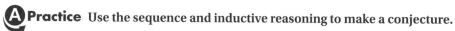

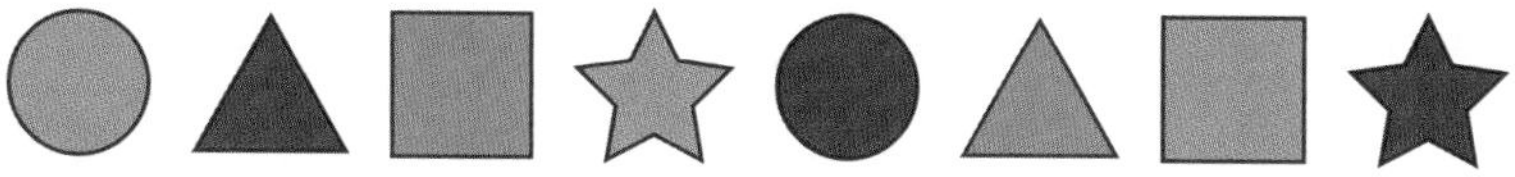

3. What is the color of the thirtieth figure?

4. What is the shape of the fortieth figure?

It is important to gather enough data before you make a conjecture. For example, you do not have enough information about the sequence 1, 3, . . . to make a reasonable conjecture. The next term could be $3 \cdot 3 = 9$ or $3 + 2 = 5$.

Problem 3 Collecting Information to Make a Conjecture

Got It? What conjecture can you make about the sum of the first 30 odd numbers?

Plan
What's the first step?

Practice **Make a conjecture for each scenario. Show your work.**

5. the sum of the first 100 positive even numbers

6. the product of two odd numbers

Problem 4 Making a Prediction

Got It? **a.** Use the graph of the sales information from Problem 4. What conjecture can you make about backpack sales in June?

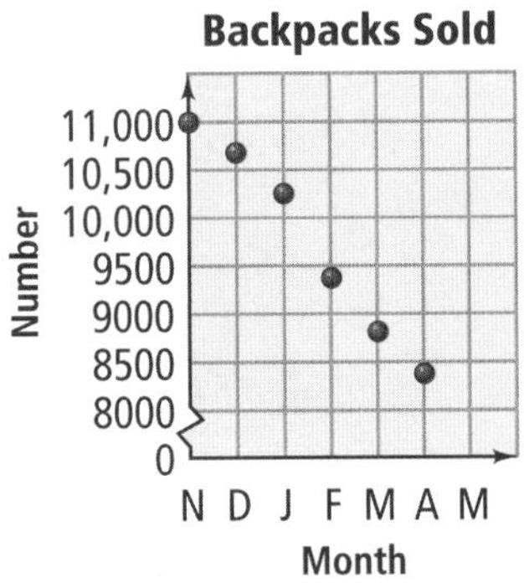

b. Reasoning Is it reasonable to use this graph to make a conjecture about sales in August? Explain.

Ⓐ Practice **Weather** **Use inductive reasoning to make a prediction about the weather.**

STEM **7.** Lightning travels much faster than thunder, so you see lightning before you hear thunder. If you count 5 s between the lightning and thunder, how far away is the storm?

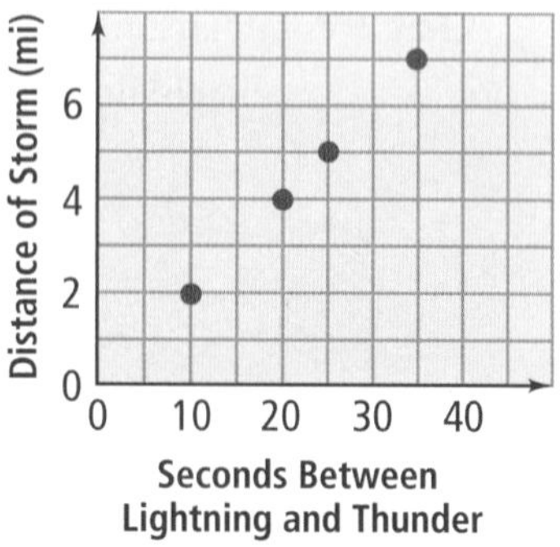

8. The speed at which a cricket chirps is affected by the temperature. If you hear 20 cricket chirps in 14 s, what is the temperature?

Number of Chirps per 14 Seconds	Temperature (°F)
5	45
10	55
15	65

Not all conjectures turn out to be true. You should test your conjecture multiple times. You can prove that a conjecture is false by finding *one* counterexample. A **counterexample** is an example that shows that a conjecture is incorrect.

Problem 5 Finding a Counterexample

Got It? What is a counterexample for each conjecture?

a. If a flower is red, it is a rose.

b. One and only one plane exists through any three points.

c. When you multiply a number by 3, the product is divisible by 6.

Practice **Find one counterexample to show that each conjecture is false.**

9. $\angle 1$ and $\angle 2$ are supplementary, so one of the angles is acute.

10. The sum of two numbers is greater than either number.

Lesson Check

Do you know HOW?

What are the next two terms in each sequence?

11. 7, 13, 19, 25, . . .

12. 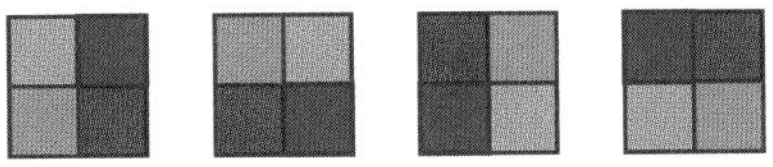

13. What is a counterexample for the following conjecture?
All four-sided figures are squares.

Do you UNDERSTAND?

MATHEMATICAL PRACTICES

14. Vocabulary How does the word *counter* help you understand the term *counterexample*?

15. Compare and Contrast Clay thinks the next term in the sequence 2, 4, . . . is 6. Given the same pattern, Ott thinks the next term is 8, and Stacie thinks the next term is 7. What conjecture is each person making? Is there enough information to decide who is correct?

More Practice and Problem-Solving Exercises

MATHEMATICAL PRACTICES

B Apply

Find a pattern for each sequence. Use inductive reasoning to show the next two terms.

16. 1, 3, 7, 13, 21, . . .

17. 1, 2, 5, 6, 9, . . .

18. 0.1, 0.01, 0.001, . . .

19. 2, 6, 7, 21, 22, 66, 67, . . .

20. 1, 3, 7, 15, 31, . . .

21. $0, \frac{1}{2}, \frac{3}{4}, \frac{7}{8}, \frac{15}{16}, \ldots$

Predict the next term in each sequence. Use your calculator to verify your answer.

22.
$12345679 \times 9 = 111111111$
$12345679 \times 18 = 222222222$
$12345679 \times 27 = 333333333$
$12345679 \times 36 = 444444444$
$12345679 \times 45 = \blacksquare$

23.
$1 \times 1 = 1$
$11 \times 11 = 121$
$111 \times 111 = 12321$
$1111 \times 1111 = 1234321$
$11111 \times 11111 = \blacksquare$

24. Patterns Draw the next figure in the sequence. Make sure you think about color and shape.

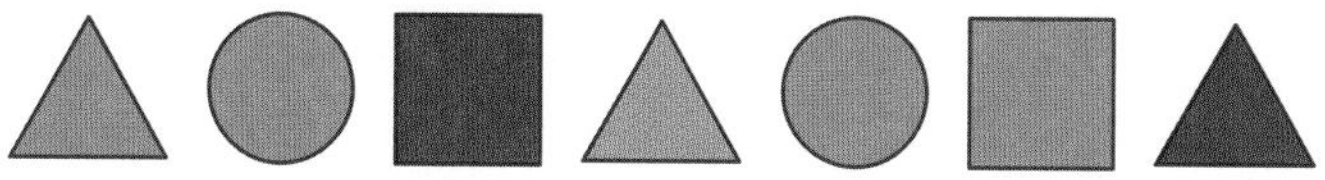

Draw the next figure in each sequence.

25. 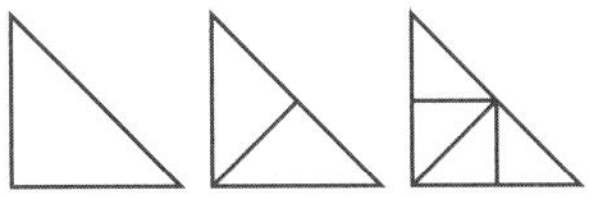

26. 

27. **Reasoning** Find the perimeter when 100 triangles are put together in the pattern shown. Assume that all triangle sides are 1 cm long.

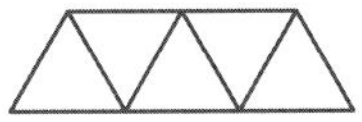

28. **Think About a Plan** Below are 15 points. Most of the points fit a pattern. Which does not? Explain.

$A(6, -2)$ $B(6, 5)$ $C(8, 0)$ $D(8, 7)$ $E(10, 2)$ $F(10, 6)$ $G(11, 4)$ $H(12, 3)$
$I(4, 0)$ $J(7, 6)$ $K(5, 6)$ $L(4, 7)$ $M(2, 2)$ $N(1, 4)$ $O(2, 6)$

- How can you draw a diagram to help you find a pattern?
- What pattern do the majority of the points fit?

29. **Language** Look for a pattern in the Chinese number system.
    a. What is the Chinese name for the numbers 43, 67, and 84?
    b. **Reasoning** Do you think that the Chinese number system is base 10? Explain.

Chinese Number System

Number	Chinese Word
1	yī
2	èr
3	sān
4	sì
5	wǔ
6	lìu
7	qī
8	bā

Number	Chinese Word
9	jǐu
10	shí
11	shí-yī
12	shí-èr
⋮	⋮
20	èr-shí
21	èr-shí-yī
⋮	⋮
30	sān-shí

30. **Open-Ended** Write two different number sequences that begin with the same two numbers.

31. **Error Analysis** For each of the past four years, Paulo has grown 2 in. every year. He is now 16 years old and is 5 ft 10 in. tall. He figures that when he is 22 years old he will be 6 ft 10 in. tall. What would you tell Paulo about his conjecture?

32. **Bird Migration** During bird migration, volunteers get up early on Bird Day to record the number of bird species they observe in their community during a 24-h period. Results are posted online to help scientists and students track the migration.
    a. Make a graph of the data.
    b. Use the graph and inductive reasoning to make a conjecture about the number of bird species the volunteers in this community will observe in 2015.

Bird Count

Year	Number of Species
2004	70
2005	83
2006	80
2007	85
2008	90

33. **Writing** Describe a real-life situation in which you recently used inductive reasoning.

Challenge

34. **History** When he was in the third grade, German mathematician Karl Gauss (1777–1855) took ten seconds to sum the integers from 1 to 100. Now it's your turn. Find a fast way to sum the integers from 1 to 100. Find a fast way to sum the integers from 1 to n. (*Hint:* Use patterns.)

35. **Chess** The small squares on a chessboard can be combined to form larger squares. For example, there are sixty-four 1×1 squares and one 8×8 square. Use inductive reasoning to determine how many 2×2 squares, 3×3 squares, and so on, are on a chessboard. What is the total number of squares on a chessboard?

36. **a. Algebra** Write the first six terms of the sequence that starts with 1, and for which the difference between consecutive terms is first 2, and then 3, 4, 5, and 6.

    b. Evaluate $\frac{n^2 + n}{2}$ for $n = 1, 2, 3, 4, 5$, and 6. Compare the sequence you get with your answer for part (a).

    c. Examine the diagram at the right and explain how it illustrates a value of $\frac{n^2 + n}{2}$.

    d. Draw a similar diagram to represent $\frac{n^2 + n}{2}$ for $n = 5$.

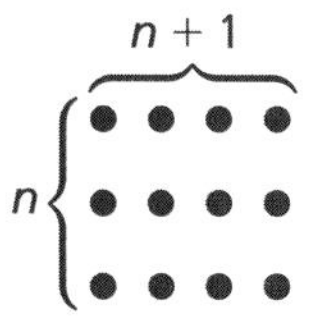

B-2 Conditional Statements

Prepares for **G.CO.10** Prove theorems about triangles . . . Also prepares for **G.CO.9, G.CO.11**

Objectives To recognize conditional statements and their parts
To write converses, inverses, and contrapositives of conditionals

Solve It! Write your solution to the Solve It in the space below.

The study of *if-then* statements and their truth values is a foundation of reasoning.

Essential Understanding You can describe some mathematical relationships using a variety of *if-then* statements.

take note

Key Concept Conditional Statements

Definition

A **conditional** is an *if-then* statement.

The **hypothesis** is the part p following *if.*

The **conclusion** is the part q following *then.*

Symbols

$p \rightarrow q$

Read as "if p then q" or "p implies q."

Diagram

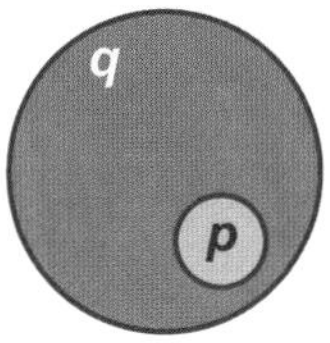

The Venn diagram above illustrates how the set of things that satisfy the hypothesis lies inside the set of things that satisfy the conclusion.

Problem 1 Identifying the Hypothesis and the Conclusion

Got It? What are the hypothesis and the conclusion of the conditional?
If an angle measures 130, then the angle is obtuse.

Think
What would a Venn diagram of the statement look like?

A Practice **Identify the hypothesis and conclusion of each conditional.**

1. If a figure is a rectangle, then it has four sides.

2. If you want to be healthy, then you should eat vegetables.

Problem 2 Writing a Conditional

Got It? How can you write "Dolphins are mammals" as a conditional?

Think

Which part of the statement is the hypothesis, (*p*)?

A Practice **3. Algebra** Write the following sentence as a conditional.

$3x - 7 = 14$ implies that $3x = 21$.

4. Write a conditional statement that the Venn diagram illustrates.

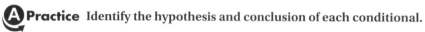

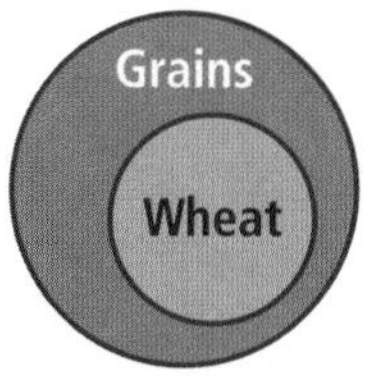

The **truth value** of a conditional is either *true* or *false*. To show that a conditional is true, show that every time the hypothesis is true, the conclusion is also true. To show that a conditional is false, find *only one* counterexample for which the hypothesis is true and the conclusion is false.

Problem 3 Finding the Truth Value of a Conditional

Got It? Is the conditional *true* or *false*? If it is false, find a counterexample.

a. If a month has 28 days, then it is February.

b. If two angles form a linear pair, then they are supplementary.

Practice **Determine if the conditional is *true* or *false*. If it is false, find a counterexample.**

5. If you live in a country that borders the United States, then you live in Canada.

6. If an angle measures 80°, then it is acute.

The **negation** of a statement p is the opposite of the statement. The symbol is $\sim p$ and is read "not p." The negation of the statement "The sky is blue" is "The sky is *not* blue." You can use negations to write statements related to a conditional. Every conditional has three related conditional statements.

take note

Key Concept Related Conditional Statements

Statement	How to Write It	Example	Symbols	How to Read it
Conditional	Use the given hypothesis and conclusion.	If $m\angle A = 15$, then $\angle A$ is acute.	$p \rightarrow q$	If p, then q.
Converse	Exchange the hypothesis and the conclusion.	If $\angle A$ is acute, then $m\angle A = 15$.	$q \rightarrow p$	If q, then p.
Inverse	Negate both the hypothesis and the conclusion of the conditional.	If $m\angle A \neq 15$, then $\angle A$ is not acute.	$\sim p \rightarrow \sim q$	If not p, then not q.
Contrapositive	Negate both the hypothesis and the conclusion of the converse.	If $\angle A$ is not acute, then $m\angle A \neq 15$.	$\sim q \rightarrow \sim p$	If not q, then not p.

Below are the truth values of the related statements above. **Equivalent statements** have the same truth value.

Statement	Example	Truth Value
Conditional	If $m\angle A = 15$, then $\angle A$ is acute.	True
Converse	If $\angle A$ is acute, then $m\angle A = 15$.	False
Inverse	If $m\angle A \neq 15$, then $\angle A$ is not acute.	False
Contrapositive	If $\angle A$ is not acute, then $m\angle A \neq 15$.	True

A conditional and its contrapositive are equivalent statements. They are either both true or both false. The converse and inverse of a statement are also equivalent statements.

Problem 4 Writing and Finding Truth Values of Statements

Got It? What are the converse, inverse, and contrapositive of the conditional statement below? What are the truth values of each? If a statement is false, give a counterexample.

If a vegetable is a carrot, then it contains beta carotene.

Practice **If the given statement is not in *if-then* form, rewrite it. Write the converse, inverse, and contrapositive of the given conditional statement. Determine the truth value of all four statements. If a statement is false, give a counterexample.**

7. Algebra If $4x + 8 = 28$, then $x = 5$.

8. Pianists are musicians.

Lesson Check

Do you know HOW?

9. What are the hypothesis and the conclusion of the following statement? Write it as a conditional.

Residents of Key West live in Florida.

10. What are the converse, inverse, and contrapositive of the statement? Which statements are true?

If a figure is a rectangle with sides 2 cm and 3 cm, then it has a perimeter of 10 cm.

Do you UNDERSTAND?

MATHEMATICAL PRACTICES

11. Error Analysis Your classmate rewrote the statement "You jog every Sunday" as the conditional below. What is your classmate's error? Correct it.

If you jog, then it is Sunday.

12. Reasoning Suppose a conditional statement and its converse are both true. What are the truth values of the contrapositive and inverse? How do you know?

More Practice and Problem-Solving Exercises

MATHEMATICAL PRACTICES

B Apply

Write each statement as a conditional.

13. "We're half the people; we should be half the Congress." —Jeanette Rankin, former U.S. congresswoman, calling for more women in office

14. "Anyone who has never made a mistake has never tried anything new." —Albert Einstein

15. Probability An event with probability 1 is certain to occur.

16. Think About a Plan Your classmate claims that the conditional and contrapositive of the following statement are both true. Is he correct? Explain.

If $x = 2$, then $x^2 = 4$.

- Can you find a counterexample of the conditional?
- Do you need to find a counterexample of the contrapositive to know its truth value?

17. **Open-Ended** Write a true conditional that has a true converse, and write a true conditional that has a false converse.

18. **Multiple Representations** Write three separate conditional statements that the Venn diagram illustrates.

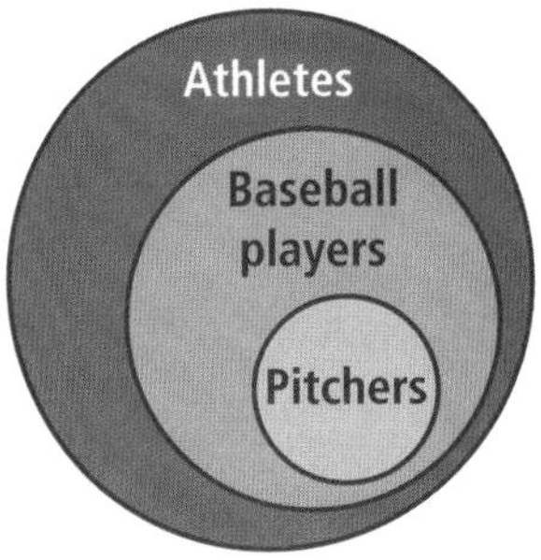

19. **Error Analysis** A given conditional is true. Natalie claims its contrapositive is also true. Sean claims its contrapositive is false. Who is correct and how do you know?

Draw a Venn diagram to illustrate each statement.

20. If an angle measures 100, then it is obtuse.

21. If you are the captain of your team, then you are a junior or senior.

22. Peace Corps volunteers want to help other people.

Algebra Write the converse of each statement. If the converse is true, write *true*. If it is not true, provide a counterexample.

23. If $x = -6$, then $|x| = 6$.

24. If y is negative, then $-y$ is positive.

25. If $x < 0$, then $x^3 < 0$.

26. If $x < 0$, then $x^2 > 0$.

27. **Advertising** Advertisements often suggest conditional statements. What conditional does the ad at the right imply?

Write each postulate as a conditional statement.

28. Two intersecting lines meet in exactly one point.

29. Two congruent figures have equal areas.

30. Through any two points there is exactly one line.

Challenge

Write a statement beginning with *all*, *some*, or *no* to match each Venn diagram.

31.

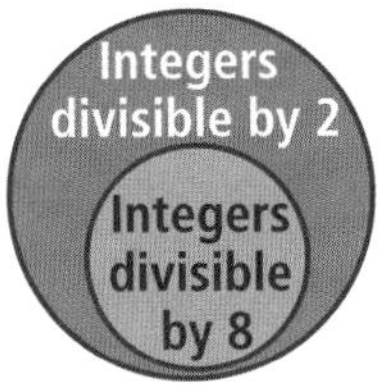

32.

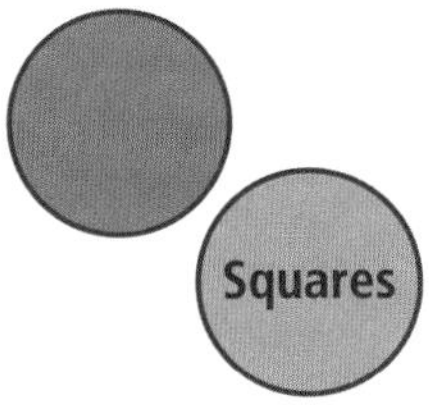

33.

34. Let a represent an integer. Consider the five statements r, s, t, u, and v.

r: a is even. s: a is odd. t: $2a$ is even. u: $2a$ is odd. v: $2a + 1$ is odd.

How many statements of the form $p \rightarrow q$ can you make from these statements? Decide which are true, and provide a counterexample if they are false.

B-3 Biconditionals and Definitions

Prepares for **G.CO.11** Prove theorems about parallelograms . . . Also prepares for **G.CO.9, G.CO.10**

Objective To write biconditionals and recognize good definitions

Solve It! Write your solution to the Solve It in the space below.

In the Solve It, you used conditional statements. A **biconditional** is a single true statement that combines a true conditional and its true converse. You can write a biconditional by joining the two parts of each conditional with the phrase *if and only if.*

Essential Understanding A definition is good if it can be written as a biconditional.

Problem 1 Writing a Biconditional

Think

How do you form the converse of a conditional?

Got It? What is the converse of the following true conditional? If the converse is also true, rewrite the statements as a biconditional.

If two angles have equal measure, then the angles are congruent.

A Practice **Each conditional statement below is true. Write its converse. If the converse is also true, combine the statements as a biconditional.**

1. Algebra If $x = 3$, then $|x| = 3$.

2. In the United States, if it is July 4, then it is Independence Day.

take note

Key Concept Biconditional Statements

A biconditional combines $p \rightarrow q$ and $q \rightarrow p$ as $p \leftrightarrow q$.

Example	Symbols	How to Read It
A point is a midpoint if and only if it divides a segment into two congruent segments.	$p \leftrightarrow q$	"p if and only if q"

You can write a biconditional as two conditionals that are converses.

ONLINE PROBLEMS

Problem 2 Identifying the Conditionals in a Biconditional

Got It? What are the two conditionals that form this biconditional?

Two numbers are reciprocals if and only if their product is 1.

A Practice **Write the two statements that form each biconditional.**

3. You live in Washington, D.C., if and only if you live in the capital of the United States.

4. Algebra $x^2 = 144$ if and only if $x = 12$ or $x = -12$.

Undefined terms such as *point*, *line*, and *plane* are the building blocks of geometry. You understand the meanings of these terms intuitively. Then you use them to define other terms such as *segment*.

A good definition is a statement that can help you identify or classify an object. A good definition has several important components.

- ✓ A good definition uses clearly understood terms. These terms should be commonly understood or already defined.
- ✓ A good definition is precise. Good definitions avoid words such as *large*, *sort of*, and *almost*.
- ✓ A good definition is reversible. That means you can write a good definition as a true biconditional.

Problem 3 Writing a Definition as a Biconditional

Think

How do you determine whether a definition is reversible?

Got It? Is this definition of *straight angle* reversible? If yes, write it as a true biconditional.

A straight angle is an angle that measures 180.

Practice **Test each statement below to see if it is reversible. If so, write it as a true biconditional. If not, write *not reversible*.**

5. A perpendicular bisector of a segment is a line, segment, or ray that is perpendicular to a segment at its midpoint.

6. Two angles that form a linear pair are adjacent.

One way to show that a statement is *not* a good definition is to find a counterexample.

Problem 4 Identifying Good Definitions

Got It? **a.** Is the following statement a good definition? Explain.

A square is a figure with four right angles.

b. Reasoning How can you rewrite the statement "Obtuse angles have greater measures than acute angles" so that it is a good definition?

Practice **Is each statement below a good definition? If not, explain.**

7. A compass is a geometric tool.

8. Perpendicular lines are two lines that intersect to form right angles.

Lesson Check

Do you know HOW?

9. How can you write the following statement as two true conditionals?

Collinear points are points that lie on the same line.

10. How can you combine the following statements as a biconditional?

If this month is June, then next month is July.

If next month is July, then this month is June.

11. Write the following definition as a biconditional.

Vertical angles are two angles whose sides are opposite rays.

Do you UNDERSTAND?

MATHEMATICAL PRACTICES

12. Vocabulary Explain how the term *biconditional* is fitting for a statement composed of *two* conditionals.

13. Error Analysis Why is the following statement a poor definition?

Elephants are gigantic animals.

14. Compare and Contrast Which of the following statements is a better definition of a linear pair? Explain.

A linear pair is a pair of supplementary angles.

A linear pair is a pair of adjacent angles with noncommon sides that are opposite rays.

More Practice and Problem-Solving Exercises

MATHEMATICAL PRACTICES

B Apply

15. Think About a Plan Is the following a good definition? Explain.
A ligament is a band of tough tissue connecting bones or holding organs in place.

- Can you write the statement as two true conditionals?
- Are the two true conditionals converses of each other?

16. Reasoning Is the following a good definition? Explain.
An obtuse angle is an angle with measure greater than 90.

17. Open-Ended Choose a definition from a dictionary or from a glossary. Explain what makes the statement a good definition.

18. Error Analysis Your friend defines a right angle as an angle that is greater than an acute angle. Use a biconditional to show that this is not a good definition.

19. Which conditional and its converse form a true biconditional?

(A) If $x > 0$, then $|x| > 0$.

(B) If $x = 3$, then $x^2 = 9$.

(C) If $x^3 = 5$, then $x = 125$.

(D) If $x = 19$, then $2x - 3 = 35$.

Write each statement as a biconditional.

20. Points in Quadrant III have two negative coordinates.

21. When the sum of the digits of an integer is divisible by 9, the integer is divisible by 9 and vice versa.

22. The whole numbers are the nonnegative integers.

23. A hexagon is a six-sided polygon.

Language **For Exercises 24–27, use the chart below. Decide whether the description of each letter is a good definition. If not, provide a counterexample by giving another letter that could fit the definition.**

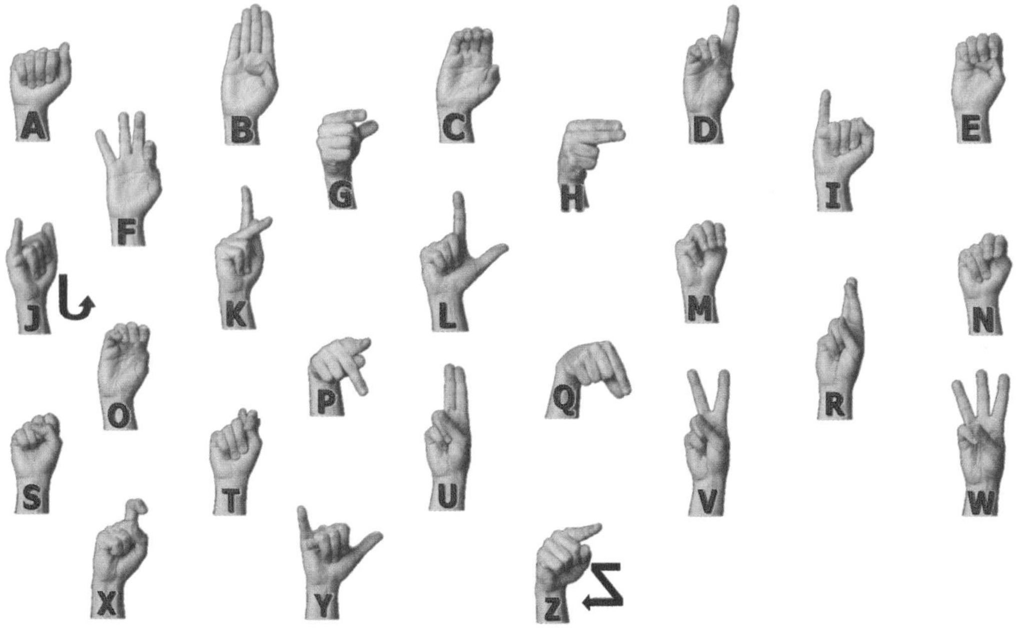

24. The letter *D* is formed by pointing straight up with the finger beside the thumb and folding the other fingers and the thumb so that they all touch.

25. The letter *K* is formed by making a *V* with the two fingers beside the thumb.

26. You have formed the letter *I* if and only if the smallest finger is sticking up and the other fingers are folded into the palm of your hand with your thumb folded over them and your hand is held still.

27. You form the letter *B* by holding all four fingers tightly together and pointing them straight up while your thumb is folded into the palm of your hand.

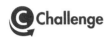

Reading Math **Let statements p, q, r, and s be as follows:**

p : $\angle A$ and $\angle B$ are a linear pair.
q : $\angle A$ and $\angle B$ are supplementary angles.
r : $\angle A$ and $\angle B$ are adjacent angles.
s : $\angle A$ and $\angle B$ are adjacent and supplementary angles.

Substitute for p, q, r, and s, and write each statement the way you would read it.

28. $p \rightarrow q$

29. $p \rightarrow r$

30. $p \rightarrow s$

31. $p \leftrightarrow s$

Challenge

32. Writing Use the figures to write a good definition of a *line* in spherical geometry.

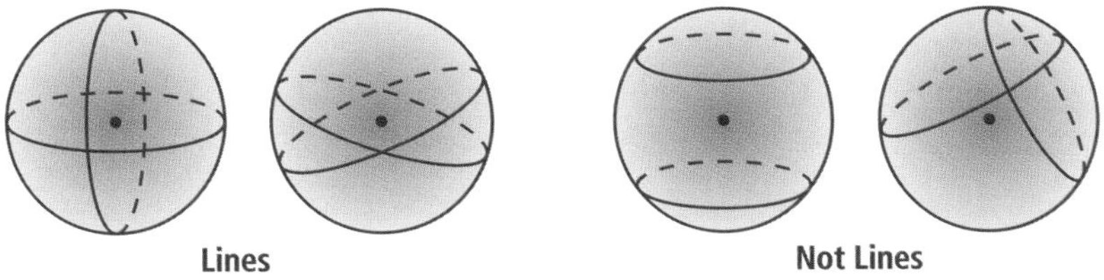

33. Multiple Representations You have illustrated true conditional statements with Venn diagrams. You can do the same thing with true biconditionals. Consider the following statement.

An integer is divisible by 10 if and only if its last digit is 0.

a. Write the two conditional statements that make up this biconditional.

b. Illustrate the first conditional from part (a) with a Venn diagram.

c. Illustrate the second conditional from part (a) with a Venn diagram.

d. Combine your two Venn diagrams from parts (b) and (c) to form a Venn diagram representing the biconditional statement.

e. What must be true of the Venn diagram for any true biconditional statement?

f. Reasoning How does your conclusion in part (e) help to explain why you can write a good definition as a biconditional?

B-4 Deductive Reasoning

Prepares for **G.CO.9** Prove theorems about lines and angles . . . Also prepares for **G.CO.10, G.CO.11**

Objective To use the Law of Detachment and the Law of Syllogism

Solve It! Write your solution to the Solve It in the space below.

In the Solve It, you drew a conclusion based on several facts. You used deductive reasoning. **Deductive reasoning** (sometimes called logical reasoning) is the process of reasoning logically from given statements or facts to a conclusion.

Essential Understanding Given true statements, you can use deductive reasoning to make a valid or true conclusion.

take note

Property Law of Detachment

Law	Symbols		
If the hypothesis of a true conditional is true, then the conclusion is true.	If	$p \rightarrow q$	is true
	And	p	is true,
	Then	q	is true.

To use the Law of Detachment, identify the hypothesis of the given true conditional. If the second given statement matches the hypothesis of the conditional, then you can make a valid conclusion.

Problem 1 Using the Law of Detachment

Got It? What can you conclude from the given information?

a. If there is lightning, then it is not safe to be out in the open. Marla sees lightning from the soccer field.

Think
What conditions must be met for you to reach a valid conclusion?

b. If a figure is a square, then its sides have equal length. Figure *ABCD* has sides of equal length.

Practice **If possible, use the Law of Detachment to make a conclusion. If it is not possible to make a conclusion, tell why.**

1. If a doctor suspects her patient has a broken bone, then she should take an X-ray. Dr. Ngemba suspects Lilly has a broken arm.

2. If three points are on the same line, then they are collinear. Points *X*, *Y*, and *Z* are on line *m*.

Another law of deductive reasoning is the Law of Syllogism. The **Law of Syllogism** allows you to state a conclusion from two true conditional statements when the conclusion of one statement is the hypothesis of the other statement.

take note

Property Law of Syllogism

Symbols			Example
If	$p \rightarrow q$	is true	If it is July, then you are on summer vacation.
and	$q \rightarrow r$	is true,	If you are on summer vacation, then you work at a smoothie shop.
then	$p \rightarrow r$	is true.	**You conclude:** If it is July, then you work at a smoothie shop.

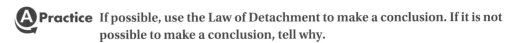

Problem 2 Using the Law of Syllogism

Got It? What can you conclude from the given information? What is your reasoning?

Think

What conditions must be met for you to reach a valid conclusion?

a. If a whole number ends in 0, then it is divisible by 10. If a whole number is divisible by 10, then it is divisible by 5.

b. If $\overrightarrow{AB}$ and $\overrightarrow{AD}$ are opposite rays, then the two rays form a straight angle. If two rays are opposite rays, then the two rays form a straight angle.

Practice **If possible, use the Law of Syllogism to make a conclusion. If it is not possible to make a conclusion, tell why.**

STEM **3. Ecology** If an animal is a Florida panther, then its scientific name is *Puma concolor coryi*.

If an animal is a *Puma concolor coryi*, then it is endangered.

4. If a line intersects a segment at its midpoint, then the line bisects the segment.

If a line bisects a segment, then it divides the segment into two congruent segments.

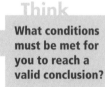

You can use the Law of Syllogism and the Law of Detachment together to make conclusions.

Problem 3 Using the Laws of Syllogism and Detachment

Got It? **a.** What can you conclude from the given information? What is your reasoning?

If a river is more than 4000 mi long, then it is longer than the Amazon.

If a river is longer than the Amazon, then it is the longest river in the world. The Nile is 4132 mi long.

b. Reasoning In Problem 3, does it matter whether you use the Law of Syllogism or the Law of Detachment first? Explain.

Practice **Use the Law of Detachment and the Law of Syllogism to make conclusions from the following statements. If it is not possible to make a conclusion, tell why.**

5. If a mountain is the highest in Alaska, then it is the highest in the United States.

If an Alaskan mountain is more than 20,300 ft high, then it is the highest in Alaska.

Alaska's Mount McKinley is 20,320 ft high.

6. If you live in the Bronx, then you live in New York.

Tracy lives in the Bronx.

If you live in New York, then you live in the eleventh state to enter the Union.

Lesson Check

Do you know HOW?

If possible, make a conclusion from the given true statements. What reasoning did you use?

7. If it is Tuesday, then you will go bowling. You go bowling.

8. If a figure is a three-sided polygon, then it is a triangle. Figure *ABC* is a three-sided polygon.

9. If it is Saturday, then you walk to work. If you walk to work, then you wear sneakers.

Do you UNDERSTAND?

MATHEMATICAL PRACTICES

10. Error Analysis What is the error in the reasoning at the right?

> Birds that weigh more than 50 pounds cannot fly. A kiwi cannot fly. So, a kiwi weighs more than 50 pounds.

11. Compare and Contrast How is deductive reasoning different from inductive reasoning?

More Practice and Problem-Solving Exercises

MATHEMATICAL PRACTICES

B Apply

12. Think About a Plan If it is the night of your weekly basketball game, your family eats at your favorite restaurant. When your family eats at your favorite restaurant, you always get chicken fingers. If it is Tuesday, then it is the night of your weekly basketball game. How much do you pay for chicken fingers after your game? Use the specials board at the right to decide. Explain your reasoning.

- How can you reorder and rewrite the sentences to help you?
- How can you use the Law of Syllogism to answer the question?

Beverages For Exercises 13–18, assume that the following statements are true.

A. If Maria is drinking juice, then it is breakfast time.

B. If it is lunchtime, then Kira is drinking milk and nothing else.

C. If it is mealtime, then Curtis is drinking water and nothing else.

D. If it is breakfast time, then Julio is drinking juice and nothing else.

E. Maria is drinking juice.

Use only the information given above. For each statement, write *must be true*, *may be true*, or *is not true*. Explain your reasoning.

13. Julio is drinking juice.

14. Curtis is drinking water.

15. Kira is drinking milk.

16. Curtis is drinking juice.

17. Maria is drinking water.

18. Julio is drinking milk.

STEM **19. Physics** Quarks are subatomic particles identified by electric charge and rest energy. The table shows how to categorize quarks by their flavors. Show how the Law of Detachment and the table are used to identify the flavor of a quark with a charge of $-\frac{1}{3}$e and rest energy 540 MeV.

Rest Energy and Charge of Quarks

Rest Energy (MeV)	360	360	1500	540	173,000	5000
Electric Charge (e)	$+\frac{2}{3}$	$-\frac{1}{3}$	$+\frac{2}{3}$	$-\frac{1}{3}$	$+\frac{2}{3}$	$-\frac{1}{3}$
Flavor	Up	Down	Charmed	Strange	Top	Bottom

Write the first statement as a conditional. If possible, use the Law of Detachment to make a conclusion. If it is not possible to make a conclusion, tell why.

20. All national parks are interesting.
Mammoth Cave is a national park.

21. All squares are rectangles.
ABCD is a square.

22. The temperature is always above 32°F in Key West, Florida.
The temperature is 62°F.

23. Every high school student likes art.
Ling likes art.

24. Writing Give an example of a rule used in your school that could be written as a conditional. Explain how the Law of Detachment is used in applying that rule.

Challenge

25. Reasoning Use the following algorithm: Choose an integer. Multiply the integer by 3. Add 6 to the product. Divide the sum by 3.

a. Complete the algorithm for four different integers. Look for a pattern in the chosen integers and in the corresponding answers. Make a conjecture that relates the chosen integers to the answers.

b. Let the variable x represent the chosen integer. Apply the algorithm to x. Simplify the resulting expression.

c. How does your answer to part (b) confirm your conjecture in part (a)? Describe how inductive and deductive reasoning are exhibited in parts (a) and (b).

STEM **26. Biology** Consider the following given statements and conclusion.

Given: If an animal is a fish, then it has gills.
A turtle does not have gills.

You conclude: A turtle is not a fish.

a. Make a Venn diagram to illustrate the given information.

b. Use the Venn diagram to help explain why the argument uses good reasoning.

B Topic Review

MathXL® for School
Go to pearsonsuccessnet.com

B-1 Patterns and Inductive Reasoning

Quick Review

You use **inductive reasoning** when you make conclusions based on patterns you observe. A **conjecture** is a conclusion you reach using inductive reasoning. A **counterexample** is an example that shows a conjecture is incorrect.

Example

Describe the pattern. What are the next two terms in the sequence?

$1, -3, 9, -27, \ldots$

Each term is -3 times the previous term. The next two terms are $-27 \times (-3) = 81$ and $81 \times (-3) = -243$.

Exercises

Find a pattern for each sequence. Describe the pattern and use it to show the next two terms.

1. 1000, 100, 10, . . .
2. 5, −5, 5, −5, . . .
3. 34, 27, 20, 13, . . .
4. 6, 24, 96, 384, . . .

Find a counterexample to show that each conjecture is false.

5. The product of any integer and 2 is greater than 2.
6. The city of Portland is in Oregon.

B-2 Conditional Statements

Quick Review

A **conditional** is an *if-then* statement. The symbolic form of a conditional is $p \rightarrow q$, where p is the **hypothesis** and q is the **conclusion**.

- To find the **converse**, switch the hypothesis and conclusion of the conditional ($q \rightarrow p$).
- To find the **inverse**, negate the hypothesis and the conclusion of the conditional ($\sim p \rightarrow \sim q$).
- To find the **contrapositive**, negate the hypothesis and the conclusion of the converse ($\sim q \rightarrow \sim p$).

Example

What is the converse of the conditional statement below? What is its truth value?

If you are a teenager, then you are younger than 20.

Converse: If you are younger than 20, then you are a teenager.

A 7-year-old is not a teenager. The converse is false.

Exercises

Rewrite each sentence as a conditional statement.

7. All motorcyclists wear helmets.
8. Two nonparallel lines intersect in one point.
9. Angles that form a linear pair are supplementary.
10. School is closed on certain holidays.

Write the converse, inverse, and contrapositive of the given conditional. Then determine the truth value of each statement.

11. If an angle is obtuse, then its measure is greater than 90 and less than 180.
12. If a figure is a square, then it has four sides.
13. If you play the tuba, then you play an instrument.
14. If you baby-sit, then you are busy on Saturday night.

B-3 Biconditionals and Definitions

Quick Review

When a conditional and its converse are true, you can combine them as a true **biconditional** using the phrase *if and only if.* The symbolic form of a biconditional is $p \leftrightarrow q$. You can write a good **definition** as a true biconditional.

Example

Is the following definition reversible? If yes, write it as a true biconditional.

A hexagon is a polygon with exactly six sides.

Yes. The conditional is true: If a figure is a hexagon, then it is a polygon with exactly six sides. Its converse is also true: If a figure is a polygon with exactly six sides, then it is a hexagon.

Biconditional: A figure is a hexagon *if and only if* it is a polygon with exactly six sides.

Exercises

Determine whether each statement is a good definition. If not, explain.

15. A newspaper has articles you read.

16. A linear pair is a pair of adjacent angles whose noncommon sides are opposite rays.

17. An angle is a geometric figure.

18. Write the following definition as a biconditional. An oxymoron is a phrase that contains contradictory terms.

19. Write the following biconditional as two statements, a conditional and its converse. Two angles are complementary if and only if the sum of their measures is 90.

B-4 Deductive Reasoning

Quick Review

Deductive reasoning is the process of reasoning logically from given statements to a conclusion.

Law of Detachment: If $p \rightarrow q$ is true and p is true, then q is true.

Law of Syllogism: If $p \rightarrow q$ and $q \rightarrow r$ are true, then $p \rightarrow r$ is true.

Example

What can you conclude from the given information?

Given: **If you play hockey, then you are on the team. If you are on the team, then you are a varsity athlete.**

The conclusion of the first statement matches the hypothesis of the second statement. Use the Law of Syllogism to conclude: If you play hockey, then you are a varsity athlete.

Exercises

Use the Law of Detachment to make a conclusion.

20. If you practice tennis every day, then you will become a better player. Colin practices tennis every day.

21. $\angle 1$ and $\angle 2$ are supplementary. If two angles are supplementary, then the sum of their measures is 180.

Use the Law of Syllogism to make a conclusion.

22. If two angles are vertical, then they are congruent. If two angles are congruent, then their measures are equal.

23. If your father buys new gardening gloves, then he will work in his garden. If he works in his garden, then he will plant tomatoes.

B Pull It All Together

PERFORMANCE TASK

Analyzing a Calendar Pattern

The figure shows a page from a calendar. Choose any four numbers from the calendar that lie inside a 2-by-2 square. One such set of numbers is shown below. Find the sum of the pair of numbers that lie on each diagonal of the square. What do you notice about the sums? Try this using other squares on the calendar and using calendar pages for different months.

MARCH						
SUN	MON	TUE	WED	THU	FRI	SAT
				1	2	3
4	5	6	7	8	9	10
11	12	13	14	15	16	17
18	19	20	21	22	23	24
25	26	27	28	29	30	31

Task Description

Use inductive reasoning to make a conjecture about the calendar pattern you observed. Then use deductive reasoning to prove your conjecture.

- How can you write your conjecture as a conditional statement?
- How can you use algebraic expressions to represent the four numbers that lie inside any 2-by-2 square on any calendar page?

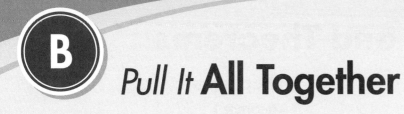

Postulates and Theorems

Postulates

Postulate 1
Perpendicular Postulate
Through a point not on a line, there is one and only one line perpendicular to the given line.

Postulate 2
Area Addition Postulate
The area of a region is the sum of the area of its nonoverlapping parts.

Postulate 3
Side-Side-Side (SSS) Postulate
If three sides of one triangle are congruent to the three sides of another triangle, then the two triangles are congruent.

Postulate 4
Side-Angle-Side (SAS) Postulate
If two sides and the included angle of one triangle are congruent to two sides and the included angle of another triangle, then the two triangles are congruent.

Postulate 5
Angle-Side-Angle (ASA) Postulate
If two angles and the included side of one triangle are congruent to two angles and the included side of another triangle, then the two triangles are congruent.

Theorems

Theorem 1
Third Angles Theorem
If two angles of one triangle are congruent to two angles of another triangle, than the third angles are congruent.

Theorem 2
Angle-Angle-Side (AAS) Theorem
If two angles and a nonincluded side of one triangle are congruent to two angles and a nonincluded side of another triangle, then the two triangles are congruent.

Theorem 3
Isosceles Triangle Theorem
If two sides of a triangle are congruent, then the angles opposite those sides are congruent.

Corollary
If a triangle is equilateral, then the triangle is equiangular.

Theorem 4
Converse of the Isosceles Triangle Theorem
If two angles of a triangle are congruent, then the sides opposite the angles are congruent.

Corollary
If a triangle is equiangular, then it is equilateral.

Theorem 5
If a line bisects the vertex angle of an isosceles triangle, then the line is also the perpendicular bisector of the base.

Theorem 6
Hypotenuse-Leg (HL) Theorem
If the hypotenuse and a leg of one right triangle are congruent to the hypotenuse and a leg of another right triangle, then the triangles are congruent.

Additional Postulates, Theorems, and Formulas

Distance Formula

The distance between two points $A(x_1, y_1)$ and $B(x_2, y_2)$ is

$$d = \sqrt{(x_2 - x_1)^2 + (y_2 - y_1)^2}$$

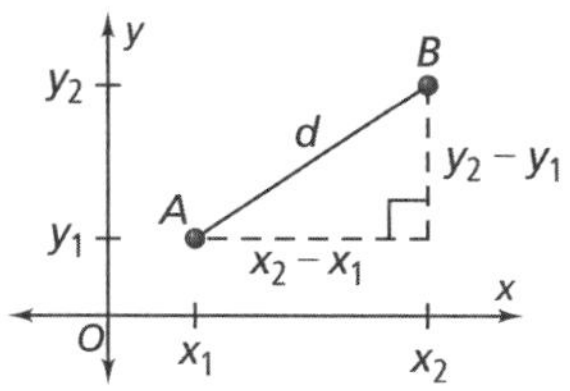

Triangle Angle-Sum Theorem

The sum of the measures of the angles of a triangle is 180.

Vertical Angles Theorem

Vertical angles are congruent.

$\angle 1 \cong \angle 3$ and $\angle 2 \cong \angle 4$

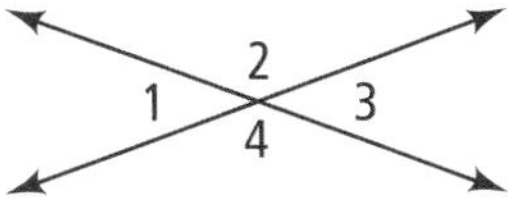

Congruent Supplements Theorem

If two angles are supplements of the same angle (or of congruent angles), then the two angles are congruent.

Triangle Exterior Angle Theorem

The measure of each exterior angle of a triangle equals the sum of the measures of its two remote interior angles.

$$m\angle 1 = m\angle 2 + m\angle 3$$

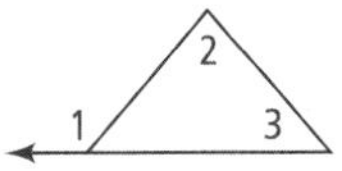

Congruent Complements Theorem

If two angles are complements of the same angle (or of congruent angles), then the two angles are congruent.

Theorem A

All right angles are congruent.

Theorem B

If two angles are congruent and supplementary, then each is a right angle.

Alternate Interior Angles Theorem

Theorem	If . . .	Then . . .
If a transversal intersects two parallel lines, then alternate interior angles are congruent.	$\ell \parallel m$ 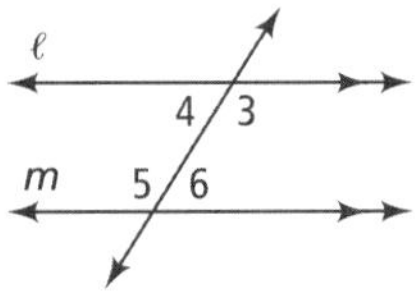	$\angle 4 \cong \angle 6$ $\angle 3 \cong \angle 5$

Corresponding Angles Theorem

Theorem	If . . .	Then . . .
If a transversal intersects two parallel lines, then corresponding angles are congruent.	$\ell \parallel m$ 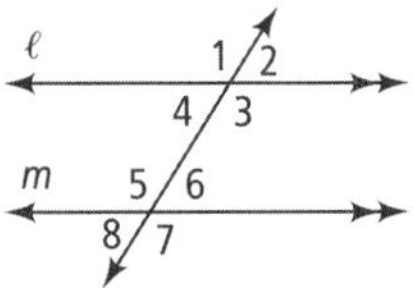	$\angle 1 \cong \angle 5$ $\angle 2 \cong \angle 6$ $\angle 3 \cong \angle 7$ $\angle 4 \cong \angle 8$

Alternate Exterior Angles Theorem

Theorem	If . . .	Then . . .
If a transversal intersects two parallel lines, then alternate exterior angles are congruent.	$\ell \parallel m$ 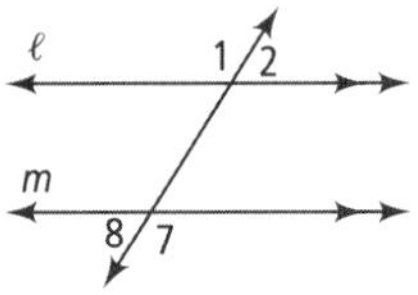	$\angle 1 \cong \angle 7$ $\angle 2 \cong \angle 8$

Same-Side Interior Angles Postulate

Postulate	If . . .	Then . . .
If a transversal intersects two parallel lines, then same-side interior angles are supplementary.	$\ell \parallel m$ 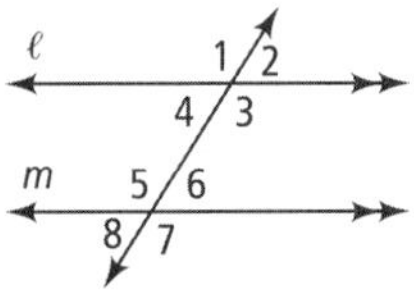	$m\angle 4 + m\angle 5 = 180$ $m\angle 3 + m\angle 6 = 180$

Visual Glossary

English | Spanish

A

Accuracy (p. 49) Accuracy is the degree of how close a measurement is to the true value of the measurement.

Exactitud (p. 49) La exactitud es el grado de lo cerca que una medición está del valor verdadero de la cantidad que se mide.

Angle of rotation (p. 493) *See* **rotation.**

Ángulo de rotación (p. 493) *Ver* **rotation.**

Area (p. 425) The area of a plane figure is the number of square units enclosed by the figure.

Área (p. 425) El área de una figura plana es la cantidad de unidades cuadradas que contiene la figura.

Example 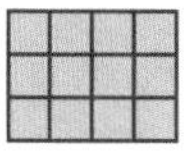 The area of the rectangle is 12 square units, or 12 units^2.

Arithmetic sequence (p. 148) A number sequence formed by adding a fixed number to each previous term to find the next term. The fixed number is called the common difference.

Progresión aritmética (p. 148) En una progresión aritmética la diferencia entre términos consecutivos es un número constante. El número constante se llama la diferencia común.

Example 4, 7, 10, 13, … is an arithmetic sequence.

Average rate of change (p. 297) The average rate of change of a function over the interval $a \leq x \leq b$ is equal to $\frac{f(b) - f(a)}{b - a}$.

Tasa media de cambio (p. 297) La tasa media de cambio de una función sobre el intervalo $a \leq x \leq b$ es igual a $\frac{f(b) - f(a)}{b - a}$.

Example The average rate of change of the function $f(x) = x^2 - 2x + 2$ over the interval $1 \leq x \leq 4$ is $\frac{f(4) - f(1)}{4 - 1} = \frac{9}{3} = 3$

B

Base(s) *See* **isosceles triangle.**

Base(s) *Ver* **isosceles triangle.**

Base angles *See* **isosceles triangle.**

Ángulos de base *Ver* **isosceles triangle.**

Biconditional (p. H74) A biconditional statement is the combination of a conditional statement and its converse. A biconditional contains the words "if and only if."

Bicondicional (p. H74) Un enunciado bicondicional es la combinación de un enunciado condicional y su recíproco. El enunciado bicondicional incluye las palabras "si y solo si".

Example This biconditional statement is true: Two angles are congruent *if and only if* they have the same measure.

English	Spanish

Box-and-whisker plot (p. 368) A graph that summarizes data along a number line. The left whisker extends from the minimum to the first quartile. The box extends from the first quartile to the third quartile and has a vertical line through the median. The right whisker extends from the third quartile to the maximum.

Gráfica de cajas (p. 368) Gráfica que resume los datos a lo largo de una recta numérica. El brazo izquierdo se extiende desde el valor mínimo del primer cuartil. La caja se extiende desde el primer cuartil hasta el tercer cuartil y tiene una línea vertical que atraviesa la mediana. El brazo derecho se extiende desde el tercer cuartil hasta el valor máximo.

Example

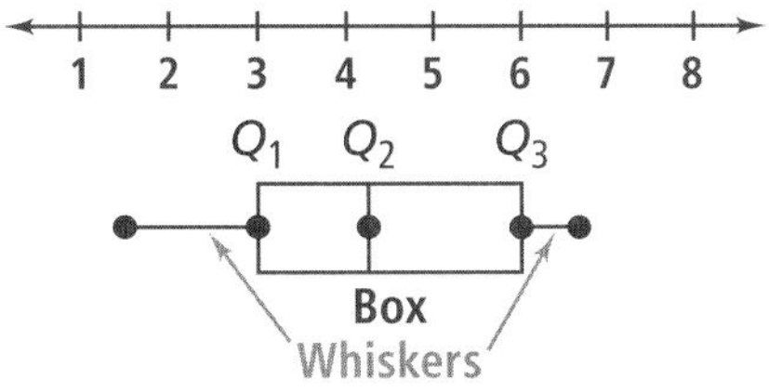

C

Causation (p. 379) When a change in one quantity causes a change in a second quantity. A correlation between quantities does not always imply causation.

Causalidad (p. 379) Cuando un cambio en una cantidad causa un cambio en una segunda cantidad. Una correlación entre las cantidades no implica siempre la causalidad.

Center (p. 493) *See* **rotation.**

Centro (p. 493) *Ver* **rotation.**

Coefficient (p. 6) The numerical factor when a term has a variable.

Coeficiente (p. 6) Factor numérico de un término que contiene una variable.

Example In the expression $2x + 3y + 16$, 2 and 3 are coefficients.

Coefficient matrix (p. H32) When representing a system of equations with a matrix equation, the matrix containing the coefficients of the system is the coefficient matrix.

Matriz de coeficientes (p. H32) Al representar un sistema de ecuaciones con una ecuación de matriz, la matriz que contiene los coeficientes del sistema es la matriz de coeficientes.

Example $\begin{cases} x + 2y = 5 \\ 3x + 5y = 14 \end{cases}$

coefficient matrix $\begin{bmatrix} 1 & 2 \\ 3 & 5 \end{bmatrix}$

Common difference (p. 148) The difference between consecutive terms of an arithmetic sequence.

Diferencia común (p. 148) La diferencia común es la diferencia entre los términos consecutivos de una progresión aritmética.

Example The common difference is 3 in the arithmetic sequence 4, 7, 10, 13, …

Compass (p. 405) A compass is a geometric tool used to draw circles and parts of circles, called arcs.

Compás (p. 405) El compás es un instrumento usado para dibujar círculos y partes de círculos, llamados arcos.

English | Spanish

Composition of transformations (p. 478) A composition of two transformations is a transformation in which a second transformation is performed on the image of a first transformation.

Composición de transformaciones (p. 478) Una composición de dos transformaciones es una transformación en la cual una segunda transformación se realiza a partir de la imagen de la primera.

Example

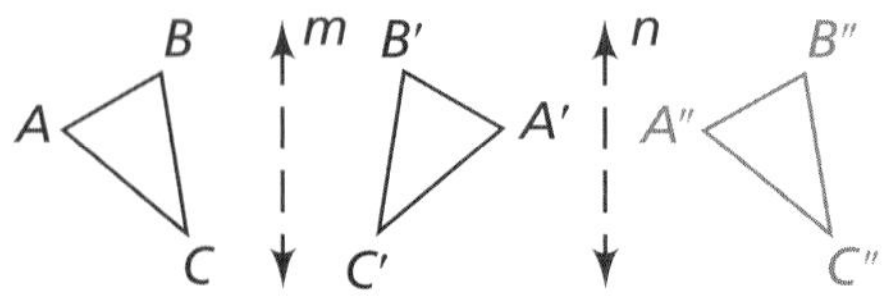

If you reflect $\triangle ABC$ across line m to get $\triangle A'B'C'$ and then reflect $\triangle A'B'C'$ across line n to get $\triangle A''B''C''$, you perform a composition of transformations.

Compound inequality (p. 70) Two inequalities that are joined by *and* or *or*.

Desigualdade compuesta (p. 70) Dos desigualdades que están enlazadas por medio de una *y* o una *o*.

Example $5 < x$ and $x < 10$
$14 < x$ or $x \leq -3$

Compound interest (p. 305) Interest paid on both the principal and the interest that has already been paid.

Interés compuesto (p. 305) Interés calculado tanto sobre el capital como sobre los intereses ya pagados.

Example For an initial deposit of \$1000 at a 6% interest rate with interest compounded quarterly, the function $y = 1000\left(\frac{0.06}{4}\right)^x$ gives the account balance y after x years.

Conclusion (p. H67) The conclusion is the part of an *if-then* statement (conditional) that follows *then*.

Conclusión (p. H67) La conclusión es lo que sigue a la palabra entonces en un enunciado (condicional), si …, entonces. …

Example In the statement, 'If it rains, then I will go outside,' the conclusion is 'I will go outside.'

Conditional (p. H67) A conditional is an *if-then* statement.

Condicional (p. H67) Un enunciado condicional es del tipo *si …, entonces.* …

Example *If* you act politely, *then* you will earn respect.

English	Spanish

Conditional relative frequency (p. 392) Conditional relative frequency is the quotient of a joint frequency in a two-way frequency table and the marginal frequency of the row or column in which the joint frequency appears.

Frecuencia relativa condicionada (p. 392) Frecuencia relativa condicionada es el cociente de una frecuencia conjunta en una tabla de frecuencias de doble entrada y la frecuencia marginal de la fila o columna en la que la frecuencia conjunta aparece.

Example

	Male	Female	Totals
Juniors	3	4	7
Seniors	3	2	5
Totals	6	6	12

The conditional relative frequency that a student is female given that she is a senior is $\frac{2}{5}$.

Congruence transformation (p. 588) *See* **isometry.**

Transformación de congruencia (p. 588) *Ver* **isometry.**

Congruent polygons (p. 523) Congruent polygons are polygons that have corresponding sides congruent and corresponding angles congruent.

Polígonos congruentes (p. 523) Los polígonos congruentes son polígonos cuyos lados correspondientes son congruentes y cuyos ángulos correspondientes son congruentes.

Example

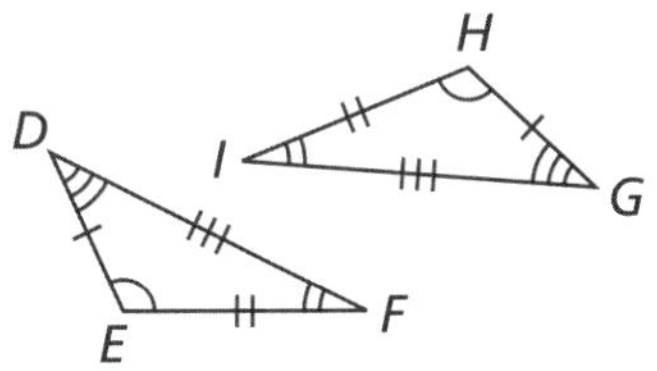

$\triangle DEF \cong \triangle GHI$

Conjecture (p. H60) A conjecture is a conclusion reached by using inductive reasoning.

Conjecture (p. H60) A conjecture is a conclusion reached by using inductive reasoning.

Example As you walk down the street, you see many people holding unopened umbrellas. You make the conjecture that the forecast must call for rain.

Consistent system (p. 226) A system of equations that has at least one solution is consistent.

Sistema consistente (p. 226) Un sistema de ecuaciones que tiene por lo menos una solución es consistente.

Example

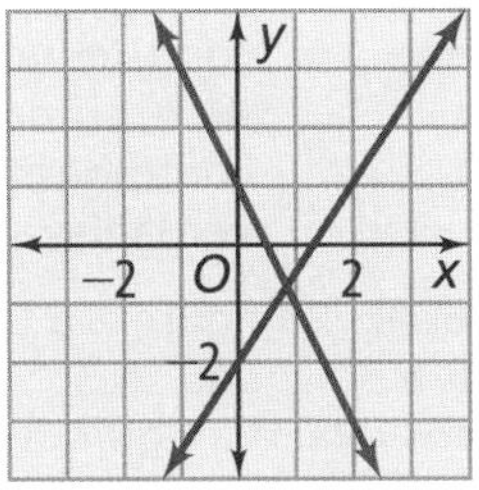

English	Spanish

Constant (p. 6) A term that has no variable factor.

Constante (p. 6) Término que tiene un valor fijo.

Example In the expression $4x + 13y + 17$, 17 is a constant term.

Constant matrix (p. H32) When representing a system of equations with a matrix equation, the matrix containing the constants of the system is the constant matrix.

Matriz de constantes (p. H32) Al representar un sistema de ecuaciones con una ecuación matricial, la matriz que contiene las constantes del sistema es la matriz de constantes.

Example $\begin{cases} x + 2y = 5 \\ 3x + 5y = 14 \end{cases}$

constant matrix $\begin{bmatrix} 5 \\ 14 \end{bmatrix}$

Constant of variation for direct variation (p. 176) The nonzero constant k in the function $y = kx$.

Constante de variación en variaciones directas (p. 176) La constante k cuyo valor no es cero en la función $y = kx$.

Example For the direct variation $y = 24x$, 24 is the constant of variation.

Construction (p. 405) A construction is a geometric figure made with only a straightedge and compass.

Construcción (p. 405) Una construcción es una figura geométrica trazada solamente con una regla sin graduación y un compás.

Example

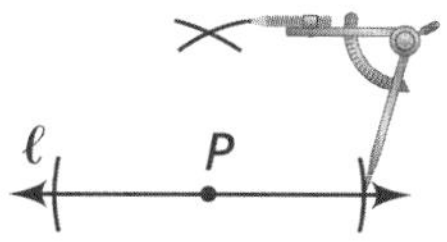

The diagram shows the construction (in progress) of a line perpendicular to a line ℓ through a point P on ℓ.

Continuous graph (p. 119) A graph that is unbroken.

Gráfica continua (p. 119) Una gráfica continua es una gráfica ininterrumpida.

Example

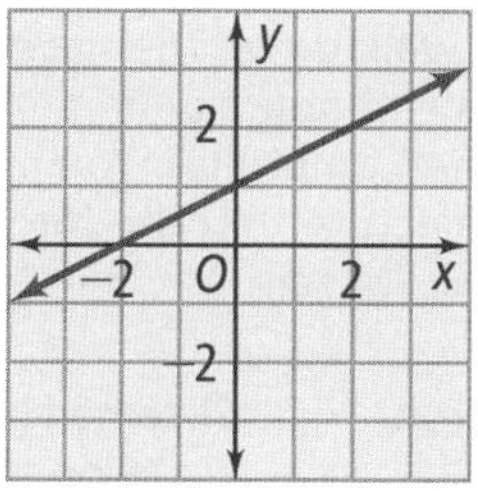

Contrapositive (p. H70) The contrapositive of the conditional "if p, then q" is the conditional "if not q, then not p." A conditional and its contrapositive always have the same truth value.

Contrapositivo (p. H70) El contrapositivo del condicional "si p, entonces q" es el condicional "si no q, entonces no p". Un condicional y su contrapositivo siempre tienen el mismo valor verdadero.

Example **Conditional:** If a figure is a triangle, then it is a polygon.
Contrapositive: If a figure is not a polygon, then it is not a triangle.

English

Spanish

Converse (p. H70) The statement obtained by reversing the hypothesis and conclusion of a conditional.

Expresión recíproca (p. H70) Enunciado que se obtiene al intercambiar la hipótesis y la conclusión de una situación condicional.

Example The converse of "If I was born in Houston, then I am a Texan" would be "If I am a Texan, then I am born in Houston."

Conversion factor (p. 38) A ratio of two equivalent measures in different units.

Factor de conversion (p. 38) Razón de dos medidas equivalentes en unidades diferentes.

Example The ratio $\frac{1\text{ ft}}{12\text{ in.}}$ is a conversion factor.

Correlation coefficient (p. 378) A number from –1 to 1 that tells you how closely the equation of the line of best fit models the data.

Coeficiente de correlación (p. 378) Número de 1 a 1 que indica con cuánta exactitud la línea de mejor encaje representa los datos.

Example

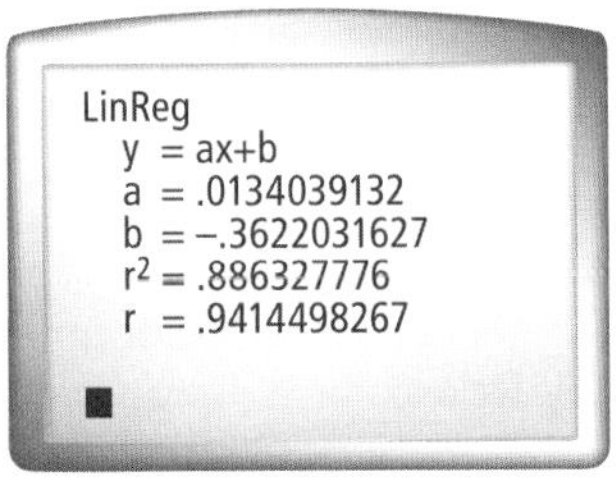

The correlation coefficient is approximately 0.94.

Corresponding elements (p. H4) Corresponding elements are elements in the same position in each matrix.

Elementos correspondientes (p. H4) Los elementos correspondientes son elementos que se encuentran en la misma posición de cada matriz.

Counterexample (p. H62) An example showing that a statement is false.

Contraejemplo (p. H62) Ejemplo que demuestra que un enunciado es falso.

Example **Statement:** All apples are red.
Counterexample: A Granny Smith Apple is green.

Cross products (of a proportion) (p. 53) In a proportion $\frac{a}{b} = \frac{c}{d}$, the products *ad* and *bc*. These products are equal.

Productos cruzados (de una proporción) (p. 53) En una proporción $\frac{a}{b} = \frac{c}{d}$, los productos *ad* y *bc*. Estos productos son iguales.

Example The cross products for $\frac{3}{4} = \frac{6}{8}$ are $3 \cdot 8$ and $4 \cdot 6$.

English

Cumulative frequency table (p. 349) A table that shows the number of data values that lie in or below the given intervals.

Spanish

Tabla de frecuencia cumulativa (p. 349) Tabla que muestra el número de valores de datos que están dentro o por debajo de los intervalos dados.

Example

Interval	Frequency	Cumulative Frequency
0–9	5	5
10–19	8	13
20–29	4	17

D

Decay factor (p. 306) 1 minus the percent rate of change, expressed as a decimal, for an exponential decay situation.

Factor de decremento (p. 306) 1 menos la tasa porcentual de cambio, expresada como decimal, en una situación de reducción exponencial.

Example The decay factor of the function $y = 5(0.3)^x$ is 0.3.

Deductive reasoning (p. H82) Deductive reasoning is a process of reasoning logically from given facts to a conclusion.

Razonamiento deductivo (p. H82) El razonamiento deductivo es un proceso de razonamiento lógico que parte de hechos dados hasta llegar a una conclusión.

Example Based on the fact that the sum of any two even numbers is even, you can deduce that the product of any whole number and any even number is even.

Dependent system (p. 226) A system of equations that does not have a unique solution.

Sistema dependiente (p. 226) Sistema de ecuaciones que no tiene una solución única.

Example The system $\begin{cases} y = 2x + 3 \\ -4x + 2y = 6 \end{cases}$ represents two equations for the same line, so it has many solutions. It is a dependent system.

Dependent variable (p. 103) A variable that provides the output values of a function.

Variable dependiente (p. 103) Variable de la que dependen los valores de salida de una función.

Example In the equation $y = 3x$, y is the dependent variable.

Determinant (p. H24) The determinant of a square matrix is a real number that can be computed from its elements according to a specific formula.

Determinante (p. H24) El determinante de una matriz cuadrada es un número real que se puede calcular a partir de sus elementos por medio de una fórmula específica.

Example The determinant of $\begin{bmatrix} 3 & -2 \\ 5 & 6 \end{bmatrix}$ is $3(6) - 5(-2) = 28$.

English | Spanish

Direct variation (p. 176) A linear function defined by an equation of the form $y = kx$, where $k \neq 0$.

Variación directa (p. 176) Una función lineal definida por una ecuación de la forma $y\ kx$, donde $k \neq 0$, representa una variación directa.

Example $y = 18x$ is a direct variation.

Discrete graph (p. 119) A graph composed of isolated points.

Gráfica discreta (p. 119) Una gráfica discreta es compuesta de puntos aislados.

Example

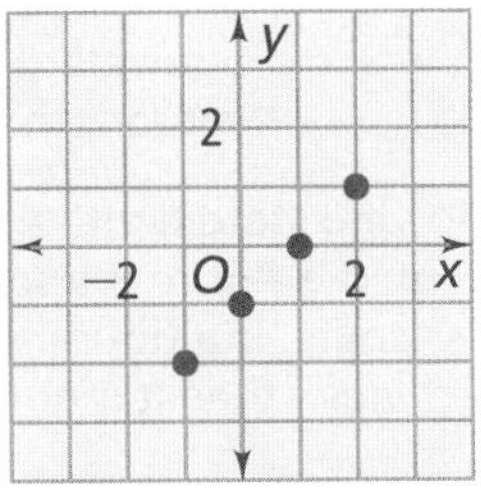

Distributive Property (p. 3) For every real number a, b, and c:

$a(b + c) = ab + ac$

$(b + c)a = ba + ca$

$a(b - c) = ab - ac$

$(b - c)a = ba - ca$

Propiedad Distributiva (p. 3) Para cada número real a, b y c:

$a(b + c) = ab + ac$

$(b + c)a = ba + ca$

$a(b - c) = ab - ac$

$(b - c)a = ba - ca$

Examples $3(19 + 4) = 3(19) + 3(4)$

$(19 + 4)3 = 19(3) + 4(3)$

$7(11 - 2) = 7(11) - 7(2)$

$(11 - 2)7 = 11(7) - 2(7)$

Domain (of a relation or function) (p. 135) The possible values for the input of a relation or function.

Dominio (de una relación o función) (p. 135) Posibles valores de entrada de una relación o función.

Example In the function $f(x) = x + 22$, the domain is all real numbers.

E

Elimination method (p. 240) A method for solving a system of linear equations. You add or subtract the equations to eliminate a variable.

Eliminación (p. 240) Método para resolver un sistema de ecuaciones lineales. Se suman o se restan las ecuaciones para eliminar una variable.

Example

$3x + y = 19$

$\underline{2x - y = \ \ 1}$ Add the equations to get $x = 4$.

$5x + 0 = 20$

$2(4) - y = 1 \rightarrow$ Substitute 4 for x in the second equation.

$8 - y = 1$

$y = 7 \rightarrow$ Solve for y.

English	**Spanish**

Equal matrices (p. H7) Equal matrices are matrices with the same dimensions and equal corresponding elements.

Matrices equivalentes (p. H7) Dos matrices son equivalentes si y sólo si tienen las mismas dimensiones y sus elementos correspondientes son iguales.

Example Matrices A and B are equal.

$$A = \begin{bmatrix} 2 & 6 \\ \frac{9}{3} & 1 \end{bmatrix} \quad B = \begin{bmatrix} \frac{6}{3} & 6 \\ 3 & \frac{-13}{-13} \end{bmatrix}$$

Equivalent statements (p. H70) Equivalent statements are statements with the same truth value.

Enunciados equivalentes (p. H70) Los enunciados equivalentes son enunciados con el mismo valor verdadero.

Example The following statements are equivalent: If a figure is a square, then it is a rectangle. If a figure is not a rectangle, then it is not a square.

Even function (p. 144) A function f is an even function if and only if $f(-x) = f(x)$ for all values of x in its domain.

Función par (p. 144) Una función f es una función par si y solo si $f(-x) = f(x)$ para todos los valores de x en su dominio.

Example $f(x) = x^2 + |x|$ is an even function because $f(-x) = (-x)^2 + |-x| = x^2 + |x| = f(x)$

Explicit formula (p. 150) An explicit formula expresses the nth term of a sequence in terms of n.

Fórmula explícita (p. 150) Una fórmula explícita expresa el n-ésimo término de una progresión en función de n.

Example Let $a_n = 2n + 5$ for positive integers n. If $n = 7$, then $a_7 = 2(7) + 5 = 19$.

Exponential decay (p. 306) A situation modeled with a function of the form $y = ab^x$, where $a > 0$ and $0 < b < 1$.

Decremento exponencial (p. 306) Para $a > 0$ y $0 < b < 1$, la función $y = ab^x$ representa el decremento exponencial.

Example $y = 5(0.1)^x$

Exponential function (p. 285) A function that repeatedly multiplies an initial amount by the same positive number. You can model all exponential functions using $y = ab^x$, where a is a nonzero constant, $b > 0$, and $b \neq 1$.

Función exponencial (p. 285) Función que multiplica repetidas veces una cantidad inicial por el mismo número positivo. Todas las funciones exponenciales se pueden representar mediante $y = ab^x$, donde a es una constante con valor distinto de cero, $b > 0$ y $b \neq 1$.

Example

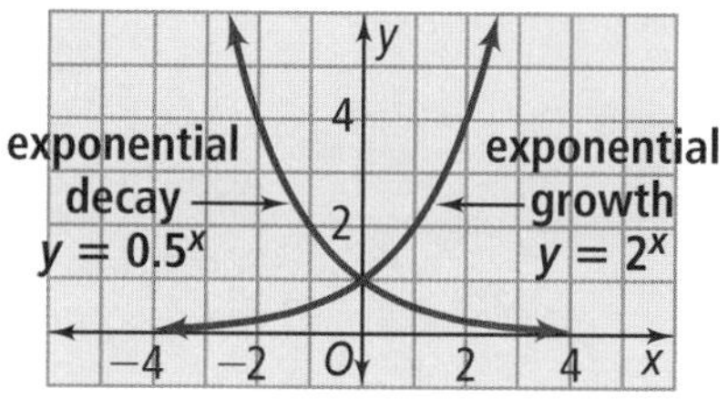

English	Spanish

Exponential growth (p. 303) A situation modeled with a function of the form $y = ab^x$, where $a > 0$ and $b > 1$.

Incremento exponencial (p. 303) Para $a > 0$ y $b > 1$, la función $y = ab^x$ representa el incremento exponencial.

Example $y = 100(2)^x$

Extrapolation (p. 375) The process of predicting a value outside the range of known values.

Extrapolación (p. 375) Proceso que se usa para predecir un valor por fuera del ámbito de los valores dados.

F

Formula (p. 31) An equation that states a relationship among quantities.

Fórmula (p. 31) Ecuación que establece una relación entre cantidades.

Example The formula for the volume V of a cylinder is $V = \pi r^2 h$, where r is the radius of the cylinder and h is its height.

Frequency (p. 345) The number of data items in an interval.

Frecuencia (p. 345) Número de datos de un intervalo.

Frequency table (p. 345) A table that groups a set of data values into intervals and shows the frequency for each interval.

Tabla de frecuencias (p. 345) Tabla que agrupa un conjunto de datos en intervalos y muestra la frecuencia de cada intervalo.

Example

Interval	Frequency
0–9	5
10–19	8
20–29	4

Function (p. 105) A relation that assigns exactly one value in the range to each value of the domain.

Función (p. 105) La relación que asigna exactamente un valor del rango a cada valor del dominio.

Example Earned income is a function of the number of hours worked. If you earn $4.50/h, then your income is expressed by the function $f(h) = 4.5h$.

Function notation (p. 137) To write a rule in function notation, you use the symbol $f(x)$ in place of y.

Notación de una función (p. 137) Para expresar una regla en notación de función se usa el símbolo $f(x)$ en lugar de y.

Example $f(x) = 3x - 8$ is in function notation.

English	Spanish

G

Geometric sequence (p. 323) A number sequence formed by multiplying a term in a sequence by a fixed number to find the next term.

Progresión geométrica (p. 323) Tipo de sucesión numérica formada al multiplicar un término de la secuencia por un número constante, para hallar el siguiente término.

Example $9, 3, 1, \frac{1}{3}, \ldots$ is an example of a geometric sequence.

Glide reflection (p. 514) A glide reflection is the composition of a translation followed by a reflection across a line parallel to the direction of translation.

Reflexión deslizada (p. 514) Una reflexión por deslizamiento es la composición de una traslación seguida por una reflexión a través de una línea paralela a la dirección de traslación.

Example

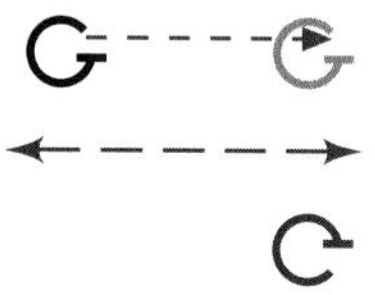

The blue G in the diagram is a glide reflection image of the black G.

Growth factor (p. 303) 1 plus the percent rate of change for an exponential growth situation.

Factor incremental (p. 303) 1 más la tasa porcentual de cambio en una situación de incremento exponencial.

Example The growth factor of $y = 7(1.3)^x$ is 1.3.

H

Histogram (p. 346) A special type of bar graph that can display data from a frequency table. Each bar represents an interval. The height of each bar shows the frequency of the interval it represents.

Histograma (p. 346) Tipo de gráfica de barras que muestra los datos de una tabla de frecuencia. Cada barra representa un intervalo. La altura de cada barra muestra la frecuencia del intervalo al que representa.

Example

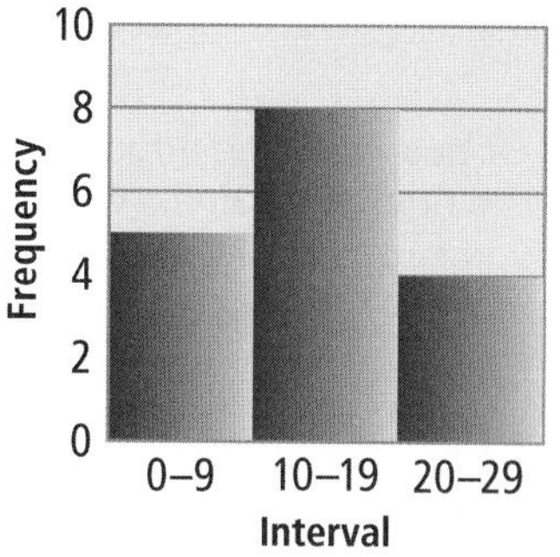

English | Spanish

Hypotenuse (p. 567) *See* **right triangle.**

Hipotenusa (p. 567) *Ver* **right triangle.**

Hypothesis (p. H67) In an *if-then* statement (conditional), the hypothesis is the part that follows *if*.

Hipótesis (p. H67) En un enunciado *si . . . entonces . . .* (condicional), la hipótesis es la parte del enunciado que sigue el *si*.

Example In the conditional "If an animal has four legs, then it is a horse," the hypothesis is "an animal has four legs."

I

Image (p. 473, H39) *See* **transformation.**

Imagen (p. 473, H39) *Ver* **transformation.**

Identity (p. 24) An equation that is true for every value.

Identidad (p. 24) Una ecuación que es verdadera para todos los valores.

Example $5 - 14x = 5\left(1 - \frac{14}{5}x\right)$ is an identity because it is true for any value of x.

Inconsistent system (p. 226) A system of equations that has no solution.

Sistema incompatible (p. 226) Un sistema incompatible es un sistema de ecuaciones para el cual no hay solución.

Example $\begin{cases} y = 2x + 3 \\ -2x + y = 1 \end{cases}$

is a system of parallel lines, so it has no solution. It is an inconsistent system.

Independent system (p. 226) A system of linear equations that has a unique solution.

Sistema independiente (p. 226) Un sistema de ecuaciones lineales que tenga una sola solución es un sistema independiente.

Example $\begin{cases} x + 2y = -7 \\ 2x - 3y = 0 \end{cases}$

has the unique solution (–3, –2). It is an independent system.

Independent variable (p. 103) A variable that provides the input values of a function.

Variable independiente (p. 103) Variable de la que dependen los valores de entrada de una función.

Example In the equation $y = 3x$, x is the independent variable.

English	Spanish

Inductive reasoning (p. H59) Inductive reasoning is a type of reasoning that reaches conclusions based on a pattern of specific examples or past events.

Razonamiento inductivo (p. H59) El razonamiento inductivo es un tipo de razonamiento en el cual se llega a conclusiones con base en un patrón de ejemplos específicos o sucesos pasados.

Example You see four people walk into a building. Each person emerges with a small bag containing food. You use inductive reasoning to conclude that this building contains a restaurant.

Initial point (p. H47) The initial point of a vector is the endpoint (not the tip) of a vector arrow.

Punto de inicio (p. H47) El punto de inicio de un vector es el extremo (no la punta) de una flecha vectorial.

Input (p. 103) A value of the independent variable.

Entrada (p. 103) Valor de una variable independiente.

Example The input is any value of x you substitute into a function.

Interpolation (p. 375) The process of estimating a value between two known quantities.

Interpolación (p. 375) Proceso que se usa para estimar el valor entre dos cantidades dadas.

Interquartile range (p. 366) The interquartile range of a set of data is the difference between the third and first quartiles.

Intervalo intercuartil (p. 366) El rango intercuartil de un conjunto de datos es la diferencia entre el tercero y el primer cuartiles.

Example The first and third quartiles of the data set 2, 3, 4, 5, 5, 6, 7, and 7 are 3.5 and 6.5. The interquartile range is $6.5 - 3.5 = 3$.

Interval notation (p. 74) A notation for describing an interval on a number line. The interval's endpoint(s) are given, and a parenthesis or bracket is used to indicate whether each endpoint is included in the interval.

Notación de intervalo (p. 74) Notación que describe un intervalo en una recta numérica. Los extremos del intervalo se incluyen y se usa un paréntesis o corchete para indicar si cada extremo está incluido en el intervalo.

Example For $-2 \leq x < 8$, the interval notation is $[-2, 8)$.

Inverse (p. H70) The inverse of the conditional "if p, then q" is the conditional "if not p, then not q."

Inverso (p. H70) El inverso del condicional "si p, entonces q" es el condicional "si no p, entonces no q".

Example **Conditional:** If a figure is a square, then it is a parallelogram. **Inverse:** If a figure is not a square, then it is not a parallelogram.

English / Spanish

Isometry (p. 510) An isometry, also known as a *congruence transformation*, is a transformation in which an original figure and its image are congruent.

Isometría (p. 510) Una isometría, conocida también como una *transformación de congruencia*, es una transformación en donde una figura original y su imagen son congruentes.

Example The four isometries are reflections, rotations, translations, and glide reflections.

Isosceles triangle (p. 558) An isosceles triangle is a triangle that has at least two congruent sides. If there are two congruent sides, they are called *legs*. The *vertex angle* is between them. The third side is called the *base* and the other two angles are called *base angles*.

Triángulo isosceles (p. 558) Un triángulo isosceles es un triángulo que tiene por lo menos dos lados congruentes. Si tiene dos lodos congruentes, éstos se llaman *catetos*. Entre ellos se encuentra el *ángulo del vértice*. El tercer lado se llama *base* y los otros dos ángulos se llaman *ángulos de base*.

Example

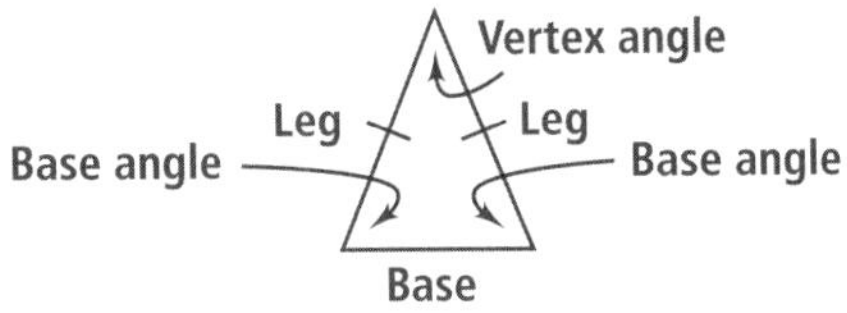

J

Joint frequency (p. 388) A joint frequency is an entry in the body of a two-way frequency table.

Frecuencia conjunta (p. 388) Una frecuencia conjunta es una entrada en el cuerpo de una tabla de frecuencias de doble entrada.

Example

	Male	Female	Totals
Juniors	3	4	7
Seniors	3	2	5
Totals	6	6	12

3 and 4 in the first row, and 3 and 2 in the second row are joint frequencies.

Joint relative frequency (p. 390) A joint relative frequency is a joint frequency in a two-way frequency table divided by the grand total of the entries in the table. It is also an entry in the body of a two-way relative frequency table.

Frecuencia relativa conjunta (p. 390) Una frecuencia relativa conjunta es una frecuencia conjunta en una tabla de frecuencias de doble entrada dividido por el total de las entradas de la tabla. Es también una entrada en el cuerpo de una tabla de frecuencias relativas de doble entrada.

L

Leg *See* **isosceles triangle**.

Cateto *Ver* **isosceles triangle.**

English	Spanish
Like terms (p. 7) Terms with exactly the same variable factors in a variable expression.	**Radicales semejantes (p. 7)** Expresiones radicales con los mismos radicandos.

Example $3\sqrt{7}$ and $25\sqrt{7}$ are like radicals.

Line of best fit (p. 378) The most accurate trend line on a scatter plot showing the relationship between two sets of data.	**Recta de mayor aproximación (p. 378)** La línea de tendencia en un diagrama de puntos que más se acerca a los puntos que representan la relación entre dos conjuntos de datos.

Example

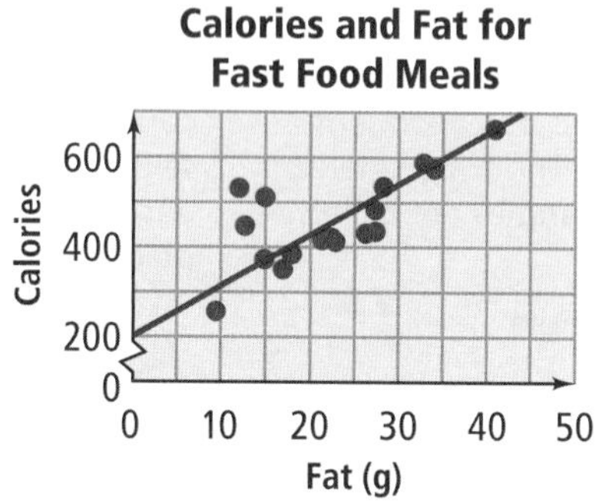

Line of reflection (p. 486) *See* **reflection.**	**Eje de reflexión (p. 486)** *Ver* **reflection.**
Line of symmetry (p. 501) *See* **reflectional symmetry.**	**Eje de simetría (p. 501)** *Ver* **reflectional symmetry.**
Line plot (p. 356) A line plot is a graph that shows the shape of a data set by stacking X's above each data value on a number line.	**Diagrama de puntos (p. 356)** Un diagrama de puntos is una gráfica que muestra la forma de un conjunto de datos agrupando X sobre cada valor de una recta numérica.

Example

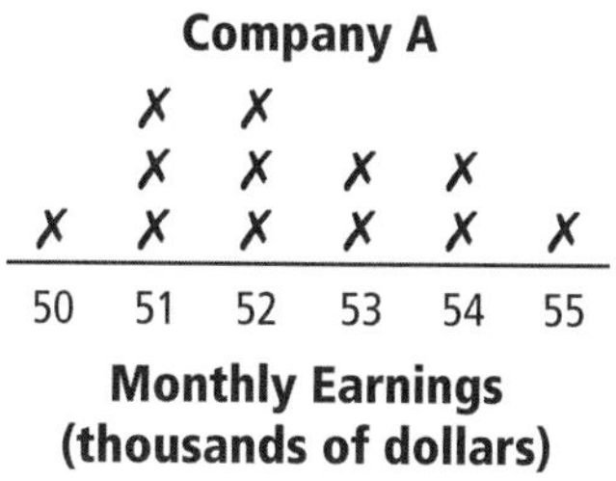

Line symmetry (p. 501) *See* **reflectional symmetry.**	**Simetría axial (p. 501)** *Ver* **reflectional symmetry.**
Linear equation (p. 186) An equation whose graph forms a straight line.	**Ecuación lineal (p. 186)** Ecuación cuya gráfica es una línea recta.

Example

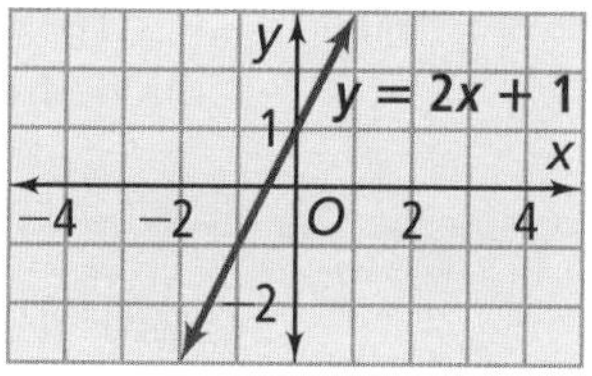

English | Spanish

Linear function (p. 105) A function whose graph is a line is a linear function. You can represent a linear function with a linear equation.

Función lineal (p. 105) Una función cuya gráfica es una recta es una función lineal. La función lineal se representa con una ecuación lineal.

Example

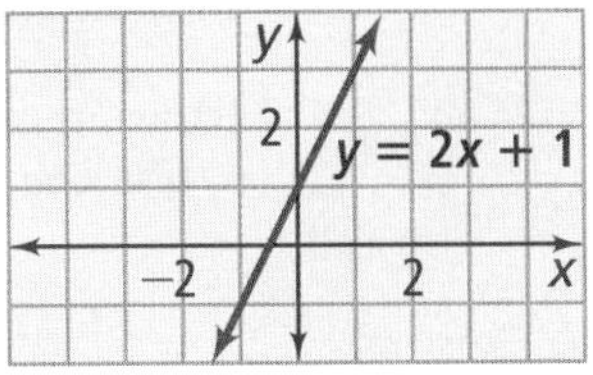

Linear inequality (p. 256) An inequality in two variables whose graph is a region of the coordinate plane that is bounded by a line. Each point in the region is a solution of the inequality.

Desigualdad lineal (p. 256) Una desigualdad lineal es una desigualdad de dos variables cuya gráfica es una región del plano de coordenadas delimitado por una recta. Cada punto de la región es una solución de la desigualdad.

Example

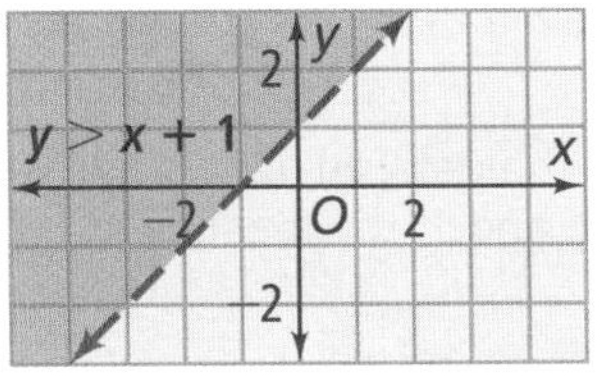

Linear parent function (p. 186) The simplest form of a linear function.

Función lineal elemental (p. 186) La forma más simple de una función lineal.

Example $y = x$

Literal equation (p. 29) An equation involving two or more variables.

Ecuación literal (p. 29) Ecuación que incluye dos o más variables.

Example $4x + 2y = 18$ is a literal equation.

M

Magnitude (p. H47) The magnitude of a vector **v** is the length of the arrow.

Magnitud (p. H47) La magnitud de un vector v es la longitud de la flecha.

Marginal frequency (p. 388) A marginal frequency is an entry in the Total row or Total column of a two-way frequency table.

Frecuencia marginal (p. 388) Una frecuencia marginal es una entrada en la fila Total o columna Total de una tabla de frecuencias de doble entrada.

Example

	Male	Female	Totals
Juniors	3	4	7
Seniors	3	2	5
Totals	6	6	12

6 and 6 in the Total row and 7 and 5 in the Total column are marginal frequencies.

English / Spanish

Marginal relative frequency (p. 390) A marginal relative frequency is a marginal frequency in a two-way frequency table divided by the grand total for the table.

Frecuencia relativa marginal (p. 390) Una frecuencia relativa marginal es una frecuencia marginal en una tabla de frecuencias de doble entrada dividido por el total de la tabla.

Matrix equation (p. H5) A matrix equation is an equation in which the variable is a matrix.

Ecuación matricial (p. H5) Una ecuación matricial es una ecuación en que la variable es una matriz.

Example

$$\text{Solve } X + \begin{bmatrix} 3 & -2 \\ 5 & 1 \end{bmatrix} = \begin{bmatrix} 4 & 0 \\ 0 & 3 \end{bmatrix}$$

$$X = \begin{bmatrix} 4 & 0 \\ 0 & 3 \end{bmatrix} - \begin{bmatrix} 3 & -2 \\ 5 & 1 \end{bmatrix} = \begin{bmatrix} 1 & 2 \\ -5 & 2 \end{bmatrix}$$

Mean (p. 353) To find the mean of a set of data values, find the sum of the data values and divide the sum by the number of data values. The mean is $\frac{\text{sum of the data values}}{\text{total number of data values}}$.

Media (p. 353) Para hallar la media de un conjunto de datos, halla la suma de los valores de los datos y divide la suma por el total del valor de los datos. La media es $\frac{\text{la suma de los datos}}{\text{el número total de valores de datos}}$.

Example In the data set 12, 11, 12, 10, 13, 12, and 7, the mean is $\frac{12 + 11 + 12 + 10 + 13 + 12 + 7}{7} = 11$.

Mean absolute deviation (MAD) (p. 362) Mean absolute deviation is a measure of the spread of a data set. For data values $x_1, x_2, \ldots x_n$, the mean absolute deviation is given by $\frac{|x_1 - \bar{x}| + |x_2 - \bar{x}| + \ldots + |x_n - \bar{x}|}{n}$, where $\bar{x}$ is the mean of the data set.

Desviación absoluta media (p. 362) Desviación absoluta media es una medida de la dispersión de un conjunto de datos. Para los datos $x_1, x_2, \ldots, x_n$, la desviación absoluta media es igual a $\frac{|x_1 - \bar{x}| + |x_2 - \bar{x}| + \ldots + |x_n - \bar{x}|}{n}$, donde $\bar{x}$ es la media del conjunto de datos.

Measure of central tendency (p. 353) Mean, median, and mode. They are used to organize and summarize a set of data.

Medida de tendencia central (p. 353) La media, la mediana y la moda. Se usan para organizar y resumir un conjunto de datos.

Example For examples, see *mean*, *median*, and *mode*.

Measure of dispersion (p. 356) A measure that describes how dispersed, or spread out, the values in a data set are. Range is a measure of dispersion.

Medida de dispersión (p. 356) Medida que describe cómo se dispersan, o esparecen, los valores de un conjunto de datos. La amplitud es una medida de dispersión.

Example For an example, see *range*.

Median (p. 353) The middle value in an ordered set of numbers.

Mediana (p. 353) El valor del medio en un conjunto ordenado de números.

Example In the data set 7, 10, 11, 12, 12, 12, and 13, the median is 12.

English | Spanish

Mode (p. 353) The mode is the most frequently occurring value (or values) in a set of data. A data set may have no mode, one mode, or more than one mode.

Moda (p. 353) La moda es el valor o valores que ocurren con mayor frequencia en un conjunto de datos. El conjunto de datos puede no tener moda, o tener una o más modas.

Example In the data set 7, 7, 9, 10, 11, and 13, the mode is 7.

Multiplicative identity matrix (p. H22) For an $n \times n$ square matrix, the multiplicative identity matrix is an $n \times n$ square matrix I, or $I_{n \times n}$ with 1's along the main diagonal and 0's elsewhere.

Matriz de identidad multiplicativa (p. H22) Para una matriz cuadrada $n \times n$, la matriz de identidad multiplicativa es la matriz cuadrada I de $n \times n$, o $I_{n \times n}$, con unos por la diagonal principal y ceros en los demás lugares.

Example $I_{2\times2} = \begin{vmatrix} 1 & 0 \\ 0 & 1 \end{vmatrix}, I_{3\times3} = \begin{bmatrix} 1 & 0 & 0 \\ 0 & 1 & 0 \\ 0 & 0 & 1 \end{bmatrix}$

Multiplicative inverse of a matrix (p. H22) If A and X are $n \times n$ matrices, and $AX = XA = I$, then X is the multiplicative inverse of A, written A^{-1}.

Inverso multiplicativo de una matriz (p. H22) Si A y X son matrices $n \times n$, y $AX = XA = I$, entonces X es el inverso multiplicativo de A, expresado como A^{-1}.

Example $A = \begin{vmatrix} 2 & 1 \\ 4 & 0 \end{vmatrix}, X = \begin{bmatrix} 0 & \frac{1}{4} \\ 1 & \frac{1}{2} \end{bmatrix}$

$AX = \begin{bmatrix} 1 & 0 \\ 0 & 1 \end{bmatrix} = I$, so $X = A^{-1}$

N

Negation (p. H70) The negation of a statement has the opposite meaning of the original statement.

Negación (p. H70) La negación de un enunciado tiene el sentido opuesto del enunciado original.

Example The angle is obtuse.
Negation: The angle is not obtuse.

Negative correlation (p. 373) The relationship between two sets of data, in which one set of data decreases as the other set of data increases.

Correlación negativa (p. 373) Relación entre dos conjuntos de datos en la que uno de los conjuntos disminuye a medida que el otro aumenta.

Example

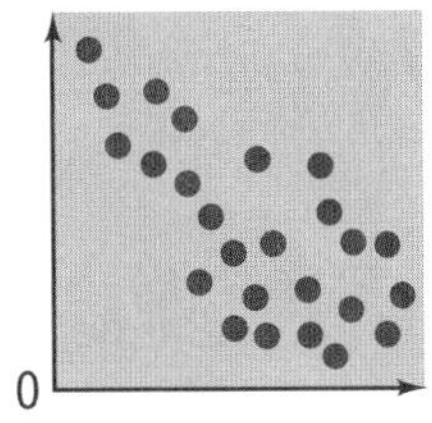

English	Spanish

No correlation (p. 373) There does not appear to be a relationship between two sets of data.

Sin correlación (p. 373) No hay relación entre dos conjuntos de datos.

Example

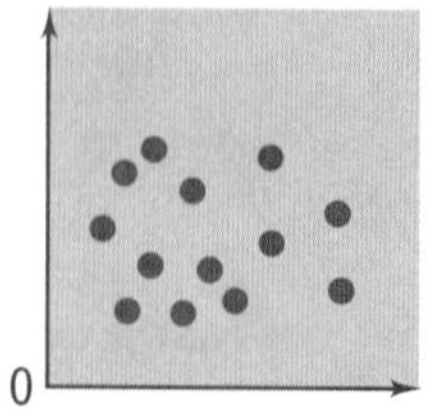

Nonlinear function (p. 110) A function whose graph is not a line or part of a line.

Función no lineal (p. 110) Función cuya gráfica no es una línea o parte de una línea.

Example

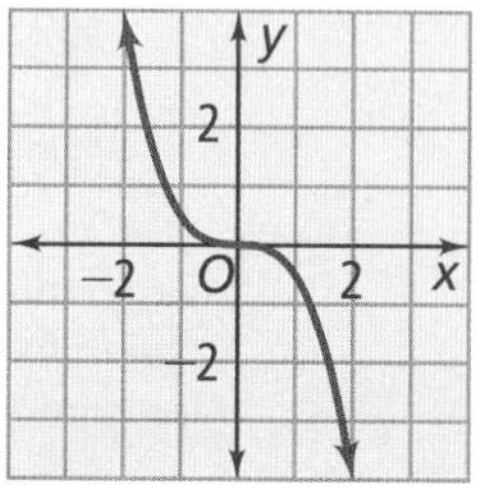

Normal vectors (p. H50) Normal vectors are perpendicular vectors. Their dot product is 0.

Vectores normales (p. H50) Los vectores normales son vectores perpendiculares. El producto escalar es 0.

O

Odd function (p. 144) A function f is an odd function if and only if $f(-x) = -f(x)$ for all values of x in its domain.

Función impar (p. 144) Una función f es una función impar si y solo si $f(-x) = -f(x)$ para todos los valores de x en su dominio.

Example The function $f(x) = x^3 + 2x$ is odd because $f(-x) = (-x)^3 + 2(-x) = -x^3 - 2x = -f(x)$

Opposite reciprocals (p. 214) A number of the form $-\frac{b}{a}$, where $\frac{a}{b}$ is a nonzero rational number. The product of a number and its opposite reciprocal is -1.

Recíproco inverso (p. 214) Número en la forma $-\frac{b}{a}$, donde $\frac{a}{b}$ es un número racional diferente de cero. El producto de un número y su recíproco inverso es -1.

Example $\frac{2}{5}$ and $-\frac{5}{2}$ are opposite reciprocals because $\left(\frac{2}{5}\right)\left(-\frac{5}{2}\right) = -1$.

Outlier (p. 353) An outlier is a data value that is much higher or lower than the other data values in the set.

Valor extremo (p. 353) Un valor extremo es el valor de un dato que es mucho más alto o mucho más bajo que los otros valores del conjunto de datos.

Example For the set of values 2, 5, 3, 7, 12, the data value 12 is an outlier.

English	Spanish

Output (p. 103) A value of the dependent variable.

Salida (p. 103) Valor de una variable dependiente.

Example The output of the function $f(x) = x^2$ when $x = 3$ is 9.

P

Parallel lines (p. 212) Two lines are parallel if they lie in the same plane and do not intersect. The symbol || means "is parallel to".

Paralle lines (p. 212) Dos rectas son paralelas si están en el mismo plano y no se cortan. El símbolo || significa "es paralelo a".

Example $\ell \parallel m$

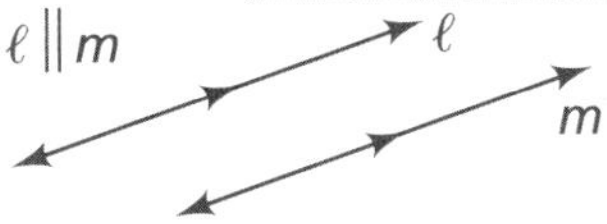

The red symbols indicate parallel lines.

Parent function (p. 186) A family of functions is a group of functions with common characteristics. A parent function is the simplest function with these characteristics.

Función elemental (p. 186) Una familia de funciones es un grupo de funciones con características en común. La función elemental es la función más simple que reúne esas características.

Example $y = x$ is the parent function for the family of linear equations of the form $y = mx + b$.

Percentile (p. 369) A value that separates a data set into 100 equal parts.

Percentil (p. 369) Valor que separa el conjunto de datos en 100 partes iguales.

Percentile rank (p. 369) The percentage of data values that are less than or equal to a given value.

Rango percentil (p. 369) Porcentaje de valores de datos que es menos o igual a un valor dado.

Perimeter of a polygon (p. 425) The perimeter of a polygon is the sum of the lengths of its sides.

Perímetro de un polígono (p. 425) El perímetro de un polígono es la suma de las longitudes de sus lados

Example

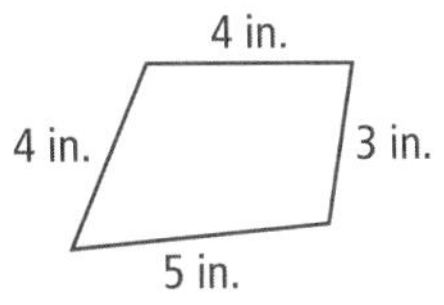

$$P = 4 + 4 + 5 + 3 \\ = 16 \text{ in.}$$

Perpendicular bisector (p. 407) The perpendicular bisector of a segment is a line, segment, or ray that is perpendicular to the segment at its midpoint.

Mediatriz (p. 407) La mediatriz de un segmento es una recta, segmento o semirrecta que es perpendicular al segmento en su punto medio.

Example

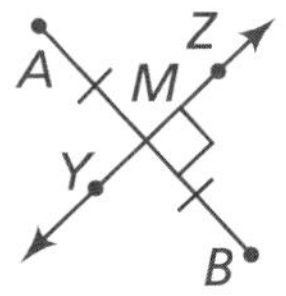

$\overleftrightarrow{YZ}$ is the perpendicular bisector of $\overline{AB}$. It is perpendicular to $\overline{AB}$ and intersects $\overline{AB}$ at midpoint M.

English	Spanish

Perpendicular lines (p. 213, 407) Perpendicular lines are lines that intersect and form right angles. The symbol $\perp$ means "is perpendicular to". Two lines are perpendicular if the product of their slopes is -1.

Rectas Perpendiculars (p. 213, 407) Las rectas perpendiculars son recta sue se cortan y frman angulos rectos. El símbolo $\perp$ significa "es perpendicular a". Dos rectas son perpendiculares si el producto de sus pendientes es -1.

Example

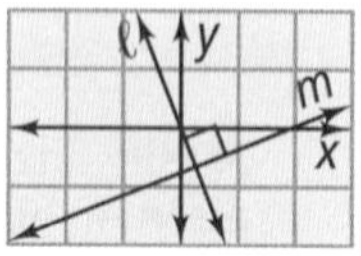

Point-slope form (p. 195) A linear equation of a nonvertical line written as $y - y_1 = m(x - x_1)$. The line passes through the point (x_1, y_1) with slope *m*.

Forma punto-pendiente (p. 195) La ecuación lineal de una recta no vertical que pasa por el punto (x_1, y_1) con pendiente m está dada por $y - y_1 = m(x - x_1)$.

Example An equation with a slope of $-\frac{1}{2}$ passing through $(2, -1)$ would be written $y + 1 = -\frac{1}{2}(x - 2)$ in point-slope form.

Point symmetry (p. 501) Point symmetry is the type of symmetry for which there is a rotation of 180° that maps a figure onto itself.

Simetría central (p. 501) La simetría central es un tipo de simetría en la que una figura se ha rotado 180° sobre sí misma.

Positive correlation (p. 373) The relationship between two sets of data in which both sets of data increase together.

Correlación positiva (p. 373) La relación entre dos conjuntos de datos en la que ambos conjuntos incrementan a la vez.

Example

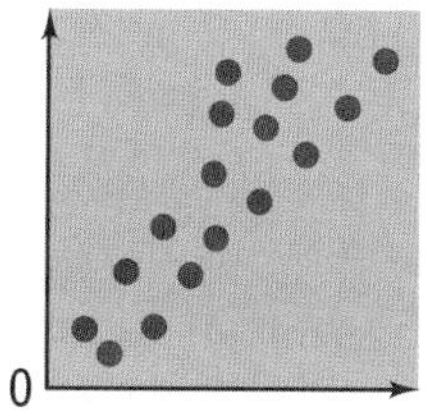

Preimage (pp. 473, H39) *See* **transformation.**

Preimagen (pp. 473, H39) *Ver* **transformation.**

Proportion (p. 52) An equation that states that two ratios are equal.

Proporción (p. 52) Es una ecuación que establece que dos razones son iguales.

Example $\frac{7.5}{9} = \frac{5}{6}$

English / Spanish

Q

Quartile (p. 366) A quartile is a value that separates a finite data set into four equal parts. The second quartile (Q_2) is the median of the data set. The first and third quartiles (Q_1 and Q_3) are the medians of the lower half and upper half of the data, respectively.

Cuartil (p. 366) Un cuartil es el valor que separa un conjunto de datos finitos en cuatro partes iguales. El segundo cuartil (Q_2) es la mediana del conjunto de datos. El primer cuartil y el tercer cuartil (Q_1 y Q_3) son medianas de la mitad inferior y de la mitad superior de los datos, respectivamente.

Example For the data set 2, 3, 4, 5, 5, 6, 7, 7, the first quartile is 3.5, the second quartile (or median) is 5, and the third quartile is 6.5.

R

Range (of a relation or function) (p. 135) The possible values of the output, or dependent variable, of a relation or function.

Rango (de una relación o función) (p. 135) El conjunto de todos los valores posibles de la salida, o variable dependiente, de una relación o función.

Example In the function $y = |x|$, the range is the set of all nonnegative numbers.

Range of a set of data (p. 356) The difference between the greatest and the least data values for a set of data.

Rango de un conjunto de datos (p. 356) Diferencia entre el valor mayor y el menor en un conjunto de datos.

Example For the set 2, 5, 8, 12, the range is $12 - 2 = 10$.

Rate (p. 37) A ratio of a to b where a and b represent quantities measured in different units.

Tasa (p. 37) La relación que existe entre a y b cuando a y b son cantidades medidas con distintas unidades.

Example Traveling 125 miles in 2 hours results in the rate $\frac{125 \text{ miles}}{2 \text{ hours}}$ or 62.5 mi/h.

Rate of change (p. 167) The relationship between two quantities that are changing. The rate of change is also called slope.

$$\text{rate of change} = \frac{\text{change in the dependent variable}}{\text{change in the independent variable}}$$

Tasa de cambio (p. 167) La relación entre dos cantidades que cambian. La tasa de cambio se llama también pendiente.

$$\text{tasa de cambio} = \frac{\text{cambio en la variable dependiente}}{\text{cambio en la variable independiente}}$$

Example Video rental for 1 day is \$1.99.
Video rental for 2 days is \$2.99.

$$\begin{aligned}\text{rate of change} &= \frac{2.99 - 1.99}{2 - 1}\\ &= \frac{1.00}{1}\\ &= 1\end{aligned}$$

Visual **Glossary**

English	Spanish

Ratio (p. 37) A ratio is the comparison of two quantities by division.

Razón (p. 37) Una razón es la comparación de dos cantidades por medio de una división.

Example $\frac{5}{7}$ and 7 : 3 are ratios.

Recursive formula (p. 149) A recursive formula defines the terms in a sequence by relating each term to the ones before it.

Fórmula recursiva (p. 149) Una fórmula recursiva define los términos de una secuencia al relacionar cada término con los términos que lo anteceden.

Example Let $a_n = 2.5a_{n-1} + 3a_{n-2}$. If $a_5 = 3$ and $a_4 = 7.5$, then $a_6 = 2.5(3) + 3(7.5) = 30$.

Reflection (p. 486) A reflection (*flip*) across line r, called the *line of reflection*, is a transformation such that if a point A is on line r, then the image of A is itself, and if a point B is not on line r, then its image B' is the point such that r is the perpendicular bisector of $\overline{BB'}$.

Reflexión (p. 486) Una reflexión (*inversión*) a través de una línea r, llamada el *eje de reflexión*, es una transformación en la que si un punto A es parte de la línea r, la imagen de A es sí misma, y si un punto B no está en la línea r, su imagen B' es el punto en el cual la línea r es la bisectriz perpendicular de $\overline{BB'}$.

Example

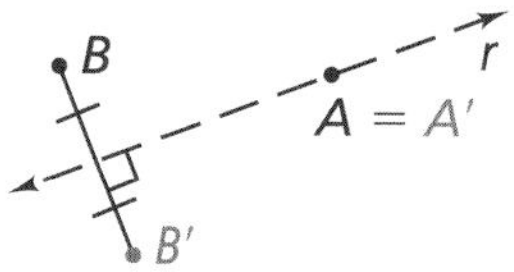

Reflectional symmetry (p. 501) Reflectional symmetry, or *line symmetry*, is the type of symmetry for which there is a reflection that maps a figure onto itself. The reflection line is the *line of symmetry*. The line of symmetry divides a figure with reflectional symmetry into two congruent halves.

Simetría reflexiva (p. 501) Simetría reflexiva, o *simetría lineal*, es el tipo de simetría donde hay una reflexión que ubica una figura en sí misma. El eje de reflexión es el *eje de simetría*. El eje de simetría divide una figura con simetría reflexiva en dos mitades congruentes.

Example

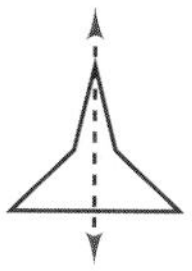

A reflection across the given line maps the figure onto itself.

Relation (p. 135) Any set of ordered pairs.

Relación (p. 135) Cualquier conjunto de pares ordenados.

Example {(0, 0), (2, 3), (2, −7)} is a relation.

Relative frequency (p. 390) The ratio of the number of times an event occurs to the total number of events in the sample space.

Freuencia relativa (p. 390) La razón del número de veces que ocurre un evento número de eventos en el espacio muestral.

Example

Archery Results

Scoring Region	Yellow	Red	Blue	Black	White
Arrow Strikes	52	25	10	8	5

$$\text{Relative frequency of spinning 1} = \frac{\text{frequency of spinning 1}}{\text{total frequencies}} = \frac{29}{100}$$

English

Spanish

Residual (p. 385) The difference between the y-value of a data point and the corresponding y-value of a model for the data set.

Residuo (p. 385) La diferencia entre el valor de y de un punto y el valor de y correspondiente a ese punto en el modelo del conjunto de datos.

Rigid motion (p. 473) A transformation in the plane that preserves distance and angle measure.

Movimiento rígido (p. 473) Una transformación en el piano que no cambia la distancia ni la medida del ángulo.

Example Translations, reflections, and rotations are rigid motions.

Rotation (pp. 493, H42) A rotation *(turn)* of $x°$ about a point R, called the *center of rotation*, is a transformation such that for any point V, its image is the point V', where $RV = RV'$ and $m\angle VRV' = x$. The image of R is itself. The positive number of degrees x that a figure rotates is the *angle of rotation*.

Rotación (pp. 493, H42) Una rotación *(giro)* de $x°$ sobre un punto R, llamado el *centro de rotación*, es una transformación en la que para cualquier punto V, su imagen es el punto V', donde $RV = RV'$ y $m\angle VRV' = x$. La imagen de R es sí misma. El número positivo de grados x que una figura rota es el *ángulo de rotación*.

Example

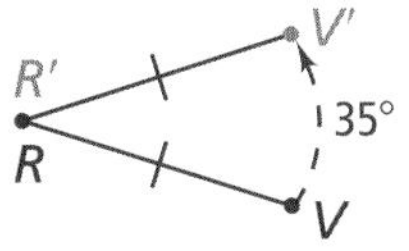

Rotational symmetry (p. 501) Rotational symmetry is the type of symmetry for which there is a rotation of 180° or less that maps a figure onto itself.

Simetría rotacional (p. 501) La simetría rotacional es un tipo de simetría en la que una rotación de 180° o menos vuelve a trazar una figura sobre sí misma.

Example

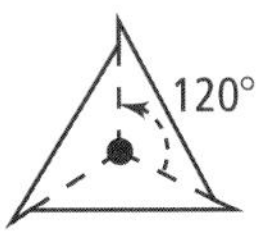

 The figure has 120° rotational symmetry.

S

Scalar (p. H12) A scalar is a real number factor in a special product, such as the 3 in the vector product 3**v**.

Escalar (p. H12) Un escalar es un factor que es un número real en un producto especial, como el 3 en el producto vectorial 3**v**.

Scalar multiplication (p. H12) Scalar multiplication is an operation that multiplies a matrix A by a scalar c. To find the resulting matrix cA, multiply each element of A by c.

Multiplicación escalar (p. H12) La multiplicación escalar es la que multiplica una matriz A por un número escalar c. Para hallar la matriz cA resultante, multiplica cada elemento de A por cs.

Example
$$2.5\begin{bmatrix} 1 & 0 \\ -2 & 3 \end{bmatrix} = \begin{bmatrix} 2.5(1) & 2.5(0) \\ 2.5(-2) & 2.5(3) \end{bmatrix}$$
$$= \begin{bmatrix} 2.5 & 0 \\ -5 & 7.5 \end{bmatrix}$$

English | Spanish

Scatter plot (p. 373) A graph that relates two different sets of data by displaying them as ordered pairs.

Diagrama de puntos (p. 373) Grafica que muestra la relacion entre dos conjuntos. Los datos de ambos conjuntos se presentan como pares ordenados.

Example

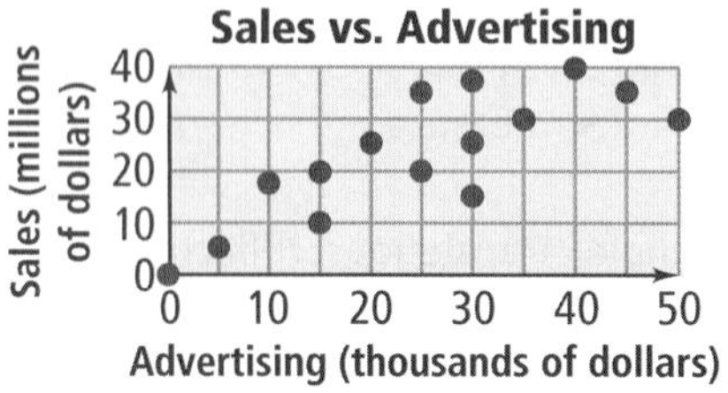

The scatter plot displays the amount spent on advertising (in thousands of dollars) versus product sales (in millions of dollars).

Sequence (p. 146) An ordered list of numbers that often forms a pattern.

Progresion (p. 146) Lista ordenada de numeros que muchas veces forma un patron.

Example $-4, 5, 14, 23$ is a sequence.

Singular matrix (p. H25) A singular matrix is a square matrix with no inverse. Its determinant is 0.

Matriz singular (p. H25) Una matriz singular es una matriz al cuadrado que no tiene inverso. El determinante de la matriz es 0.

Slope (p. 168) The ratio of the vertical change to the horizontal change.

slope $= \frac{\text{vertical change}}{\text{horizontal change}} = \frac{y_2 - y_1}{x_2 - x_1}$, where $x_2 - x_1 \neq 0$

Pendiente (p. 168) La razón del cambio vertical al cambio horizontal. pendiente cambio vertical cambio horizontal. pendiente $= \frac{\text{cambio vertical}}{\text{cambio horizontal}} = \frac{y_2 - y_1}{x_2 - x_1}$, donde $x_2 - x_1 \neq 0$

Example

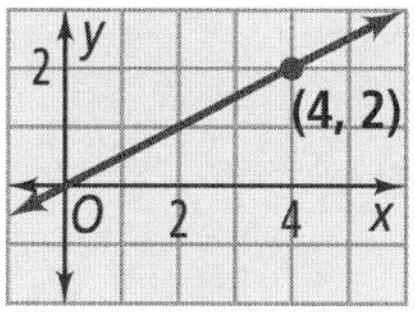

The slope of the line above is $\frac{2}{4} = \frac{1}{2}$.

Slope-intercept form (p. 186) The slope-intercept form of a linear equation is $y = mx + b$, *where m is the slope of the line and b is the y-intercept.*

Forma pendiente-intercepto (p. 186) La forma pendiente-intercepto es la ecuación lineal $y = mx + b$, en la que m es la pendiente de la recta y b es el punto de intersección de esa recta con el eje y.

Example $y = 8x - 2$

English | Spanish

Solution of a system of linear equations (p. 224) Any ordered pair in a system that makes all the equations of that system true.

Solución de un sistema de ecuaciones lineales (p. 224) Todo par ordenado de un sistema que hace verdaderas todas las ecuaciones de ese sistema.

Example (2, 1) is a solution of the system
$y = 2x - 3$
$y = x - 1$
because the ordered pair makes both equations true.

Solution of a system of linear inequalities (p. 264) Any ordered pair that makes all of the inequalities in the system true.

Solución de un sistema de desigualdades lineales (p. 264) Todo par ordenado que hace verdaderas todas las desigualdades del sistema.

Example

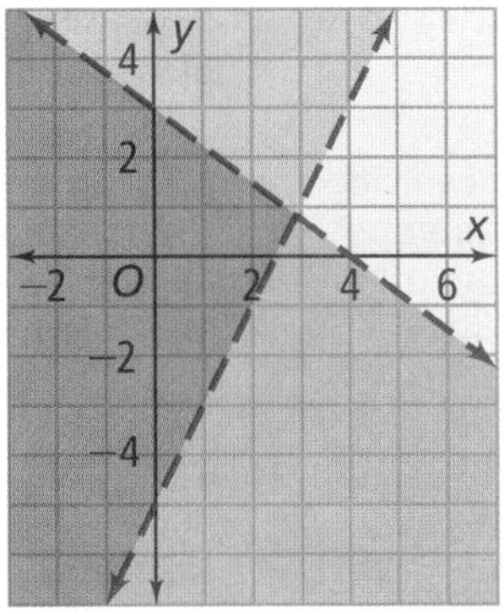

The dark shaded area shows the solution of the system $y > 2x - 5$
$3x + 4y < 12$.

Solution of an inequality (two variables) (p. 256) Any ordered pair that makes the inequality true.

Solución de una desigualdad (dos variables) (p. 256) Cualquier par ordenado que haga verdadera la desigualdad.

Example Each ordered pair in the shaded area and on the solid red line is a solution of $3x - 5y \leq 10$.

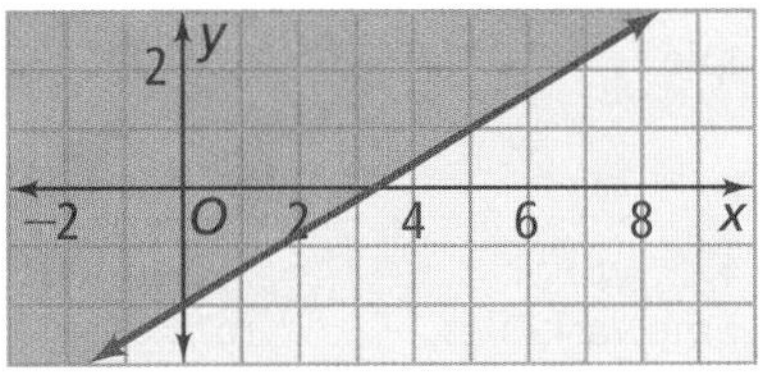

Square matrix (p. H22) A square matrix is a matrix with the same number of columns as rows.

Matriz cuadrada (p. H22) Una matriz cuadrada es la que tiene la misma cantidad de columnas y filas.

Example Matrix A is a square matrix.

$$A = \begin{bmatrix} 1 & 2 & 0 \\ -1 & 0 & -2 \\ 1 & 2 & 3 \end{bmatrix}$$

English	Spanish

Standard deviation (p. 364) A measure of how data varies, or deviates, from the mean.

Desviación típica (p. 364) Medida de cómo los datos varían, o se desvían, de la media.

Example Use the following formula to find the standard deviation.

$$\sigma = \sqrt{\frac{\Sigma(x - \bar{x})^2}{n}}$$

Standard form of a linear equation (p. 203) The standard form of a linear equation is $Ax + By = C$, where A, B, and C are real numbers and A and B are not both zero.

Forma normal de una ecuación lineal (p. 203) La forma normal de una ecuación lineal es $Ax\ By\ C$, donde A, B y C son números reales, y donde A y B no son iguales a cero.

Example $6x - y = 12$

Straightedge (p. 405) A straightedge is a ruler with no markings on it.

Regla sin graduación (p. 405) Una regla sin graduación no tiene marcas.

Substitution method (p. 233) A method of solving a system of equations by replacing one variable with an equivalent expression containing the other variable.

Método de sustitución (p. 233) Método para resolver un sistema de ecuaciones en el que se reemplaza una variable por una expresión equivalente que contenga la otra variable.

Example If $y = 2x + 5$ and $x + 3y = 7$, then $x + 3(2x + 5) = 7$.

Symmetry (p. 501) A figure has symmetry if there is an isometry that maps the figure onto itself. *See also* **point symmetry; reflectional symmetry; rotational symmetry.**

Simetría (p. 501) Una figura tiene simetría si hay una isometría que traza la figura sobre sí misma. *Ver también* **point symmetry; reflectional symmetry; rotational symmetry.**

Example

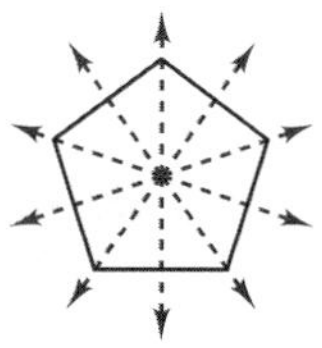

A regular pentagon has reflectional symmetry and 72° rotational symmetry.

System of linear equations (p. 224) Two or more linear equations using the same variables.

Sistema de ecuaciones lineales (p. 224) Dos o más ecuaciones lineales que usen las mismas variables.

Example $y = 5x + 7$

$y = \frac{1}{2}x - 3$

System of linear inequalities (p. 264) Two or more linear inequalities using the same variables.

Sistema de desigualdades lineales (p. 264) Dos o más desigualdades lineales que usen las mismas variables.

Example $y \leq x + 11$

$y < 5x$

T

Term (p. 6) A number, variable, or the product or quotient of a number and one or more variables.

Término (p. 6) Un número, una variable o el producto o cociente de un número y una o más variables.

Example The expression $5x + \frac{y}{2} - 8$ has three terms: $5x$, $\frac{y}{2}$, and -8.

English | Spanish

Term of a sequence (p. 146) A term of a sequence is any number in a sequence.

Término de una progresión (p. 146) Un término de una secuencia es cualquier número de una secuencia.

Example −4 is the first term of the sequence −4, 5, 14, 23.

Terminal point (p. H47) The terminal point of a vector is the tip (not the endpoint) of a vector arrow.

Punto terminal (p. H47) El punto terminal de un vector es la punta (no el extremo) de una flecha vectorial.

Transformation (p. 473) A transformation is a change in the position, size, or shape of a geometric figure. The given figure is called the *preimage* and the resulting figure is called the *image*. A transformation *maps* a figure onto its image. *Prime notation* is sometimes used to identify image points. In the diagram, X' (read "X prime") is the image of X.

Transformación (p. 473) Una transformación es un cambio en la posición, tamaño o forma de una figura. La figura dada se llama la preimagen y la figura resultante se llama la *imagen*. Una transformación *traza* la figura sobre su propia imagen. La *notación prima* a veces se utilize para identificar los puntos de la imagen. En el diagrama de la derecha, X' (leído X prima) es la imagen de X.

Example

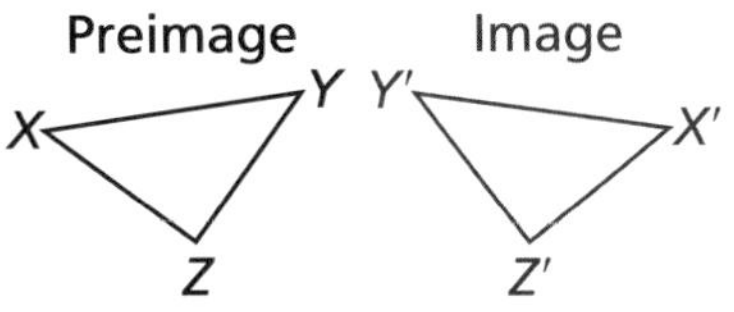

$\triangle XYZ \rightarrow \triangle X'Y'Z'$

Translation (p. 476) A translation is a transformation that moves points the same distance and in the same direction.

Traslación (p. 476) Una traslación es una transformación en la que se mueven puntos la misma distancia en la misma dirección.

Example

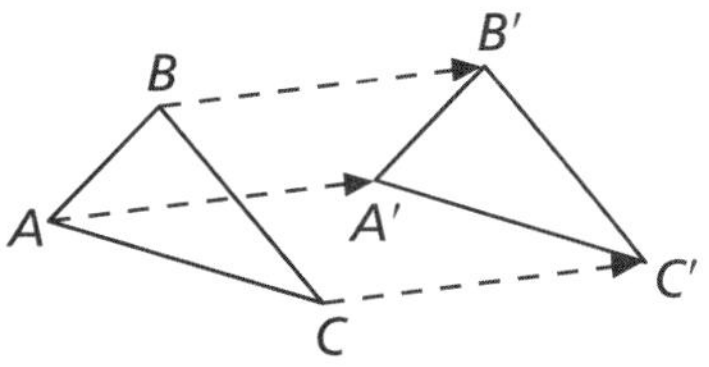

Trend line (p. 375) A line on a scatter plot drawn near the points. It shows a correlation.

Línea de tendencia (p. 375) Línea de un diagrama de puntos que se traza cerca de los puntos para mostrar una correlación.

Example

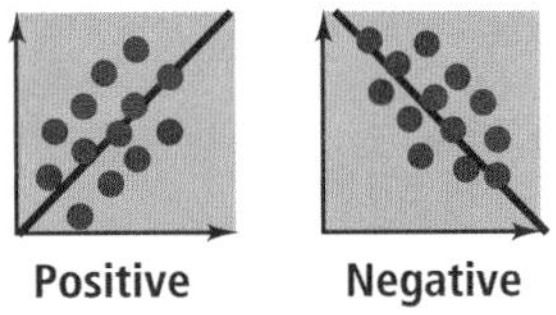

Truth value (p. H69) The truth value of a statement is "true" or "false" according to whether the statement is true or false, respectively.

Valor verdadero (p. H69) El valor verdadero de un enunciado es "verdadero" o "falso" según el enunciado sea *verdadero* o falso, respectivamente.

English / Spanish

Two-way frequency table (p. 388) A table that displays frequencies in two different categories.

Table de frecuencias de doble entrada (p. 388) Una tabla de frecuencies que contiene dos categorias de datos.

Example

	Male	Female	Totals
Juniors	3	4	7
Seniors	3	2	5
Totals	6	6	12

Two-way relative frequency table (p. 390) A two-way relative frequency table shows joint relative frequencies and marginal relative frequencies for two categories of data.

Tabla de frecuencias relativas de doble entrada (p. 390) Una tabla de frecuencias relativas de doble entrada muestra las frecuencias relativas conjuntas y las frecuencias relativas marginales para dos categorías de datos.

U

Unit analysis (p. 39) Including units for each quantity in a calculation to determine the unit of the answer.

Análisis de unidades (p. 39) Incluir unidades para cada cantidad de un cálculo como ayuda para determinar la unidad que se debe usar para la respuesta.

Example To change 10 ft to yards, multiply by the conversion factor $\frac{1\text{ yd}}{3\text{ ft}}$.

$$10\text{ ft}\left(\frac{1\text{ yd}}{3\text{ ft}}\right) = 3\tfrac{1}{3}\text{ yd}$$

Unit rate (p. 37) A rate with a denominator of 1.

Razón en unidades (p. 37) Razón cuyo denominador es 1.

Example The unit rate for 120 miles driven in 2 hours is 60 mi/h.

V

Variable matrix (p. H32) When representing a system of equations with a matrix equation, the matrix containing the variables of the system is the variable matrix.

Matriz variable (p. H32) Al representar un sistema de ecuaciones con una ecuación de matricial, la matriz que contenga las variables del sistema es la matriz variable.

Example $\begin{cases} x + 2y = 5 \\ 3x + 5y = 14 \end{cases}$

variable matrix $\begin{bmatrix} X \\ Y \end{bmatrix}$

Vector (p. H47) A vector is a mathematical object that has both magnitude and direction.

Vector (p. H47) Un vector es un objeto matemático que tiene tanto magnitud como dirección.

Vertex angle (p. 558) *See* **isosceles triangle.**

Ángulo del vértice (p. 558) *Ver* **isosceles triangle.**

English	Spanish

Vertical line test (p. 136) The vertical-line test is a method used to determine if a relation is a function or not. If a vertical line passes through a graph more than once, the graph is not the graph of a function.

Prueba de la recta vertical (p. 136) La prueba de recta vertical es un método que se usa para determinar si una relación es una función o no. Si una recta vertical pasa por el medio de una gráfica más de una vez, la gráfica no es una gráfica de una función.

Example

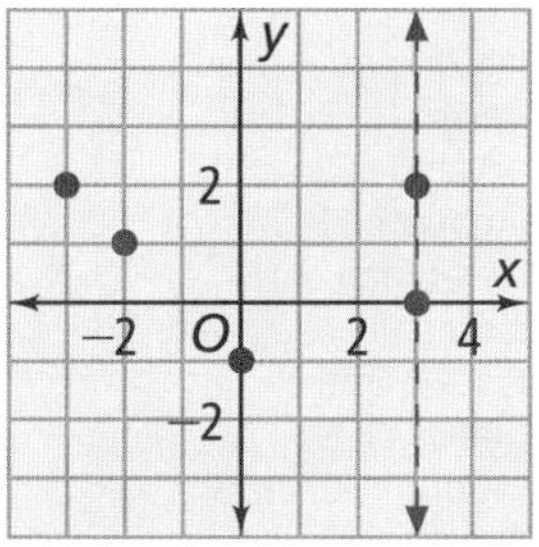

A line would pass through (3, 0) and (3, 2), so the relation is not a function.

X

***x*-intercept (p. 203)** The *x*-coordinate of a point where a graph crosses the *x*-axis.

Intercepto en *x* (p. 203) Coordenada *x* por donde la gráfica cruza el eje de las *x*.

Example The *x*-intercept of $3x + 4y = 12$ is 4.

Y

***y*-intercept (p. 186)** The *y*-coordinate of a point where a graph crosses the *y*-axis.

Intercepto en *y* (p. 186) Coordenada *y* por donde la gráfica cruza el eje de las *y*.

Example The *y*-intercept of $y = 5x + 2$ is 2.

Z

Zero matrix (p. H6) The zero matrix O, or $O_{m \times n}$, is the $m \times n$ matrix whose elements are all zeros. It is the additive identity matrix for the set of all $m \times n$ matrices.

Matriz cero (p. 766) La matriz cero, O, o $O_{m \times n}$, es la matriz $m \times n$ cuyos elementos son todos ceros. Es la matriz de identidad aditiva para el conjunto de todas las matrices $m \times n$.

Example $\begin{bmatrix} 1 & 4 \\ 2 & -3 \end{bmatrix} + O = \begin{bmatrix} 1 & 4 \\ 2 & -3 \end{bmatrix}$

Index

A

B

C

D

E

F

G

Index

H

I

J

K

L

M

Index

Q

R

S

Index

W

X

Y

Z

Acknowledgments

Staff Credits

The people who made up the High School Mathematics team—representing composition services, core design digital and multimedia production services, digital product development, editorial, editorial services, manufacturing, marketing, and production management—are listed below.

Patty Fagan, Suzanne Finn, Matt Frueh, Cynthia Harvey, Linda Johnson, Roshni Kutty, Cheryl Mahan, Eve Melnechuk, Cynthia Metallides, Hope Morley, Michael Oster, Wynnette Outland, Brian Reardon, Matthew Rogers, Ann-Marie Sheehan, Kristen Siefers, Richard Sullivan, Susan Tauer, Mark Tricca, Oscar Vera, Paula Vergith

Additional Credits: Emily Bosak, Olivia Gerde, Alyse McGuire, Stephanie Mosely

Illustration

Jeff Grunewald: 101, 102, 134, 464, H73, H87; **Christopher Wilson:** 351; **Stephen Durke:** 436, 443, 478, 528, 537, 551, 558, 568, 585; **Phil Guzy:** 503; **XNR Productions:** H28.

Technical Illustration

Aptara, Inc.; Datagrafix, Inc.; GGS Book Services

Photography

Every effort has been made to secure permission and provide appropriate credit for photographic material. The publisher deeply regrets any omission and pledges to correct errors called to its attention in subsequent editions.

Unless otherwise acknowledged, all photographs are the property of Pearson Education, Inc.

35, Reuters/Corbis; **158,** John Glover/Alamy Images; **158,** Bob Gibbons/Alamy Images; **492,** North Wind Picture Archives/Alamy Images; **500,** Alan Copson/City Pictures/ Alamy Images; **552,** Viktor Kitaykin/iStockphoto; **562,** John Wells/Photo Researchers, Inc; **573,** Image Source Black/Jupiter Images; **593 l,** M.C. Escher's "Symmetry E56" © 2009 The M.C. Escher Company-Holland. All rights reserved. www.mcescher.com; **593 r,** M.C. Escher's "Symmetry E18" © 2009 The M.C. Escher Company-Holland. All rights reserved. www.mcescher.com; **H3** (T) Jim Sanborn; **H15** (TR, TL) iStockphoto; **H41** (TC) Wolfgang Spunbarg/PhotoEdit, Inc.; **H80,** Material courtesy of Bill Vicars and Lifeprint.

Chapter 1: Whole chapter taken from Chapter 1 of *Pearson High School Math 2014 Common Core Integrated Math 1 Write-In Student Edition Volume 1.*

Chapter 2: Whole chapter taken from Chapter 2 of *Pearson High School Math 2014 Common Core Integrated Math 1 Write-In Student Edition Volume 1.*

Chapter 3: Lessons 1-6 taken from Chapter 3, Lessons 1-6 of *Pearson High School Math 2014 Common Core Integrated Math 1 Write-In Student Edition Volume 1.*

Chapter 4: Whole chapter taken from Chapter 4 of *Pearson High School Math 2014 Common Core Integrated Math 1 Write-In Student Edition Volume 1.*

Chapter 5: Lessons 1-7 taken from Chapter 5, Lessons 1-7 of *Pearson High School Math 2014 Common Core Integrated Math 1 Write-In Student Edition Volume 1.*

Chapter 6: Whole chapter taken from Chapter 6 of *Pearson High School Math 2014 Common Core Integrated Math 1 Write-In Student Edition Volume 1.*

Chapter 7: Lesson 1 taken from Chapter 10, Lesson 1 of *Pearson High School Math 2014 Common Core Integrated Math 1 Write-In Student Edition Volume 2.* Lesson 2 taken from Chapter 11, Lesson 6 of *Pearson High School Math 2014 Common Core Integrated Math 1 Write-In Student Edition Volume 2.*

Chapter 8: Whole chapter taken from Chapter 9 of *Pearson High School Math 2014 Common Core Integrated Math 1 Write-In Student Edition Volume 2.*

Chapter 9: Whole chapter taken from Chapter 8 of *Pearson High School Math 2014 Common Core Integrated Math 1 Write-In Student Edition Volume 2.*

Chapter 10: Whole chapter taken from Chapter 12 of *Pearson High School Math 2014 Common Core Integrated Math 1 Write-In Student Edition Volume 2.*

Honors Appendix: Whole Topic A taken from Chapter 12 of *Algebra 2 Common Core Edition.* Lessons B-1 through B-4 taken from Chapter 10, Lessons 2-5 from *Pearson High School Math 2014 Common Core Integrated Math 1 Write-In Student Edition Volume 2.*